The

# Primary Healthcare Management Handbook

Consultant Editors: Brenda Sawyer & Helen Kogan

The **A**ssociation of Managers in General Practice (AMGP)

KOGAN
PAGE

Published in 1997

Kogan Page Ltd
120 Pentonville Road
London N1 9JN
kpinfo@kogan-page.co.uk

© Kogan Page 1997

**British Library Cataloguing in Publication Data**

ISBN 0 7494 2259 9


Typeset by BookEns Ltd, Royston, Herts
Printed and bound in Great Britain by Clays Ltd, St Ives plc

# Contents

# Foreword

The Secretary of State for Health, Rt Hon Stephen Dorrell MP, has described primary care as the 'jewel in the NHS crown'. As it is often the first and only point of contact for most patients for healthcare services, it has also to be robust and accessible. The increasing number of changes that have taken place over the past few years within the Health Service, and in particular primary care, have demanded efficient working practices and enormous flexibility from all members of the practice team. The role of the practice manager has also changed dramatically, particularly with the advent of fundholding and practices purchasing and providing services, changes within legislation and the continued integration of attached staff and professionals allied to medicine within the primary care team.

Patients also play a significant role in the quality issues of delivery of care. The establishment of complaints procedures and patient involvement regarding purchasing decisions means patients' views are taken into consideration in greater proportion within all aspects of practice life. The manager, therefore, has to be both an ambassador and advocate on behalf of patients and the practice. Financial management, interpersonal communication and the management of change have all required high levels of expertise and skill. It is quite clear good management is now an essential part of general practice life and managers have a responsibility to use the resources effectively, cope with the demands and changes imposed by government, and be aware of public accountability.

All members of the primary care team are expected to avail themselves of the highest quality training to keep up to date, relevant and evidence based. None more so than the manager, whose role demands commitment, enthusiasm, self-development, and continuing education. I have met many managers and practices in my role as Chairman of the Association of Managers in General Practice and am impressed with the openness and willingness to learn and share information between themselves. This handbook, written specifically for general practice, comes with the authority and credibility of expertise from both working managers and others who work closely with the real issues in general practice. The Association has striven to raise the standards of management in primary care and is delighted to be associated with such a worthy publication. I know the manager will find much to commend this book to their armoury of information and I am sure it will be an invaluable resource.

Jackie Maun FAMGP
*Chairman AMGP*

# List of Contributors

**Kathie Applebee** of Practice Consultancy Services, Swindon is a psychologist and management consultant who specialises in general practice. In addition to sixteen years' experience, she has a master's degree in GP computing and is researching GP stress at doctorate level.

**David Barber** is a principal consultant with Environmental Resources Management (ERM), one of the leading environmental consultancies in the UK. He has specialised in the assessment of the environmental impacts and health and safety issues associated with waste management for over eight years.

**Dr Harry Burns** followed a career as first a general, and then a consultant surgeon until 1989. Following changes in the organisation of the NHS, he entered healthcare management and was, for a time, medical director of the Royal Infirmary in Glasgow. Since 1993 he has been director of public health for Greater Glasgow Health Board, which is responsible for organising healthcare and maintaining the health of one million people in the West of Scotland.

**Barbara Daniels** works as a practice manager for a three-partner, non-fundholding practice operating from a health centre in the Vale of Glamorgan. She has the AMGP (formerly AHCPA) Diploma in practice management and is a training NVQ Assessor. She was Chairman of the Cardiff and District AMGP Branch, Regional Education Co-ordinator for Wales, National Education Co-ordinator and now Vice-Chairman of AMGP.

**Rosemary Day** is chairman of the London Ambulance Service, as well as being director and board member for many organisations. Previously, she was an executive director of London Transport; an operations director for Allied Dunbar; and, after 18 years working for the Greater London Council, she was the assistant director general.

**Bill Edwards** has been Practice Manager at the Hillsborough Medical Centre, County Down, Northern Ireland for the last four years.

**Dr Philip Evans** is a general practitioner in the St Leonard's Medical Practice, a four-partner practice in Exeter. He is the lead researcher within the practice which is an NHS research general practice. He is also a Research Fellow at the Institute of General Practice of the University of Exeter.

**Rosey Foster** was appointed Chief Executive of AMGP in 1994 and elected Chairman of the Alliance of Primary Care in 1996. She is also a King's Fund Organisational Audit surveyor, a member of the editorial board of the *British Journal of Health Care Management* and council member of the Medical Insurance Agency.

**Bob Gann** is Director of The Help for Health Trust, a registered charity involved in communication of healthcare information to patients and the public, and also heads the central support unit for the NHS freephone Health Information Service (HIS). He is a member of the steering groups of the NHS Centre for Reviews and Dissemination and the UK Outcomes Clearinghouse and sits on the Standing Advisory Group on Consumer Involvement in NHS R&D.

**Sandra E A Gower** is practice business and development manager of Bennetts End Surgery, Hertfordshire, a nine-partner training and first-wave fundholding practice with a very large progressive primary care team. She is also a practice diagnostic consultant, King's Fund surveyor, and NVQ assessor and external examiner for the Institute of General Practice, University of Exeter. She is a Fellow of AMGP and past chairman, and co-author with Rosey Foster, AMGP Chief Executive, and Andrew Hepworth, management consultant, of the AMGP Code of Principles.

**John Hearle** is a Fellow of the Royal Institution of Chartered Surveyors, an Associate of the Chartered Institute of Arbitrators and a Director of Aitchisons Raffety Buckland, Surveyors Valuers and Property Consultants specialising in surgery premises.

**Dr Robin Hopkins** is senior lecturer in the Institute of General Practice, University of Exeter, with a special interest in medical informatics as well as being a practising GP in Exmouth, Devon.

**Dr Colin Hunter** became a member of the RCGP in 1985; he has been an honorary secretary of the North East Scotland Faculty for seven years, and in 1993 became the first member of the college in Scotland to become a Fellow by Assessment. He is currently vice chairman and honorary treasurer of Scottish Council and a member of both the Finance Committee and the CME Working Party at the college. In 1991 he was nominated as a director of the Rowett Postgraduate Nutrition and Dietetic Centre, and he is also a member of the Royal College of Physicians Working Party on obesity.

**Andrea J Jones** is in an almost unique position of having worked both as a manager in general practice and then in a senior management position with an FHSA and latterly a new health authority. As such her perceptions of the latest reforms are developed from an understanding of both interests and environments.

**Clare Landymore** is practice manager at Wyndham House Surgery, Silverton, a rural dispensing practice in Devon, and course organiser for practice management at the Institute of General Practice, Exeter University.

**Graeme Love** is a chartered valuation surveyor who has more than ten years' experience specialising in GP surgeries. He is a director of Medi-Commercial Ltd which provides healthcare premises and facilities.

**Lorna M G McMillan** is general manager of Abington Health Complex, a member of AMGP and was involved in the development of the new Diploma. She is currently the centre co-ordinator for the AMGP approved NVQ centre.

**Gerald Malone**, MP for Winchester, was appointed Minister for Health in July 1994. An Arts and Law graduate from Glasgow University, he practised as a solicitor in Glasgow until election to Parliament in 1983. He is married to Dr Anne Blyth, an anaesthetist in the NHS, and has three children.

**Professor Geoff Meads** is Professor of Health Services Development in the Health Management Group at the City University in London, which is responsible for the highest number of graduates in health management in the UK. Previously director of purchaser performance management for the NHS Executive, South and West Region and director of primary and community care for the Wessex Regional Health Authority.

**Lindley Owen** is Director of Performance Management and Deputy Chief Executive of Cornwall & Isles of Scilly Health Authority. He has been an NHS manager since 1973 in South West Thames, Northern, Wessex and South West Regions.

**Mike Pringle** is the Professor of General Practice in Nottingham and a partner in a rural dispensing practice on the Nottinghamshire-Lincolnshire border. He is a Fellow by Assessment and now manages the Fellowship by Assessment programme on behalf of the Royal College of General Practitioners.

**Brenda Sawyer** is Education Adviser to the Association of Managers in General Practice, a Research Fellow at the Institute of General Practice in Exeter, and a Visiting Fellow to the Institute of Health Policy Studies at Southampton University. She is now a consultant in management training and development and is undertaking research.

**Robert Sloane** is chief executive of a combined hospital and community service NHS trust in central Hampshire, which has attracted a national focus for being a model of change for the 21st century. He joined the NHS in 1964 and progressed through a series of operational posts in general hospitals before moving to work in a teaching hospital environment at a senior level in 1971. In the late 1970s he was appointed to head the planning and commissioning of the first Nurcleus Hospital in England. This provided a springboard in the early 1980s for private sector consultancy which involved working in different parts of the world. Returning to the NHS in 1984, he managed a range of development project for Wessex RHA, culminating with the implementation of the government's NHS Reform Programme in the region.

**Timothy Smith** is the practice manager of the St Leonard's Medical Practice. Formerly Colour Sergeant in the Royal Marines he has experienced the transition from his practice undertaking research prior to NHS recognition to the practice being appointed as an NHS research general practice.

**David M Towner**, a qualified occupational psychologist, is an independent management consultant. Over recent years he has undertaken substantial work in primary care, focusing on bringing enhancements to the management and work arrangements of GP practices. He also specialises in the development of competence profiling, staff appraisal systems and change management, working in both the private and public sectors. He is a member of the Institute of Personnel and Development (UK) and the American Society for Training and Development (USA).

**Dr Colin Waine** is director of health programmes and primary care development with Sunderland Health Authority. Previously, he was a principal in general practice in Bishop Auckland, his home town. In the RCGP he was successfully the chairman of the Publications Committee, Communications Division, Clinial and Research Division and Council. In 1990 he was awarded the OBE for Services to Medicine.

**John Walker** is a chartered engineer with more than twenty years' experience in estate management in the NHS. He is a director of Medi-Commercial Ltd which provides healthcare premises and facilities.

**Merrill Whalen** has been an adviser in practice management at the Medical and Dental Defence Union of Scotland since April 1995. She admits to being 'passionate' about general medical practice, lectures and works regularly with groups of doctors, managers, nurses, staff and has written extensively on a wide range of organisational and management subjects.

# PART ONE

# OVERVIEW

# Introduction

*Brenda Sawyer, AMGP, and*
*Institute of General Practice*
*Exeter University*

A primary care led NHS indicates the enormous change that has taken place in the provision and delivery of healthcare in the nineties. It has meant that the evolution of the manager in general practice from the administrative role of the past has gathered momentum and is developing further into the role of managing the primary health care team. This strategic position brings new responsibilities and requires different knowledge and understanding. The three government White Papers, *Primary Care − The Future, Choice and Opportunities* and *The NHS: A Service with Ambitions* and *Primary Care: Delivering the Future* emphasise the need for professional development and for multi-professional working and learning across the boundaries of primary and secondary care. One of the aims is to concentrate on the individual patient, to bring purchasing and commissioning of healthcare to locality level and the delivery of that care as close to the patient as possible. This move towards a primary care led NHS has resulted in the piloting of new models of primary care organisations. The latest White Papers pave the way for experimenting with different kinds of contracting for primary healthcare services.

The aim of this book is to stimulate the thinking of managers and to provide them with some examples of current initiatives, and future thinking on the provision of primary healthcare and the commissioning and purchasing of secondary care services.

**Part One** provides an overview of some of these initiatives in the south through locality purchasing in south west Hampshire and the setting up of a Primary Care Agency in Andover.

The work of a manager in primary care involves working on many projects and **Part Two** includes a model of how to go about this in an effective manner and ways of identifying and handling risks in service management. A high-quality team is the basis of a high standard of delivery of patient care. The chapter on how to build a secure foundation of human resource management is essential knowledge.

**Part Three** covers the need for the continual development of the team through traditional and new methods. The chapter on training gives numerous ways of identifying and meeting the training needs of the team and that on Fellowship by Assessment describes ways in which the manager can assist general practitioners who wish to take this route of professional development. There is a growing demand for more research in primary care and for some actions to be based on evidence. A chapter describes the newly appointed research general practices in primary care and another discusses evidence-based management.

**Part Four** on managing relationships deals with the important areas of a Code of Principles for managers in their working environments; key issues relating to relationships with consumers; and how relationships are changing and progressing with the newly formed health authorities.

There is no doubt that innovations in information technology are changing our lives, not least those of managers in primary care. **Part Five** gives a glimpse of the future in the management of information; how this might affect us and what we need to do about it.

**Part Six** addresses changes in financial areas. One chapter is a live case study on the innovative way in which one practice has gone about meeting future needs in extending the services offered from their site. They obtained finance to provide extensive premises from which a range of professionals provide both traditional and new services. Another deals with the all-important issues of obtaining value for resources in primary care. It is necessary for all those dealing with partners' finance to understand the new tax rules on self-assessment and this is covered in full.

The management of premises and equipment grows in importance as the provision of services provided from primary healthcare premises expands. The first chapter in **Part Seven** covers the area of waste management which is both of environmental and health and safety importance. It is important that a systematic approach is used when purchasing equipment of any kind and a model for the procurement of equipment, in this case IT equipment, is provided. The importance of valuation of premises and the use of private finance in obtaining premises are two often neglected aspects which are explored in this section.

One of the largest and most complex issues facing the nation is the rationing and prioritising of healthcare. There are not infinite resources to meet the demands of the future. **Part Eight** addresses these issues which were confronted at the Association of Managers in General Practice 21st Annual Course at Glasgow. Managers attended workshops to extend their skills in decision-making and then went on to practise these skills. This involved exploring how practices can cope with the ever-rising demands of the public, through prioritising patient treatments and debating whether or not people with self-inflicted illness should receive different priority for treatment. These experiences are shared in the AMGP section of this book, and provide the opportunity, and the tools, for managers to explore and discuss these issues within their own teams.

For managers working within primary care to face the new challenges of change they need the support of their professional association. A major part of this support is provided in the form of the AMGP Code of Principles which is explained in Part 4 of this book. Membership of the Association involves signing up to this Code of Principles. This means that managers can face the new challenges with confidence.

In 1997, The British School of Osteopathy celebrates 80 years as one of the world's centres for osteopathic excellence. Over the years, the BSO has made a significant contribution not only to the education of the nation's osteopaths but in raising public awareness of osteopathy as a profession and the value of holistically diagnosing and treating musculoskeletal pain and disability.

In our central London clinics, we see over 800 patients each week, in general and specialised areas. In the General Clinic patients are treated by senior students under supervision of fully qualified osteopathic practitioners. The specialised areas, currently managed as demonstration clinics, are Children, Expectant Mothers, Sports Injury and Tempero-mandibular.

The BSO is pleased to accept GP or self referrals. Osteopathy is concerned with total body health, not claiming to be a cure all, and therefore complementary to the use of orthodox medicine in treatment plans. Patients can be seen within 24 hours of an initial enquiry, however an emergency service is available. There is full disabled access to the clinic. Since the introduction of the Osteopaths Act in 1995, the BSO~ has been at the forefront of fostering close working relationships with other healthcare professionals. It is usually possible to arrange a familiarisation tour for other professionals interested in knowing more about our work. Enquires regarding this opportunity should be directed to the Clinic General Manager.

*To make an appointment or further enquiry about the available services, please call 0171 930 9254. The BSO is a registered charity, no: 312873.*

# ALLERGY TESTING AT THE TOUCH OF A BUTTON
## *MODERN "COMPUTERISED" ALLERGY TESTING SOLVES MANY HEALTH PROBLEMS BY TAKING THE HUMAN ELEMENT OUT OF DIAGNOSIS*

Scientists have found that we are constantly doing damage to our nervous system by simply eating everyday foods. When you think that its our nervous system (brain) which runs everything in our body, it doesn't make sense to poison it. Modern U.S. technology has now brought allergy testing into the 21st century - no more patch testing - needles, or waiting for results. At Health Scan results are instant - accurate - pain free and non-invasive, all you feel is a little pressure on your finger. They have screened adults and children of all ages without any problems, and results are amazing as their many testimonial letters will confirm. They have received so many letters of thanks from people who previously suffered with conditions such as ECZEMA-ARTHRITIS-MIGRAINE-EPILEPSY-ASTHMA-DIGESTIVE-WEIGHT-LETHARGY-HAY FEVER-ATHLETES FOOT-CATARRH, and all corrected with just a single scan!

### HOW IT WORKS

Your brain is a computer which runs on electricity, this feeds all your organs etc., via the nerves and keep you alive. (If your arm did not have electricity through it, it would be paralysed)! You **DO NOT** generate **ELECTRICITY** in order to stay alive so you **MUST** put it into your body. You do this each and every day by eating drinking, also by injecting, inhaling or absorbing items through your skin. Some charges are more acceptable to the nervous system (brain) than others.

### 108 DIFFERENT FOODS

In a standard test the Health Scan computer reproduces electrical charges from 108 different foods and drink and measures the reaction of the brain to each of these. The items tested include everything from dairy products to sardines and spinage, and red wine to rhubarb. Health Scan also tests reaction to 9 major "E" numbers (i.e. food colours, which can cause a large number of problems, including hyperactivity in children). Also checked are the bodies levels of 29 "ESSENTIAL" vitamins and minerals, as well as a sensitivity check of respiratory problems such as **ASTHMA** and **HAY FEVER**.

Everyone undergoing a Health Scan receives an instant printout detailing the items which are acceptable and unacceptable to their nervous system (brain). It is simply a case of avoiding the offending items where possible, **FOODS ARE THE BIGGEST CULPRITS OF ALL**, when you DO NOT poison you nervous system in this way it is quite amazing how problems seem to clear up, and how your general health improves dramatically.

The cost of a scan is £67 + VAT a total of £79, one is normally enough to achieve desired results.

Health Scan have a network of Agents such as Doctors, Dentists and Chemists that send people to them on a regular basis, in some cases a small renumeration is paid directly to the agent or to a charitable cause. *Should you require further information on this scheme or would like a copy of their standard brochure then please telephone 0181 399 2644.*

# Purchasing by Practices and Localities: Which Way Forward?

*Angela Jeffrey,*
*Southampton and South West*
*Hampshire Health Authority*

### Achieving a primary care led NHS

Late in 1994 the circular 'Towards a Primary Care Led NHS' (EL(94)79) was published. This document has acted as a major focus for work that has been ongoing within Southampton and South West Hampshire Health Authority. It also acted as a catalyst for a stocktake as to how the Authority should take the development of the primary care led NHS forward within a structured framework, particularly as one of its strategic aims is to make primary care the principal focus of responsibility for health.

As there has been confusion over the exact meaning of the term 'a primary care led NHS,' it is important to be clear about the definitions. The term concerns shifting the focus of decision-making about health and healthcare as close as possible to patients, in a primary care setting, on the grounds that this is the best place to trade off effectiveness, quality, access and cost, taking account of the patient as a whole (with those individual decisions informed by public health priorities).

The term also concerns the process of delivering care, with the GP as co-ordinator, not just of the primary care team, but of the whole care system. This seeks to avoid the patient being 'passed' from one part of the system to another. It does not preclude specific clinical responsibility being held by different professionals at different times, but it does provide a single point of perception of primary care as the 'feeder' of secondary care services.

This requires effective partnerships between primary care professionals and health authorities, between primary and secondary care professionals, between primary care professionals and social care providers, and between primary care professionals and patients. To a certain extent the GP becomes one of the key guides through the health and social care maze.

## The Southampton context

The Southampton and South West Hampshire Health Authority is responsible for commissioning health services for a population of 530,000. There are 79 GP practices of varying sizes with only a handful of single-handed practitioners. There are 317 GPs in total.

The Authority relates to three main provider trusts: Southampton University Hospitals NHS Trust, Southampton Community Health Services NHS Trust and Winchester and Eastleigh Care NHS Trust. The total budget is £305.9 million. Of this sum, £121.3 million is now directly influenced by primary care (see Table 1.2.1).

At present, services are commissioned within Southampton and South West Hampshire by complementary but distinctive healthcare purchasers, as follows:

- The Health Authority which (either solely or with other agencies) purchases all healthcare for 42 per cent of the population and purchases services not included in the GP fundholding scheme for 95 per cent of the population.
- GP fundholding practices ('standard' and 'community') which purchase a specified range of healthcare for 53 per cent of the population. This will rise to 71 per cent in 1997–98.

**Table 1.2.1** *Primary care budget, Southampton and South West Hampshire Health Authority (excluding general dental services)*

| Expenditure | £m |
|---|---|
| GPFH budgets | 59.8 |
| Total purchasing project | 6.1 |
| General medical services cash limited | 6.3 |
| General medical services non-cash limited | 24.0 |
| Prescribing (non GPFH) element) | 20.0 |
| Optical services | 1.8 |
| Pharmaceutical services | 3.3 |
| Total | £121.3m |

- The Romsey Total Purchasing Project (three Fundholding practices working collaboratively) which purchases all healthcare for 5 per cent.
- Southampton East Multifund Consortium (12 GPFH practices).
- Eastleigh Consortium (4 GPFH practices).
- The Shirley Commissioning Group (Community Fundholders, West City Centre).

## Purchasing in partnership with GPs

In Southampton and South West Hampshire all GPs, including GP fundholders, are encouraged to work together to influence the commission of health and social care. We have specified that in working with all GPs (both GP fundholders and non-fundholders) key development areas are as follows:

- **Strategy development.** Ensuring that all GPs are involved from the outset and that the strategic objectives for the development of local health services encompass the views of GPs, other co-purchasers and stakeholders. This includes discussion with local providers.
- **Agreement and commitment to strategy.** Harnessing the joint purchasing power of GP fundholders and the Health Authority to achieve agreed objectives and sharing and managing the risks involved in major strategic shifts.
- **Strategy implementation.** Taking account of the views of the GPs about the content of detailed investment programmes, approving investment programmes, including priority setting.

## Localities – lead GPs

The mechanisms for participation and collaboration continue to be developed through discussions with local GPs and representatives of the Local Medical Committee (the profession's representative body), the GP Fundholding Forum (for standard fundholding practices) and the Core Commissioning Board, (membership consists of ten lead GPs representing ten localities, plus the chief executive and directors), representing all GPs.

## The Core Commissioning Board

The functions of the Core Commissioning Board are to:

- co-ordinate the work of the ten localities;
- tackle district-wide issues;

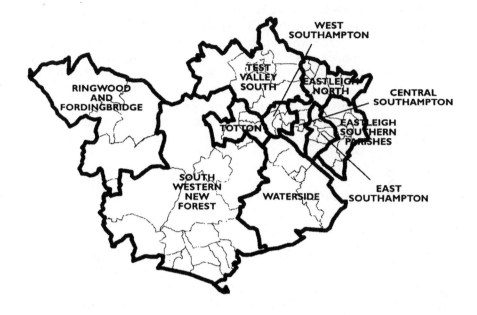

**Figure 1.2.1**  *Locality map*

- contribute to and influence the Health Authority's work across all the areas of commissioning, including strategy, contracting, joint commissioning and accountability;
- encourage the commitment and involvement of all GPs and the primary healthcare team in influencing the future of local healthcare;
- make links to the provision of services in primary care settings;
- act as a channel of communication and information between GPs, the Health Commission and providers.

There is co-terminosity between the localities in Figure 1.2.1 and medical practice areas for general practice. Groupings of the localities are also co-terminus with social service area boundaries. This facilitates the links and ensures networks are developed with local authorities and the voluntary sector. The key potential benefits of defining health localities and commissioning responsively for them are seen as follows:

- **A better focus for community involvement**. Better communication, assistance in the prioritisation of health needs, better understanding of unmet need for all of the agencies involved, and a greater local ownership of health programmes – resulting in improved local accountability for the Authority.

9

- **A more flexible response to local need.** Encouraging joint working between agencies and between providers.
- **A more targeted response to local needs.** Improving local needs assessment and building up a more accurate picture of what health services people need in order to enable the purchasing of health services to match those needs.
- **Increased scope for integration of health and social care.** Enabling closer working between primary care and social services teams in the areas where their responsibilities meet, to the considerable benefit of patients and clients.

### General practice involvement in purchasing

#### General practice fundholding

From April 1997, 71 per cent of the population will be registered with a fundholding practice. This will consist of 35 standard fundholding practices, covering 50 per cent of the population and a further 17 community fundholding practices, covering 21 per cent of the population.

The Community Fundholding Scheme covers practice staffing,

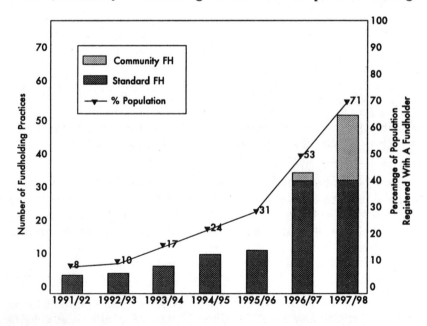

**Figure 1.2.2** *Number of standard and community fundholders and the percentage of the population registered with fundholders*

practice prescribing costs, pathology tests, radiology tests, paramedic services and district nurses, health visitors and specialist nurses. In addition, Standard Fundholding covers most elective inpatient and daycase procedures, most outpatient services and community mental health and learning disability services.

## The Romsey Total Purchasing Project

The Romsey Total Purchasing Project covers a population of 29,000 and involves 19 GPs in three general practices. The total budget including the GPFH element is £9 million. The project is managed by a project manager, a project group and a steering committee which report to the Health Authority. There has been a small investment in an IT system to support the project.

The project operates within a defined locality and has a common boundary with social services. There is a 26-bed Community Hospital in Romsey providing a range of local facilities. The project went live on 1 April 1996. Its aims are to:

- develop healthcare services which are locally focused, reflect local priorities, and are responsive to local need;
- evaluate the effectiveness and efficiency of GPs purchasing the full range of healthcare.

The key objectives for 1996–97 were to:

- improve mental health services;
- develop rehabilitation services in Romsey;
- improve maternity services and increase the number of domino deliveries.

Good progress has been made against each of these objectives. For the financial year 1997–98, the practices' priorities are to:

- develop further the services at Romsey Hospital;
- achieve closer integration of health and social care;
- identify the potential benefits of introducing nursing homes as new providers of care;
- link GP 'out of hours' arrangements with a low-tech minor injuries unit;
- improve discharge planning;
- purchase mental health services on a locality as opposed to practice basis.

Two other groups of GP fundholders have expressed an interest in total purchasing.

## Southampton East Multifund (SEM)

There is a multifund (12 GPFH practices) on the east side of South-ampton covering a population of about 76,000, with a budget of £16 million. It is managed by a GPFH manager working across all 12 practices with support staff and input from lead GPs.

The Multifund aims to stimulate practice developments in primary care and the strategic development of secondary care provision to primary care. The Multifund is committed to developing effective locally based services and working with customer focused providers.

For 1997–98, the SEM is looking to develop one-stop and direct access approaches to care across a range of specialities. Particular priorities are:

- to develop cardiac surgery protocols;
- to improve ECG reporting;
- to improve the waiting times in rheumatology;
- to develop protocols for orthopaedic joint replacements;
- to develop gynaecology outreach outpatients;
- to develop more integrated back pain service.

Medium-term priorities are to develop a more holistic approach to orthopaedics, to develop locally based services for sigmoidoscopy and colposcopy services, rheumatology and cardiology services and the development of a back pain strategy.

Mental health and counselling services remain a high priority for investment as well as the need to develop primary healthcare teams and improve co-ordination with the community nurses to ensure value for money.

Fundholding has facilitated the development of information technology within the practices. It is intended to build on this strong base and work towards improving information reporting from providers and waiting list management.

## The Eastleigh Consortium

On 1 April 1996 the Authority became responsible for practices in Eastleigh and Chandlers Ford. Six of the practices form the Eastleigh GP Fundholding Consortium. One GPFH manager co-ordinates the work of the Consortium. Resolving their funding position and their relative equity position compared to other fundholders was their main priority for 1996–97. The Consortium's key objectives relate to:

- decreasing waiting times for outpatients and surgery, particularly cardiothoracic services;
- developing more locally based outpatient services with the Winchester and Eastleigh NHS Trust;

- improving joint working with social services;
- decreasing follow-up outpatient activity in secondary care.

The Consortium is also seeking funding to appoint a care manager to work with the practices.

## Commitment to GP involvement

Local developments continue to demonstrate commitment by both general practitioners and the Authority to the involvement of GPs in the commissioning and purchasing of health services both now and in the future. GP involvement in and influence on purchasing is now a major factor, which also underpins the development of a primary care led NHS.

## Purchasing perspectives

However, there are a number of perspectives that need to be considered in taking stock of current developments and seeking some clarity about future direction. They are not unique to Southampton and include:

- the patient;
- the GP practice;
- the provider;
- the purchaser.

### The patient

From the patients' perspective their main concern is how to access health services without unreasonable waiting times. Recent financial difficulties have resulted in a higher profile in the local press relating to a 'two-tier service'. This has raised awareness among the general public to a more informed level of understanding as to how the purchasing of healthcare is currently organised. It has also caused considerable anxiety.

### The GP practice

Most GP practices are involved in influencing the commissioning of healthcare through a variety of means. Much has been achieved through fundholding. However, once initial objectives have been met by practices, what is the best way to influence more major changes in clinical service delivery if the practice continues to operate in isolation from others in a locality? The motto of the Southampton East Multifund is 'Practices working together for better patient care'.

SEM has approached locality purchasing while retaining the

Multifund is 'Practices working together for better patient care'.

SEM has approached locality purchasing while retaining the objective for purchasing at an individual level, but in a way that has the ability to affect real change in service delivery through working together – 'Practice based locality purchasing'. An example is an attempt with cardiology to ensure that all post-myocardial infarctions are followed up in a dedicated clinic rather than in an undedicated outpatient system.

Similarly, the Total Purchasing Project practices purchase all healthcare currently excluding fundholding activity on a locality basis.

Other practices have little desire to become actively involved in 'hands on purchasing' but want their voices heard, so real communication links to the Health Authority (with demonstrable outcomes) are vital.

A number of practices is considering the benefits of working together, rather than in isolation. For some the way forward at the current time points to practices working together in a locality to have an influence directly or indirectly on commissioning; rather than as individual fund units. This approach relates to a balance between the following:

- practice willingness to be involved;
- practice capacity to be involved;
- incentives for the practice to devote time and effort to influencing the commissioning of health services for the benefit of its population;
- which health services are best commissioned on an individual practice basis (e.g. minor surgery) and which on a group basis for a locality (e.g. mental health services);
- the need to maintain individual practice identity;
- the need to safeguard patient choice.

### The provider

To a certain extent increasing numbers of GP fundholding practices have decreased the ability of providers to respond individually to practices' requirements. Larger numbers are in some cases stifling a provider's ability to be innovative.

The convergence to a 'group' approach that is emerging in Southampton and South West Hampshire is welcomed by one of our providers who states that 'the critical mass approach reduces fragmentation and offers a provider some hope for focusing on areas of innovation which are critical to a particular area or group of practices'. It can also be used as a mechanism for facilitating initiatives between GPFHs and non-fundholders in a locality. In addition, if locality based or outreach services are to be developed on an effective basis, they require a number of practices to subscribe in order to make them viable (e.g. minor surgery, outpatients). For the future one trust hopes that there will be a degree of cohesion among practices which will allow for individual patient flexibility. Another factor relates to increasing demands on management and transaction costs.

There are also issues relating to service provision and equity which are genuinely difficult to manage when many small purchasers are involved with a myriad different requirements.

## The purchaser

There are a number of issues that are facing the Authority as a result of the development of a multiplicity of purchasing arrangements. The purchasing environment has been in a state of continual change and at present this is particularly challenging. Current issues relate to the following:

- There needs to be equity in the allocation of resources between the services purchased by the Authority, GP fundholders and the Total Purchasing Project.
- Co-ordination of its role in the identification of health needs for the whole population alongside those identified by individual practices and localities.
- Development and implementation of health strategies in working with a number of co-purchasers (GPFHs/TPP) and achieving consensus and financial commitment.
- Ensuring there is adequacy of risk-sharing arrangements at practice, locality and Health Authority level and for what activity, for example:
  (a) high cost, low volume procedures;
  (b) extra contractual referrals;
  (c) emergency and urgent workload.
- The need to allow innovations and achievements in service provision without extreme 'tierism', perhaps through different ways of managing the pace of change (e.g. 'variety within a banding' of waiting time targets, i.e. no major outliers).
- The contracting 'currency' for purchasing services which varies between the Authority, GPFHs and the TPP.
- When major problems arise (e.g. financial difficulties) the lack of clarity about accountability of GP fundholders to the Health Authority.
- Reduction of management costs of the Health Authority, working in a more complex environment, coupled with increasing expenditure in management costs by GP fundholders.

## The future

The Authority's aims for the future include the following:

1. Continue to involve GPs in commissioning in order to develop health services.
2. Ensure GP/clinician dialogue continues to develop and service developments are clinically led.
3. Recognise and agree that GP fundholding needs to evolve. It is currently 'cherry picking' but this has been productive and has fuelled innovation. Local evolution is pointing to a convergence to localities, GPFHs working together in groups and Total Purchasing (again for a locality).
4. Develop capable and professional practice, GPFH and locality TPP managers to underpin the implementation of primary care led purchasing. This will allow GPs and their teams to direct and guide and the manager to implement and effect change, thereby reducing GP and professional day-to-day input to an appropriate minimum.
5. Ensure skill mix in primary care is appropriate to underpin changing working practices across secondary/primary/social care.
6. Use the investment in practice IT systems (now and in the future) to improve clinical IT systems to support the identification of health needs and outcomes and reduce transaction costs.
7. Ensure consumer involvement to provide the best service for patients.
8. Develop the role of GP tutors (postgraduate education), Department of Primary Medical Care, Southampton University Medical School, local trusts and Wessex Faculty of the RCGP and the Health Authority (through the programmes run in the Primary Care Development and Resource Centre) in supporting and developing GPs' role in commissioning.
9. Ensure clarity about priority setting mechanisms.
10. Facilitate opportunities to make links between health and social care.
11. Continue to take stock of current purchasing initiatives, evaluate and learn from them in order to determine their future shape.

# The Primary Care Agency: Starting with a Blank Sheet

*Robert Sloane*
*Andover District Community Health Care NHS Trust*

## Introduction

Through a planning process believed to be unique in the recent history of the NHS a community NHS trust and five GP fundholding practices have been shaping their future — with better patient care in mind.

The outcome of the planning process is pointing them firmly down the pathway of integration — a radical solution which appears neatly to anticipate changing health policy and the move towards a primary care led NHS. Important issues of value for money, public accountability and where hard decisions about priorities are best taken have all come in for open scrutiny.

## Background

Few would disagree that the adoption of fundholding by the five main practices in the Hampshire town of Andover from 1992 onwards and the formation of the Andover NHS Trust in 1993 have led to more local influence and involvement in the way health services are organised for this distinct community of 80,000 people who live in the town and encircling rural villages.

Fundholding has allowed clinical decisions to be backed with purchasing power. The trust mechanism has enabled developments to take place which would have been inconceivable under the old order.

As a result, local people are being provided with increased choice and improved accessibility to health services.

The people of Andover who funded the War Memorial Hospital in 1925 have retained a lively civic interest in health affairs and have been encouraged to play an active role in the future planning and delivery of their health services. Substantial sums of money to augment state funding continue to be raised annually. Co-terminosity with social services has facilitated joint working between the statutory agencies and excellent relationships exist between statutory and voluntary agencies.

The newly formed North and Mid-Hampshire Health Authority is committed to the idea of locality purchasing to reflect the distribution of population rather than any historical pattern of healthcare. An Andover-based Locality Purchasing Group was formed in February 1995 to help consolidate the local commissioning of services. Senior partners of the fundholding practices meet quarterly with the Andover Trust Board in a 'Health Consortium' mode designed to improve the planning and delivery of local health services.

Open communication has been established with the local authority and an annual exchange takes place with councillors on local health priorities. Conscious steps have been taken by GPs and the trust, acting in partnership with the North and Mid-Hampshire Health Authority and Winchester and Central Hampshire Community Health Council, to map the prevailing health needs of the community and ascertain their views about priorities.

In each of its first three years the Andover NHS Trust has developed new services, lowered operating costs, consistently achieved contractual requirements and met all statutory financial duties. The special relationship between the hospital and its local general practitioners has been at the heart of this success. The NHS trust culture has sparked a flourishing creativity which GPs have supported and sustained with the funds at their disposal.

## Need for change

After a long history of resource deprivation in an acute services/ hospital dominated system, the NHS reforms have undoubtedly worked to greater benefit for the people of Andover. Early in 1995 the Andover NHS Trust and senior partners of the local general practices took stock of the local health system. Positive aspects of the current arrangements include:

- all five main practices firmly embracing fundholding, operating within a locality purchasing framework – a sixth practice – not eligible for fundholding but nevertheless fully engaged in the collective activity;

- a demonstrably successful locality-based NHS trust comprising an unusual breadth of acute, community and mental health services for a small organisation;
- national health policy inclining towards primary care and the evolution of a rich diversity of primary care led service models;
- a strong collaborative culture engendered between the trust, neighbouring district general hospitals and other players in the health system (the Andover NHS Trust is by no means the sole provider of healthcare to local people);
- clearly articulated public support for local health services and a realistic expectation of service improvements in the future.

They were however mindful too of the risks to the established position:

- the resource allocation to GP fundholders appears to be far from equity within the health authority area;
- the NHS financial regime perpetuates the historical model of healthcare which works to Andover's disadvantage;
- North and Mid-Hampshire Health Authority face severe financial problems, requiring firm resolution and new solutions which may have to include trust mergers;
- predatory moves have been made and continue to be made by neighbouring trusts;
- under local government reorganisation, the new social service area will be based on a combined Andover and Winchester population;
- disproportionate transaction costs are almost certainly incurred in the management of six small individual healthcare businesses, i.e. the Andover NHS Trust and the five GP fundholding practices.

In addition to the continuous process of change affecting the health service, the next twelve months would also see a general election which will add to the climate of uncertainty.

## Andover Health Inquiry

Following analysis, the Andover NHS Trust and Locality Purchasing Group agreed on the need actively to plan a local future rather than let the tide of inevitable change dictate circumstances.

The idea of a planning style inquiry seemed to be both highly original and reflective of the part played by the local community in the running of a publicly funded service. There was an initial reserve about the use of the word inquiry, suggestive perhaps of a judicial investigation into untoward incidents, but this concern was soon overcome and has not surfaced subsequently.

Willing partners were found in the form of the North and Mid-

Hampshire Health Authority which welcomed the inquiry as part of their Framework for Change programme of strategic change, and Winchester and Central Hampshire Community Health Council which applauded the public participation foundations.

Sponsorship funding for the inquiry was committed from the NHS Executive South and West Region which also involved an experienced primary care manager in an observer role.

A key decision was the appointment of an independent chairman and the team were delighted when Professor Robinson, Director of the Institute for Health Policy Studies, Faculty of Social Science, Southampton University, accepted the invitation to fulfil this role.

At their first meeting the inquiry team decided three principal objectives:

1. to review the scope and effectiveness of the current health service model in Andover;
2. to review the equity of resource allocation;
3. to recommend a future service model which would:
   - secure increased health gain or service capacity for the benefit of patients;
   - reduce operating costs.

### Process and programme

The timetable was of necessity tight, spanning the four-month period June, July, August and September 1996. A variety of mechanisms was devised by which evidence was to be gathered:

- **Mapping** – to gain a better understanding of how patient referrals and funds flow in the system. A specific goal was to compare a future weighted capitation 'community resource' allocation against current contractual spend.
- **Visioning** – which involved leading practitioners in the country sharing their motivations and aspirations in the field of primary and community care within a 'think tank' environment. Linking health professionals and community interests emerged as a dominant theme.
- **Consulting** – a well attended public meeting offered some clear insights about the desire of the local community to continue to play an active part in the planning and delivery of their health services, even if this would inevitably involve hard decisions about priority setting.

Users and carers contributed in full to a half-day workshop designed to elicit the issues which they believed to be the most important in building a future pattern of local health services.

Individual practitioners from the statutory, voluntary and

private sectors were invited to share their views about the way health and health-related services could be developed.

Neighbouring NHS trusts responded to the 'greenfield' approach of the Inquiry and, favouring a collaborative approach, made a series of presentations illustrating how greater gain could be derived from the global health system.

- **Visits** – although fewer in number than originally planned, visits were made to primary care development sites in the UK. International references were drawn to the health maintenance organisations in the USA.

Throughout the process each of the participating organisations fed in comments of both an individual and corporate nature. A particularly helpful contribution came from the Chief Executive of the North and Mid-Hampshire Health Authority and it was upon this submission that the final recommendations of the Inquiry were based. The recommendations were the product of a final session which involved the team in an intensive distillation of key issues.

## Inquiry recommendations

The Inquiry concluded that while there was nothing fundamentally flawed with the existing service model, the sponsoring organisations were right to think in terms of risk and opportunity regarding the means of future delivery. Recommendations were grouped around four main themes:

- provision of services;
- locality commissioning;
- public accountability;
- transaction costs.

### Provision of services

A process of elimination was followed to arrive at the range of services which might be provided in (as opposed to for) the local community in the future. Despite the rapidly expanding population, few had ever foreseen the justification for a District General Hospital/ High Technology Centre in Andover. Rather, the first building block should be around primary and community care, services which should be controlled and provided locally wherever possible.

A second group of services that bridges primary and community care would present an opportunity for review, particularly where there were genuine options about the balance in how services were delivered, notably:

- patient rehabilitation;
- maternity;
- mental health.

An inherent expectation in arriving at a future pattern of services would be a continuation of the process of remodelling and re-engineering, 'providing more for less', which had hallmarked the collaborative working between trust and GPs.

### Locality commissioning

Perhaps the recommendation of greatest significance turned upon the issue of how best to retain and increase local influence over the commissioning of health services for Andover residents. This debate began with a definition of locality which at the base level was taken as the aggregate of the practice lists of the six GP practices in the town, a total of 50,000 people.

The rooting of fundholding within the practices had clearly illustrated the benefit of the new instrument, particularly where purchasing decisions had been co-ordinated on a global basis. Nevertheless, the actual funds within the standard fundholding scheme were relatively small compared to the scope of total fundholding which would increase local leverage by a factor of four times. From this notion the idea of the 'total health resource for Andover' was born with both HCHS and GMS coming under local control.

While this thinking was not entirely new, the Inquiry considered and agreed to look further at a bolder and more far-reaching stage of evolution. This would entail the coalescing of fundholding and the trust into a form of primary care agency which carried both purchasing and providing responsibility. The benefits of such integration could be described in a number of ways:

- providing the opportunity for more effective management of GMS and HCHS funding;
- by subsuming parts (and only parts) of the current trust framework into the agency immediate business management economies could result.

But, perhaps the most powerful consequence would be in following the primary care maxim to 'provide what you can, purchase what you can't'. In this way the agency could concentrate mainly on the direct provision of locally accessible high-quality primary and community care. With three district general hospitals in a close encirclement of 15 miles, this appears to be a viable way forward, provided that the overall strategic balancing of services is preserved. This approach also seems to address one of the central problems of a primary care led NHS, namely, how to incentivise primary care and ensure that resources are geared to where the care is actually being delivered.

What is perhaps key about this possible stage of development, colloquially referred to as 'a merger' of the trust and fundholders, is that it is not a takeover of one partly by another. Rather, it would be a voluntary fusion of organisational frameworks in the interests of providing better local care.

## Public accountability

The dual roles of such an agency would of necessity dictate the highest standards of public accountability and demonstrable probity in the management of substantial sums of public money. Not only would this concern accounting for how state funds were being committed, but also promoting informed debate about difficult choices. Yet in this challenge lies one of the greatest opportunities actively to involve social services, education, housing and voluntary sector partners in a more effective and joint commissioning process.

## Conclusion

Following the publication of *Primary Care: The Future* and the White Paper on Choice and Opportunity (October 1996), the moment for primary care adventure has never been better.

Following agreement by all the interested parties, a second stage of the Andover Health Inquiry has been commissioned. This will concentrate on examining the feasibility of moving forward in the way that the Inquiry has suggested. By 1 March 1997 the team had set a new deadline of devising a firm implementation plan.

In what seems to be an inexorable movement towards a primary care led NHS the ideas that have been spawned in Andover seem to be of immense local relevance and an important contribution to the national debate.

*Stuart Chidgey - Director - UK Primary and Community Healthcare*
*International Hospitals Group*

# PRIMARY CARE - FUTURE, PAST AND PRESENT

Primary Care is set to witness profound change as it becomes, for the first time in its 50 year history, fully integrated with the rest of the NHS.

Primary Care, and in particular General Medical Services (GMS), have enjoyed through the first half century of the NHS, a 'semi-detached' arrangement with the more dominant Hospital and Community Health Services (HCHS). Amongst the main differences between GMS and HCHS have been: distinct employment contact arrangements (ie GPs self-employed status), resource allocation (both capital and revenue), purchaser/provider responsibilities, and performance management approaches.

The dawn of a primary care led NHS in the mid 1990s has signalled for the first time, a full recognition of the leading role primary care services represent within the NHS. This recognition has evolved through the 1991 internal market reforms which introduced General Practice Fundholding (GPFH). GPs have increasingly through the extension of the GPFH scheme, culminating in total fundholding pilots, been given enhanced authority over the determination of how HCHS resources are spent.

EL(94)79 *Developing NHS purchasing and GP Fundholding* heralded the commencement of a primary care led NHS.

Defining what a primary care led NHS means gathered pace through 1996 with a ministerial 'listening tour' of the country leading to the publication in June 1996 of *Primary Care: The Future* a consultation document which distilled a '...set of principles which should govern primary care services and, through primary care, access to secondary care'. These principles are: quality, fairness, accessibility, responsiveness and efficiency. This was followed in October 1996 by a White Paper *Choice and Opportunity Primary Care: The Future* which included amongst its proposals the opportunity to pilot new arrangements for delivering primary care.

These proposals include:

- a salaried option for GPs, either within partnerships or with other bodies, such as NHS Trusts
- practice based contracts
- a single budget for general medical services, other hospital and community health services, and prescribing with the practice responsible for purchasing or providing services within it.

Enabling legislation *National Health Service (Primary Care) Bill* was introduced to parliment in November 1996. The Primary Care Act received its Royal Assent in March 1997 enabling the first pilots to operate from April 1998. Prior to this through 1997/98 GPs, NHS Trusts and Health Authorities can expect an intensive preparatory period.

A second White Paper *Primary Care: Delivering the Future* was published in December 1996. This White Paper unveils 70 new initiatives for primary care including:

- practice staff eligible for NHS pensions
- nurse prescribing pilots in 500 practices
- an enhanced role for private finance for premises development
- a doubling of the primary care research budget to £50 million
- a more equitable distribution of GMS funds

For 1997/98 £100 million is being made available to develop primary and community services. £5 million has been set aside for preparatory work for primary Care Bill pilots, with a separate £2 million challenge fund to promote progress on Primary Care White Paper proposals.

Together this represents an enormous challenge for Primary Care Teams. As *Primary Care: Delivering the Future* concludes:

*They should seize the opportunities on offer to initiate change and improvements to services.*

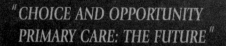

# PART TWO

# MANAGING SERVICE DELIVERY

## 2.1

# The Foundations of Effective Human Resource Management

*David M. Towner*
*Occupational Psychologist and*
*Independent Management Consultant*

---

### Introduction

With the move to fundholding and taking charge of the business development of the practice, GPs and their managers are increasingly taking on more responsibility for the human resource management issues within the practice. As a result, many practices are faced with having to establish and introduce sound policies and procedures for human resource management. This, in many cases, is a new experience for GPs and their managers.

The purpose of this chapter is to examine the fundamental human resource management and procedures needed to ensure the smooth running of a GP practice. In consideration of these we will also look at how to introduce changes in existing human resource operations within the practice and implement new policies and procedures. This will also take account of how effectively to introduce change to staff to ensure their commitment and understanding.

The examination of these issues is structured so as to provide response to the following questions:

- What is the context or domain of human resource management, policies and procedures within an organisation?
- What are the fundamental planks that need to be in place, in terms of human resource policies, procedures and structures within a GP practice?
- How are these planks developed and then introduced to staff?

- Sound management – the critical ingredient for effectiveness in the management and development of human resources at the practice, what is required?

Throughout the chapter we will examine both human resource management theory and case study material from GP practices.

## The context of human resources in an organisation

When planning to make improvements in human resource management and operations of a GP practice, it is useful to have a broad framework for understanding the areas that this might encompass. To proceed without this understanding might lead to the development of a new procedure or policy in one area of human resource management which may not integrate well with another developed at a later date.

For example, take an instance when job descriptions were developed at one point in the practice and then, at a later date, a new staff appraisal system was implemented. If job descriptions for all posts within the practice had been developed without consideration of how they will link and relate to the staff appraisal systems, problems could occur.

Let us assume that the job descriptions were set out so that they described the key tasks and responsibilities of each post, and to whom the job holder reports and is accountable. This type of job description helps an individual understand what work they are expected to carry out within the practice and provides a reference point for decision-making and accountability, but it is limited.

Further on in this scenario, let us assume that, one year later, the practice decides to develop and implement a new staff appraisal system that will encompass both the assessment of job performance and the identification and planning of training and development for staff. To develop an appraisal system of this type requires a full understanding of the tasks, activities and areas of responsibility for each post and, additionally, it requires a full understanding of the skills, knowledge, abilities and experience (competencies) that support effective job performance in each post.

In attempting to develop and implement this type of staff appraisal system, the practice would find that its job descriptions narrowly focus individuals on the tasks and activities of their jobs, but do not help them understand the competencies required of them. Although staff would be able to undertake assessment of their job performance against what is expected of them in terms of tasks and activities, it would be difficult for them to assess their training and development needs, as their job descriptions do not contain an explanation of the skills mix or competencies needed for the post.

The obvious lesson here is that the practice needed to develop job descriptions so they would relate to the future development of a staff appraisal system and that they should be structured so as to integrate effectively with the type of system envisaged by the practice.

To minimise the risks identified above, the planning and introduction of new human resource management initiatives should always be done by considering the impact individual initiatives could have on the full context of human resource areas of the practice. So what does the big picture of human resource management in an organisation look like?

A useful way to conceptualise the full picture of the activities involved in human resource management within an organisation is provided by Leonard Nadler, and as summarised by Rothwell and Kazanas in their book, *Strategic Human Resource Development* (1989). Within this description, Nadler sets out three domains for all human resource management activities. These are:

- Human Resource Utilisation (HRU);
- Human Resource Engineering/Environment (HRE);
- Human Resource Development (HRD).

For each domain, the specific human resource management activities encompassed and the external factors needing to be taken into account are shown in Figure 2.1.1.

What Figure 2.1.1 shows is that when considering the introduction of a new element or change in any one existing element within a given domain reference should be made to the elements within that precise domain and to those in the other two. When considering the recruitment of new employees (HRU domain), consideration should be given to elements within that domain (i.e. job descriptions, pay, etc.) as well as to elements of the other two domains (e.g. those in HRE – work space, use of IT, etc. – and those in HRD – induction, training, appraisal, etc.).

Additionally, when planning the introduction of new human resource management initiatives, consideration needs to be given to factors outside the organisation, such as government legislation (e.g. employment law, health and safety legislation, etc.), the labour market, local conditions and the current socio-economic conditions. If this is the context within which to undertake effective planning of human resource management, what are the critical elements for GP practices?

## Key human resource policies and procedures with a GP practice

During the past two years this author has had several opportunities to work, in various capacities, with practices in undertaking thorough reviews of their existing work arrangements and staffing structures.

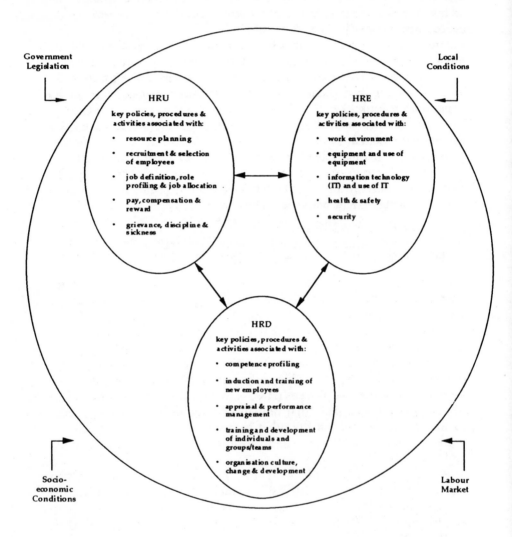

**Figure 2.1.1** *The three domains of human resource management activities*
*Source:* Based on the categories devised by Leonard Nadler (1984)

This work involved implementing radical and far-reaching change. The need for this substantial change was to prepare practices to undertake their roles effectively as fundholders and to establish the organisation and human resource foundations from which to achieve their identified development goals.

During this period of providing external consultancy within GP practices and other organisations, several human resource management issues emerged as being particularly common and critical with GP practices. The first of these sits within the Human Resource Utilisation domain and is concerned with moving decision-making about staff management issues onto a more objective and equitable basis within the practice.

A practice must establish a clear set of policies and procedures that help guide behaviour and serve as a reference point for staff management decision-making. The key thrust of these policies and procedures is to set out clearly what the practice can expect of its employees and what they in turn can expect from the practice. The key policies and procedures that help to provide this guide for behaviour and reference point for decision-making are set out below.

## Terms and conditions of employment

As stated above, the key thrust of these policies and procedures is to make clear what the practice can expect of its employees and what they can expect from this practice. The fundamental building block for all policies and procedures of this type is an umbrella document that covers all essential aspects of employment within the practice, and is normally referred to as Terms and Conditions of Employment.

A standard Terms and Conditions of Employment document will usually set out the following:

- **Hours of work**, specified for each individual employee and conditions relating to work attendance (further details of work attendance, covering absence is then provided in an Absence from Duty policy document).
- Statement of **Continuous Service**, as required by Section 1 (2)(c) of the Employment Protection (Consolidation) Act 1978.
- Details of **Place of Employment** and conditions relating to potential and future changes in hours, work and place of work.
- **Payment** details, specified for each individual employee and conditions relating to changes in pay.
- **Annual Leave**, providing details of holiday entitlement and holiday booking arrangements.
- Conditions for giving **Notice** to terminate employment by either side (i.e. the practice and the employee).

- **Standards of Conduct and Work,** a set of expectations relating to how employees are to conduct themselves while at work (e.g. maintaining confidentiality, security, dealing with patients, standards for appearance and dress, complying with reasonable instructions, standards of honesty and integrity and professional standards) and producing work of acceptable standards.
- An overview of the **Disciplinary and Grievance Policy and Procedures.** Detailed explanations of these are contained in separate policy documents.
- A policy statement relating to conditions for **Maternity Leave.**
- An overview of the practice's **Health and Safety Policy.** Detailed explanation of the policy and related procedures are contained in a separate policy and procedures document.
- A statement outlining the responsibility for **Personal Property** of employees while at work.
- An overview of the practice's **Equal Opportunities Policy.** A detailed policy document is provided separately.
- A statement regarding fitness and **Health** to undertake the duties of the post, to which the employee has been appointed.
- **Form of Acceptance,** this is the final section of a standard Terms and Conditions of Employment that states an employee has agreed to the terms specified in the document. Signatures of both the partnership and the individual employee are required for formal acceptance.

The additional policy and procedure documents referred to within the Terms and Conditions of Employment are outlined below.

### Absence from duty

This should encompass both a policy guideline for absence as well as a set of procedural documents for recording and monitoring absence. The policy guideline should set out the following:

- A Notification procedure explaining what is expected of an employee when they are absent.
- Conditions for payment during sickness and conditions for requiring an independent medical examination.
- Certification procedures of absence up to and exceeding seven consecutive days.
- Circumstances of special compassionate leave.
- Absences for reasons other than of sickness and compassionate nature.

Three key procedural documents support the implementation and maintenance of the policy document. These are:

- An Absence from Duty Record form upon which are recorded each absence from duty (other than holidays), stating date of absence, reason, number of days, whether self-certified or doctor's certificate is required and space for noting special remarks.
- A Sickness Absence Form which is to be started upon notification of absence and completed upon an employee's return to work following an absence (other than holidays).
- A combined Holiday Request Form and Record, providing detail of holiday entitlement, dates of requests and number of days requested, authorisation of requests and cumulative total (descending from entitlement) showing outstanding holiday entitlement.

## Performance standards

Many organisations are instituting procedures for performance management, appraisal of job performance and assessment of training needs. The main emphases of these procedures are to ensure that employees carry out their work effectively and to help them develop competence within their jobs.

In support of these procedures many organisations also have policies on performance standards. A key thrust of these policies is to move poor job performance or performance where there is need to improve out of being a disciplinary matter and into one that focuses on providing opportunity to make improvements.

These policies also provide a means for being able to address poor performance immediately, rather than waiting for an annual appraisal meeting to occur. In this manner, appraisal of performance and the ability to help individuals improve performance or acquire new skills becomes a continual process.

The policy should provide a means for identifying and addressing poor performance. It should provide a way to set out and record areas that need improvement, potential causes of the poor performance (e.g. lack of skill, poor motivation, unclear instruction), action to be taken to achieve the improvement, mechanism for assessing outcome and a way for individuals to lodge a 'right of appeal' under the grievance policy.

To support the policy a procedural form is required. This serves as an action plan for addressing the poor performance and a record of areas identified for improvement along with causes that needed to be addressed.

## Discipline

One hopes that only on rare occasions will a practice need formally to discipline one of its employees. However, if the need arises, and to ensure that this is done on a fair and equitable basis, the practice requires both a policy and procedures for handling disciplinary matters.

The main emphasis of a disciplinary policy is to have problems resolved through informal discussions with an immediate senior. Only if informal discussions have failed to bring about a satisfactory solution should they be escalated to more formal and documented procedures.

The policy should set out procedures for dealing with discipline so that they escalate from the issuing of a verbal warning, through two stages of written warnings. At each of these stages, the manager of the practice is responsible for issuing all warnings and for convening disciplinary interviews. The policy should allow for an individual to have the right of representation at any point in the disciplinary proceeding.

In addition to setting out the stages in the disciplinary proceedings, the policy needs to provide some definition of what behaviour constitutes gross misconduct and for which an employee could be summarily dismissed. In most cases the type of conduct would include:

- wilful disregard of reasonable instructions;
- wilful disregard of the practice's rules, procedures, statutory requirements and conditions of employment;
- disclosure of confidential information;
- bringing the practice into disrepute;
- dishonesty in dealings with patients or other members of the practice;
- violent or aggressive behaviour or language towards patients or other members of the practice;
- wilful damage to or theft of the property of patients, the practice or other members of staff;
- irresponsible or obstructive behaviour which seriously damages working relationships.

Given the serious nature of these types of behaviour, summary dismissal should only be authorised by the full partnership of the practice and not take place until the partnership has full investigated the matter and discussed it with the individual concerned. To provide scope to undertake the investigation within these circumstances, the Disciplinary Policy should provide for suspension of an employee from work on full pay pending such investigations.


### Grievance

Matters dealing with staff grievance should encompass both a policy guideline as well as a set of procedural documents for recording and monitoring any grievance that require formal handling.

As with the Disciplinary Policy, the main emphasis of a Grievance Policy is to have problems resolved through informal discussions with an immediate senior and only escalated for formal proceedings if informal discussions have failed to bring about a satisfactory resolution.

The policy guideline should reaffirm the principle that most problems should be handled by an employee's immediate senior. If this is not possible, the policy should state what formal course of actions are then available. Normally, this will comprise three stages of escalation. Stage 1 should be a formal written statement of the grievance to the manager of the practice. This is then followed by a meeting of those involved in the grievance with a view to resolving the matter at that meeting.

If the problem is not resolved or if there is dissatisfaction, employees should have a next step recourse. This Stage 2 of the policy would again require a written submission of the grievance along with reasons for taking it further. The manager of the practice then submits the written document to the partnership for consideration. The partnership takes the lead in settling the grievance at this stage.

The third and final stage normally takes the form of a written 'right of appeal' to the partnership against the decisions made at Stage 2. Once the partnership has made its decision, the outcome is final and there is no further 'right of appeal'.

A single key procedural document supports the implementation and maintenance of the policy document. This is a form upon which the date of lodging the formal grievance, along with details of the grievance and subsequent action taken to resolve the problem, can be written and recorded.

## Equal opportunities

This policy, based on the Race Relations Act 1976, provides pro-tection to employees against unfair discrimination and ensures that all are provided with reasonable and equitable opportunities without prejudice. Any breach of the policy could result in disciplinary action and any employee believing they have received treatment contrary to the policy, should be enabled to pursue this through the Grievance Policy.

## Conclusion

The above policies and procedures along with the Terms and Conditions of Employment, the employee's job description and offer of letter of employment constitute the employment contract with the practice. As such, they form the cornerstones of human resource management within the practice.

These fundamental planks are the policies and procedures from which all other human resource management initiatives within the other two domains will be built upon and need to have integration. Examples of these later developments will include issues such as health and safety (HRE domain), staff appraisal systems (HRD domain) and training and development policies (HRD domain).

A useful resource for helping to establish these fundamental policies and procedures is the *Using Information in Practice Management*, Greenhalgh and Company Ltd with a consortium of NHS organisations.

## Developing and implementing changes in human resource management

Development and implementation of the policies and procedures identified above, will support the effective management of human resources within a practice. There is however the risk that their development will largely be seen as a pen and paper exercise. In other words, that in order to set up effective policies and procedures for human resource management one simply goes away and writes them.

The danger with this viewpoint is that taking this course of action will lead to policies and procedures that get filed away or lodged on a manager's bookshelf. To prevent this from occurring, clear steps need to be taken to ensure that staff are involved in the process of establishing improvements in human resource management and the introduction of new policies and procedures.

This needs to happen on several fronts. First, Dawson (1986) in her model of the change processes in organisations identifies that a critical stage is 'Members felt need for change'. Employees of an organisation need to want to see change, or at least have some understanding of the need for change, or accept the fact that change will improve circumstances.

The lead in creating this climate for change must come from top management within the organisation. For a GP practice this would be the partnership and executive management (e.g. practice manager fundholding manager). To help establish this climate, the group must commit itself to undertaking a programme of change and to take the lead in developing a picture of how the practice is to develop, by identifying current problems and areas where a change in policy or procedure will ultimately benefit the practice.

Second, this group must identify ways to involve staff in the development of this 'big picture' and the actions that will be required for implementation. This means creating forums whereby staff can provide inputs to discussions about the current state of affairs of the practice and contribute views on proposals for its development and changes to be implemented. Within this context, the top management group of the practice must continue to provide leadership throughout the process and maintain their role as the final decision-makers of the organisation. The case study presented below, helps to illustrate these principles.

## Case study: Planning and implementing a programme of change

This case study is based on work that the author has undertaken with the partnership and staff of The Freemen's Common Health Centre. The health centre provides a health service to students and staff of Leicester University and the local population. Details of the case study are presented here with the permission of the partnership.

The process of change within the health centre was initiated by the partnership. They had clear ideas about how they wanted the health centre to develop over the next five-year period. To commence a major programme of change, the partnership instituted a major review of all the health centre's internal and external operations. The review set out to identify:

- problems and areas needing improvement at the health centre;
- its existing strengths and capabilities;
- opportunities for development of the health centre.

The review involved all staff and partners on both an individual and group basis as well as meetings with key personnel at the University of Leicester and the health agency.

Outcomes from the review were used to develop an action plan to set right the immediate problems facing the health centre and to establish the fundamental organisation and human resource management blocks for the future development of the health centre. Stages in the development of the action plan were:

- Consideration of the full findings from the review by the partnership and devising a draft action plan on the basis of these findings. Within the draft action plan, each doctor undertook lead responsibility for specific action points. This helped to ensure ownership of the action plan and provided for long-term responsibility for these areas.
- Presentation of the draft action plan to all staff of the health centre and reaching agreement on a final version. Within the final version of the action plan, staff were encouraged to identify specific actions in which they wanted to be involved.

The action plan was timetabled for implementation over a six-week period. Within this period, small working groups were established to produce drafts of the various policies and procedures identified in the plan. These in turn were circulated to all staff for consideration prior to being discussed and finalised at full staff meetings.

At the conclusion of this process the health centre had established the following changes:

- a new job rota system for its reception team;
- new structure for its internal business and clinical meetings;
- a set of human resource management policies and procedures on matters covering: personnel records, employment contracts, grievance, discipline, performance management, staff appraisal, sickness, terms and conditions of employment, equal opportunities;
- a health and safety policy and set of procedural guidelines;
- implementation of an education programme for staff on fundholding;
- establishment of a new executive management structure for the health centre.

The manner in which the partnership led the change process provided opportunity for all staff to contribute to the identification of the problems facing the health centre. It also gave staff opportunity to contribute ideas for the development of the health centre and to work on the various initiatives involved in the change programme. This meant that everyone at the health centre was able to recognise the need to change, identify the benefits of change and take ownership for implementing change.

## The critical role of sound management

The Massachusetts Institute of Technology's research study (*Management Into the 1990s* upon which Morton's book *The Corporation of the 1990s* is based) into the reasons why some organisations grew and developed in the 1980s while others failed miserably, identified that a key ingredient of successful organisations was an effective integration between their business, human resource and information technology planning and activities. In developing this concept, the study came up with what has been termed the Strategic Alignment paradigm (see Figure 2.1.2).

What was also identified in the study, and can be seen in Figure 2.1.2, is that for this integration to be achieved successfully, sound management processes must be at the centre. Managers and the management processes by which they operate are at the centre of all the other activities within the organisation and have the potential to draw across all other dimensions to achieve integration. It was also demonstrated in the case study in the previous section that for the change process to be effective, strong management is needed to provide leadership and direction for staff.

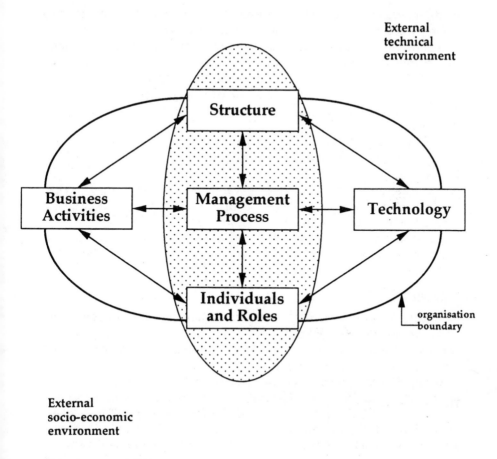

**Figure 2.1.2** *Management into the 1990s paradigm of Strategic Alignment*

As with organisational effectiveness and effective change management, the critical role that a manager has with regard to human resource management policies and procedures cannot be under-estimated. A manager within a GP practice is at the core of making these policies and procedures workable.

One of the important roles of the manager within many of the human resource management policies and procedures set out earlier in this chapter is that of being the focal point for decision-making. For example, within the grievance and disciplinary policy, the manager of the practice is the one to whom employees will direct their issues and it is the manager of the practice who is responsible for the resolution of these issues. At later stages within these policies, the manager also has the important role of escalating issues if they cannot be resolved at immediate levels and needs to liaise between staff and the partnership.

Another important role of the manager is to ensure that the procedures contained within the policies are being used by staff. It is one thing to have the policies and procedures implemented within the practice but another for staff to be actively using these in their day-to-day work.

Finally, the emphasis of the human resource management policies and procedures is to focus the management of staff at the management levels within the practice, so that the partnership is enabled to concentrate on the business and clinical developments of the practice. The manager of the practice has a critical role to ensure that effective management is being undertaken at the practice and that the staff management processes are being carried out within the policy and procedural guidelines.

## References

Bennison, M and Casson, J (1984) *The Manpower Planning Handbook*, McGraw-Hill, Maidenhead.

Davies, P and Towner, D M (1996) 'Partners in change', to be published in *PULSE*, London.

Dawson, S (1986) *Analysing Organisations*, Macmillan, London.

Greenhalgh and Company Ltd with a consortium of NHS organisations (1994) *Using Information in Practice Management (The Rainbow Pack)*, 8 vols, British Crown Copyright.

Morton, Michael S Scott (1991) *The Corporation of the 1990s — Information Technology and Organizational Transformation*, Oxford University Press, New York.

Nadler, L (ed.) (1984) *The Handbook of Human Resource Development*, Wiley-Interscience, New York.

Rothwell, W and Kazanas, H (1989) *Strategic Human Resource Development*, Prentice-Hall, Englewood Cliffs, New Jersey.

Towner, D M (1989) 'Training needs analysis: incorporating dimensions of organisation behaviour and the learning needs of employees', MSc thesis, Birkbeck College, University of London.

# Risk Management

*Merrill Whalen*
*Adviser in Practice Management*

## Introduction

This chapter is not intended to be academic, nor can it be comprehensive. The purpose is quite simply to take any mystique out of this relatively new responsibility called risk management, yet emphasise just how crucially important it has become in organising and managing successful and safe general practice.

The chapter will address and highlight what could be termed the common pitfalls in practice and is based on the wide experience and collected evidence of the Medical and Dental Defence Union of Scotland (MDDUS). By necessity, many important issues are simply raised in checklist form.

In the first instance let us consider the term risk management. Like so many unfamiliar words and phrases that have slowly yet surely been edging their way into the general practice vocabulary, strip away the jargon and there is something more meaningful and relevant. If we look at the example of business planning for many healthcare workers, the very thought of it conjures a vision and concept of a maze of figures, clever words and an enormous document usually relating to one or other giant business corporation. While the underlying principles will undoubtedly be similar, business planning is about helping to take a practice or indeed any organisation forward, careful consideration of what the organisation is doing at the present time, what it really wants to be doing and setting out how to get there – no more, no less.

What is the first thing that springs to mind when the term risk management is mentioned?

- 'Forced on us from the Americans.'
- 'Too busy to take on anything else.'
- 'Another buzz phrase that doesn't involve us.'
- 'We're not ready for it.'
- 'What does it mean anyway?'
- 'It will cost far too much!'

Risk management is a process, a continuous process, that must by necessity have a beginning, but once started will never end. The successful caring and careful practice will ensure that risk management is totally integrated into the very culture of the organisation. Like quality and continuous improvement, risk management will need to be led. But achievement is everyone's business and is dependent upon personal and team ownership and accountability. Risk management is a process that:

- identifies hazards and associated risks;
- has a good look at these hazards and risks, assesses them and evaluates the situation and circumstances;
- then, most importantly is prepared to do something about it.

Life is full of risks, is it not? Simply getting out of bed in the morning, using an electric kettle to make tea, crossing the road, travelling by bus/car, etc., all of course carry an element of risk. In terms of healthcare risk means anything that can have an adverse effect on the quality of care for patients and also for staff and visitors. Think too of the general practitioners and members of staff who, one or all, could find themselves involved, totally responsible or party to a complaint from patients, or a claim for negligence. Professional reputation, months if not years of anxiety, issues of registration with regulating bodies such as GMC, UKCC, financial implications, one's very liberty are all at stake and undoubtedly, at all levels, will have profound and serious effects on individuals. In essence risks are present. Patients do and no doubt will continue to suffer harm from an adverse effect of one sort or another. Doctors and staff suffer too. There has been a steady rise in the number of claims alleging medical negligence against general practitioners over the last decade. Why should this be so? Some of the suggested reasons are listed as follows:

1. Patients' expectations.
2. In a general sense, society is more litigation conscious than ever before.
3. Patient advocacy (local health councils, citizens advice bureaux).
4. The media give a lot of publicity to medical matters and settlements of successful claims.
5. 'Me too' claims (such as Benzodiazepines).
6. In some instances, the positive action of the legal profession.

To be successful in a case of medical negligence a patient must prove that:

- there was an existing duty of care owed by the doctor to the patient;
- there was a breach in that duty of care;
- the loss or damage suffered by that patient resulted directly from that breach.

There is no statute law in medical negligence. Cases are judged on their own particular merits and circumstances and in the light of previous important cases. To manage risks effectively so that these can be at very best eliminated or, possibly more realistically, reduced or minimalised, a number of foundation stones need to be firmly in place.

## Think and breathe quality

Is there a demonstration from the top of genuine belief and commitment that only the best will do: 'Our practice is about doing the right thing at the right time and getting it right first time.'

## An active process

Act on the basis that prevention is better than cure. Act before a problem arises. Standards and expectations have to be set out so that people are left in no doubt what is expected of them. Like mountains, expectations need to be high and visible.

## A positive approach

Is effective leadership in place that demonstrates risk management as a positive, exciting and challenging responsibility and not one of negatives and problems? There is no place for a punitive approach which will ultimately result in lack of morale and motivation and an unwillingness to accept anything innovative. The Japanese were noted to 'rejoice' in a mistake as it was an opportunity to learn. Understandably one may have some hesitation at the thought of actually rejoicing, but the opportunity to learn is important.

## An organisation that involves and values people

Effective communications, forums for discussion where people's views and ideas are generally considered, all help to create an open and honest culture. Line management, who is responsible for what and reporting systems must be clear to individuals and shared with all members of the team.

## Audit

Audit involves the ability to look carefully and critically at systems and services so that the purpose is clear and the outcome able to be measured. Selling the idea is not straightforward and it would be fool-hardy to state otherwise. Like health promotion, it is not that easy, in fact sometimes impossible, to demonstrate a quick return for any investment. However, benefits could be summarised as follows:

- continuous improvement in the quality of care delivered to patients;
- a reduction in complaints and claims for damages;
- all round, a much safer environment for patients, doctors and staff;
- feeling good, feeling in control, knowing the scope of work, standards and expectations, all of which should lead to an increase in morale and motivation;
- reduction in costs (stress and anxiety for all concerned, having to repeat procedures/tasks because they were not done correctly first time, settlement for successful claims).

At this point the reader could be forgiven for thinking that this is all a bit nebulous. Writing about culture and openness does little to help the manager who is more or less on the shop floor daily and expected to act practically and with common sense.

## What do I actually have to do to avoid risks?

All staff must be aware of risks – ignorance will be no defence whatsoever.

- Why is filing letters regularly and accurately important?
- The abnormal cervical cytology result that fails to reach the patient could have disastrous consequences because ...
- Noting the time against the request for a home visit could prove extremely important because ...

A young mother was excited about her new appointment – two night shifts a week on telephone duty at a recently set up co-operative for out-of-hours work. 'Off the job and on the job training – what do you mean? I was a telephonist for years prior to having my family.' Here was an enthusiastic and intelligent lady with no knowledge, understanding or awareness of risks, until they are pointed out and explanations given of serious consequences.

Address fairly and seriously the issue of quality versus quantity. A problem of accessibility, particularly in relation to telephones, will not be solved by a new, improved super deluxe telecommunications system if there are quite simply not enough hands to answer lines. On the other hand, constant hurly-burly and complaints of busyness are unlikely to be solved simply by providing another member of staff.

Appropriate and proper delegation of tasks and responsibilities is a key factor in managing risks. How often do we see around us abdication and examples of dumping which invite problems, and again no defence. Delegation entails assessing a person's competence and keeping a finger on the pulse, as well as being available for advice and support. There is a responsibility, of course, on members of staff also to work within their own competence and not to take on tasks for which they have had no training or experience. The practice that puts time, effort and money into training, education and development of the primary healthcare team invests wisely, again making a large contribution towards success, care and safety.

Mention was made earlier of the need to make everyone aware of risks. Awareness of legislation is also important and can be dealt with in a simple straightforward way. An explanation of the key elements of the complaints route open to patients, the claims route, patients' rights under Access to Health Records Act, Access to Medical Reports Act, Health and Safety Legislation, Employment Law, etc., assists the development and commitment of individuals and of the team.

Paper, paper and yet more paper to be read, dealt with, filed or filled in as a form for further action is a regular heartfelt cry. Yet setting out what has been agreed in the form of systems of working, protocols and guidance notes is to be recommended — and not as a one-off exercise in a folder, gathering dust on a shelf, but as working documents to be acted upon and reviewed at regular intervals.

This section so far has attempted to set out the importance of quality management and put in place some foundation stones. Now the day-to-day grassroots issues are examined. Risk areas can be categorised into three main headings:

- providing the service;
- the premises;
- risks to those providing the service (the GPs and staff).

## Providing the service

### Communications

Is there a standard for the humble message (and a plea to dispense with post-its that all too easily come off and are lost)? Do regular meetings take place where all members of staff are valued and involved for contributions they may make? Technology continues to forge ahead: answering machines, portable telephones, pagers, faxes, etc. The need to address access codes, confidentiality, maintenance and simply ensuring that their work cannot be understated.

---

Communicate, **Communicate, Communicate**

---

## Medical records

Attention should be given to whether they are:

- chronological;
- contemporaneous;
- each sheet headed with name, date of birth, address of patient;
- adverse reactions/allergies prominently displayed;
- summaries available;
- medication (present and past) easily identified;
- a practice statement about confidentiality of medical records;
- abbreviations confined to those recognised by the medical profession. Avoid idiosyncratic, sarcastic or insulting comment. Remember it will not be amusing if asked to clarify in court.

---

Record, **Record, Record**

---

**NB:** Medico/legal correspondence and insurance reports do not form part of the patient's health record and as such should be filed separately.

## Dealing with the mail and giving out results

Is there a:

- protocol for review, initialling and action of all mail?
- procedure for informing patients of all clinically significant laboratory results?
- procedure for informing patients of normal results?
- a log of outgoing specimens that can be checked against incoming?

## Failure to visit

A method of recording home visit requests and a system for ensuring action must sound pretty mundane to most, yet time and again this has proved to be an area of risk.

### Telephone advice

Whether morning, afternoon, evening or overnight, every effort should be made to ensure entries are made in the health record.

### Practice nurse issues

For the purpose of this brief section comment is contained to delegation of duties. The advice which follows is that which is standard to MDDUS members. Cognisance is taken of the following:

- The nurse considers her/himself competent to undertake the proposed delegated tasks.
- The nurse's competence is personally assessed by the doctor who is delegating tasks and responsibilities (guidance on delegating duties is given in the GMC booklet *Professional Conduct and Discipline — Fitness to Practice*).
- Account is taken of UKCC Code of Professional Conduct, Scope of Professional Practice, Exercising Accountability; RCN Standards of Care.
- Where relevant, protocols are discussed, agreed, set down and regularly reviewed.
- Should the nurse work in isolation then she/he must be adequately prepared and consider her/himself competent to manage anaphylactic reaction.

### Minor surgery

- Is the correct equipment available and a system in place for the regular maintenance of that equipment?
- Has the technical skill of those performing the surgery been assessed or verified?
- Support from nursing staff.
- Are explanations given to patients of the normal and expected course of events?
- Are explanations given to patients of the more common adverse reactions?
- Are the records noted that such discussions have taken place?
- Are there clear procedures for follow-up of patients following surgery?
- Are patients given explanatory back-up leaflets of information?

### Fundholding (contracting within and without the NHS e.g. counsellors, physiotherapists)

- Has competence been assessed or verified?

- Is there regular assessment of that competence?
- Has there been confirmation of recognised qualifications and registration with such professional bodies? Ask for sight of documents, noting registration details.
- Has indemnity been discussed and it is clear?
- Are the contracted parties clear about pathways of referral?
- Has confidentiality been addressed and set down in a policy?
- What arrangements are there for feedback and review?
- Is there absolute clarity on who is doing what and who is taking responsibility for what?

## Premises

- Are there designated confidential areas?
- Is there privacy for patients and are there clear policies about entering consulting/treatment rooms?
- Are there clear arrangements for dealing with clinical waste, sharps, confidential material?
- Does every one know what to do in the event of an accident affecting staff, patients or visitors?
- Are owner/occupier liabilities clear and certificates displayed?
- Is equipment (medical, nursing, general office) safe and regularly maintained?

## General practitioner and staff safety

### Visiting patients in their homes

People doing a wide variety of jobs face aggression and violence in the course of their work. Those involved in the delivery of healthcare are no exception. Healthcare workers are vulnerable, and particularly those involved in psychiatric care, accident and emergency, the community and general practice. Most healthcare workers will experience hassle and verbal abuse.

All too frequently headlines appear in the press of alarming stories where doctors and other healthcare workers have been the victims of threats, intimidation and violence. Certain measures that are reasonably simple and practical can and should become standard practice.

- Does someone know of my whereabouts?
- Am I traceable?
- Am I clear about where I am going? Instructions from patient, map of the area held at base, and also one in the car.

## Driving and parking

Guidance includes the following:

- Lock yourself in.
- Handbag, case, phones, etc. locked in boot until required.
- Don't stop to offer assistance to anyone (drive on and telephone police).
- Ensure that you never run out of petrol.
- Park in a well-lit area where you can have a quick get-away if required.
- Always ensure your keys are to hand when approaching the car.
- Don't try to be a hero if there are people hanging around the car when returning from a home visit.
- Walk away until you can safely contact police.

Techniques for assessing a situation on the doorstep, the decision to go in, ending the visit and leaving need to be talked through, sharing experiences and agreeing policies where at all possible. Quite simply, home visiting is a vulnerable area of work that carries added risk.

## Dealing with abuse and avoiding physical assault at surgery premises

The following is a brief checklist only. Much has been written and supportive material is available. The message is straightforward — address the issue and manage it so that staff feel supported, cared for and as safe as possible.

- Invest in training so that staff are first and foremost aware of risks and then able to deal with people who have become aggressive, or are about to do so. Training should include customer care and interpersonal skills.
- Ensure regular review of the arrangements for appointments so that reception staff are clear about procedures for routine, urgent and emergency appointments. Does the practice meet reasonable demands? Is there a different way of arranging appointments that could alleviate frustration and ease access for patients?
- Assess and do something about potential weapons (e.g. vases, heavy staplers).
- Secure storage for prescription pads and drugs.
- Have a clearly identified and genuinely welcoming reception area.

In some respects what has been set out in this chapter so far has been relatively straightforward. The reader will either be feeling confident and reassured that all is well back at base and that managing the risks is indeed part of his or her day-to-day work. On the other hand, this might simply act as a reminder that there are still a number of issues to be addressed. There has been little that one could term controversial or an ethical dilemma or downright difficult (accepting of course that managing the complexity of general practice and the people who work there is akin to managing General Motors).

However, a brave new healthcare world has been emerging and continues to forge ahead. Changed days indeed:

- A primary care led NHS;
- purchasers and providers;
- accountability;
- internal market;
- needs assessment;
- health gain;
- finite resources;
- priorities;
- choices;
- standards;
- audit and peer review;
- charters;
- customer focused;
- community based care.

Are these new threats or new opportunities? Whatever way these issues are perceived they bring with them new and increased responsibilities for doctors and managers, as well as an increased level of accountability.

---

What if you contract with a counsellor to undertake three sessions per week at your practice? The counsellor is self-employed. What consideration must you give to this contract?

---

Considerations would include an assessment of competence, training and qualifications, ensuring that the counsellor is a member of an accredited professional body and has indemnity. There should be discussion, clarity and an agreement about the range of services to be offered, arrangements for continuity of care, regular reviews and referrals to counsellor.

---

What if a patient's relative challenges a purchasing decision on the grounds that scrutiny of league tables of successful outcomes for coronary artery bypass surgery would have been better placed at hospital A opposed to hospital B? The patient died following surgery.

---

General practice fundholders are required to set up and run practice-based complaints procedures in the same way as other general practitioners. This will need to cover both general medical and purchasing decisions. A purchasing decision will be expected to be taken properly and reasonably with regard to priorities and availability of resources.

> What if a patients' group in the community becomes aware that women presenting with carcinoma of the breast have the best care and treatment with the highest level of successful outcomes if referred to a specialist unit some hundred miles outwith the practice's normal contracted unit for such services. One of the group's members with carcinoma of the breast challenges the practice's decision to refer her locally.

Considerations would include the extent to which it is reasonable for a practice to hold information and knowledge about specialist services and outcomes, as well as contractual relationships between practices, trust, health authorities etc.

> What if a child has normally been looked after in the hospital setting for his chronic renal condition? Prescribing of expensive, complex drugs, and monitoring of such drugs has lain squarely with the hospital consultant and his team.
>
> Due to a dedicated primary healthcare team and advanced technology the child can now spend periods of time at home with regular hospital review.

Considerations must include:

- dialogue to ensure absolute clarity;
- who is doing what;
- who is taking responsibility for what;
- prescribing budgets.

> What if you are responsible for managing the practice, which includes managing the fund. The partners call a meeting to discuss a proposed waiting list initiative for patients with cataracts. As the meeting progresses, the partners have differing views on priorities. Cataracts: hip replacement. As a responsible, accountable professional, what information might you be able to put forward from a managerial standpoint to assist the decision-making process?

Considerations would include:

- national, local and practice plans;
- data on practice patients awaiting elective surgery;
- hospital availability

By now the reader will most certainly be feeling the weight of responsibility. However, any self-respecting manager is aware that managing healthcare is not about maintaining the status quo. Management is more to do with achieving. The successful effective manager will understand the past, be critically aware of the present and keep a watchful eye on the future. Nobody has ever said it would be easy.

# PART THREE

# TRAINING

# Training and Development: A Continuing Process

*Brenda Sawyer and Barbara Daniels*
*Association of Managers in General Practice*

---

How often do you hear a colleague or member of your team state that they have been doing the job so long that they know it backwards and do not need any training?. Anyone who does not address the need for continuing personal and professional development will stagnate. Not only can they be left behind, but they can adversely affect the development of their organisation – the provision of a high quality of patient care.

The focus for patient care is now in the primary care led NHS. During this period of rapid and constant change, it is necessary for those working in the sector to ensure that they are prepared to meet new challenges. There is an increasing demand for qualified staff, in particular for highly skilled and knowledgeable managers. For managers, or aspiring managers, who have been working in general practice for a number of years, there is the challenge from those managers 'outside' who often come with a multitude of high level qualifications. But, they, too, need to develop because they do not have the 'culture' of general practice.

How can you ensure that you and your team are continuing to develop yourselves and your organisation? Three important components need to be considered: knowledge, understanding and competence. It is possible to be:

- knowledgeable, to have acquired many facts, but not have a good understanding;
- knowledgeable and skilled, but not have an in-depth understanding;

- to be skilled but not have knowledge or understanding;
- to have knowledge and understanding, but not be skilled.

When assessing and choosing suitable training these three areas need to be taken into consideration.

### Assessment of training needs

Assessing training needs is a continuing process, not just a one-off event. It is something that should become part your own self-development and the development of the individual team members whom you manage. It should be both informally and formally applied. There are many occasions when assessment can take place and these include the following.

- **The recruitment and selection period.** Gaps in knowledge and skills can be detected from an application form and on informal and formal interview. The training and development needs of an individual can be assessed at this stage. It is advisable to decide how much resource, in terms of finance, time and energy, can be used to support an individual and how the needs might be met. You need to obtain commitment to such development from the prospective employee at interview.
- **The induction period.** While a new employee is getting to know colleagues, to understand working practices and to gain in-depth knowledge of the roles, responsibilities and duties associated with the job, any gaps in knowledge and lack of skills may become apparent.
- **At appraisal and job reviews.** During the two-way exchange of views on achievements, problems, strengths and weaknesses, training needs can be identified both by the appraiser and the appraised.
- **Change of role, responsibilities and duties.** If promotion or change of job is in prospect different knowledge and skills maybe needed.
- **Introduction of new equipment or different working practices.** If new methods of working are to be introduced or, for instance, a new computer system or new software is to be installed, an assessment of people's current expertise and future training needs to implement the changes must be undertaken.
- **When undertaking organisational audit.** Some practices are working with the King's Fund Organisational Audit standards for general practice. During this process training needs of the practice team can be identified.
- **When working for Investors in People.** A main component of this quality award is that the team undergoes a training needs analysis.

- **When something goes wrong.** It may be that on such an occasion the need for further training becomes evident.

Methods of assessment include the following.

- **A job description** will provide a framework to match the ability of a job applicant. An application form should be designed to elicit the information needed to assess whether or not a person has had previous experience in carrying out the duties listed, or holds relevant qualifications. For existing staff, a regular review of job descriptions is necessary and this can include an exercise in assessing the knowledge and skills against the role and responsibilities. This is usually carried out at appraisal.
- **Questioning during interview** will provide the opportunity to clarify or obtain fuller information on an applicant's capabilities and to ascertain where they may need support and training.
- **During the induction period** a useful tool to assess competence is a set of standards. This may be one of the national standards, or those set by the practice. For receptionists and secretaries the Administration and Customer Services standards are the most relevant. For supervisors such as a senior receptionist, the Management Charter Initiative (MCI) Supervisory Standards are suitable. For managers the MCI Management Standards at Level I for first line managers, Level II for middle managers and the Strategic standards at Level III can be used. These are broken down into key roles, then units, elements and finally performance criteria (see the section on 'Evidence-based Management'). Therefore, competence can be assessed to a very fine level.

  One method of using these standards is to ask the member of staff to indicate whether or not they feel they are competent, or not yet competent,against each performance criterion. The manager or supervisor then makes their assessment alongside. This then provides an opportunity for discussion when there is a discrepancy in perception of competence and identifies the areas in which a person thinks they are not yet competent and may need training.

## How do we meet the training and development needs?

### Learning styles

First, you need to consider that everyone learns in different ways. What might be a suitable method for one person might not produce the desired results with another. Many of you will have heard of the Honey and Mumford learning styles. These were developed by Peter

Honey and Alan Mumford in the 1980s. They suggest that we are a mixture of four learning styles, but usually we have one or two of these styles that are predominant. It explains why people with equal intelligence and ability faced with a similar learning experience react differently. How often does one person in the team appear to be motivated by such an opportunity to learn and another feel that it was of no use to them whatsoever? It helps to have an understanding of how people learn best. Then we can endeavour to choose methods of training that suit them best.

The four learning styles identified by Honey and Mumford are: activists, reflectors, theorists and pragmatists.

## Activists

Activists like anything new. They throw themselves wholeheartedly into activities, often without thought of the consequences of acting immediately. Their attitude is 'I'll try anything once'. They are gregarious, enjoy being the centre of attention, like the challenge of change, but are bored once the initial enthusiasm has died down and they are into the implementation stage. They brainstorm problems.

## Reflectors

Reflectors are the opposite to Activists. They prefer to take their time, to look at things from every angle, in fact, to reflect. Before coming to any decision they like to assemble all the facts and to think about them. There is a tendency to postpone reaching decisions for as long as possible. In meetings they tend to be quiet, observing and absorbing what is going on, before putting their own point of view. They like to include past and present, their own and other's observations.

## Theorists

Theorists like everything to fit neatly and tidily into the scheme of things. 'If it's logical it's good'. They approach problems in a step-by-step way, rationally and logically. They do not like subjective judgements or lateral thinking. Therefore, they have a tendency to reject anything that does not 'fit'. There is no room for ambiguity. They like to analyse and synthesise.

## Pragmatists

Pragmatists are practical people who seek new ideas and ways of doing things. Problems are seen as opportunities and challenges. They act quickly and do not spend time reflecting when they are taken with an idea: 'If it works it's good'. They are usually confident and return from courses full of good ideas that they want to experiment with in practice.

Do you recognise yourself and members of your team? It is very useful to find out the learning styles of the whole practice team. This will explain why one doctor dictates his letters immediately and another puts them in the drawer to think about; why one receptionist learns a new procedure immediately and rushes in to try it, and another wants to read it up first. How does this help in terms of meeting the training needs? In considering the training methods, you will be able to think which suits each of the learning styles best and how some might be adapted to suit, say, a high Activist, or a high Reflector.

## Training methods

Methods of meeting the training needs include: shadowing, external shadowing, taught courses, distance learning and open learning.

### 'Sitting by Nellie' shadowing

Did you think that this method is old fashioned? The current expression used is 'shadowing'. There is still much to be gained from a new member of staff spending time with experienced, efficient and knowledgeable team members. Be sure that they do not have any 'bad habits' that you would not like to have passed on.

The Activists are going to want to 'have a go' straight away. It may be possible arrange this, but remember, that the high Reflectors will want to observe, think, reflect and, be sure before they try it out. It is possible that the Pragmatists may suggest ways of doing it differently!

For any person joining the practice, GP registrar, new partner or new member of staff, it can be a rewarding experience, as well as a training exercise, for them to spend a period of time with the nursing team, including district nurses, health visitors and community psychiatric nurses, with the receptionists, with the secretarial and administrative staff, with the general practitioners and with the manager, or managers. With the multiplicity of practice organisations, some will also have fundholding teams, a commissioning group, and a dispensing team. Other staff might include; midwives, speech therapists, physiotherapists, podiatrists – an ever-expanding primary healthcare team. It is of the utmost importance that all team members understand the roles and responsibilities of their colleagues. It also helps if they understand the pressures of the various jobs.

It is usually assumed that only new members of the team benefit from this shadowing inhouse. In many practices there are instances where one team thinks that another team has 'an easy ride'. It can promote improved team working and greater understanding if existing members of the various inhouse teams shadow one another.

*External shadowing*
A visit to the pharmacist and local social services office might also be included in an induction programme or in a programme set up for the existing team.

With the advent of the purchaser and provider split and the merging of the FHSAs and District Health Authorities, managers in primary care have to work with new external teams. Often the culture difference between those working in primary care and those in the new Health Authorities and provider Trusts is enormous. Each does not understand the other's world. In the main, each thinks they are the only ones with all the anxiety, stress and pressures to perform and meet targets. A period of time spent shadowing managers in a Trust and a Health Authority, and a reciprocal arrangement, could alleviate some of the misunderstandings that arise. Collaboration is better than competition.

*Taught courses*
Some people need the discipline of attending courses and working with others to encourage and motivate them to achieve their aims. This might involve a regular day, or half-day, or evening, a week attendance or blocks of several days.

A taught course provides the opportunity for exchange of problems, ideas and learning. As managers often work in isolation within practices this is an ideal way of both giving and obtaining support. The presence of a tutor during the learning process is an important resource. They can be questioned, provide guidance, encouragement and help.

*Distance learning and correspondence courses*
This method is suited to those who like working alone and have the discipline to ensure that they can achieve their goals. It is usual for distance learning programmes, such as those offered by AMGP and the Open University, to have supporting tutorials, often at weekends. There are usually workbooks containing reading material and activities and these are sometimes supplemented by video or audio cassettes and other reading matter.

Correspondence courses are a form of distance learning but without face-to-face tutor support. They would be suitable for those sufficiently disciplined to work in isolation without the interaction of a group and the input of a tutor.

*Open learning*
This is a term used for a variety of learning situations. It is sometimes confused with distance learning. It tends to fall between taught courses and distance learning. Occasionally the same materials are

used for both types of study. However, with Open Learning, there are usually regular meetings with the tutor and other students. It is a method often used in larger organisations such as in the wider NHS.

## Qualifications

Increasingly managers are becoming aware of the necessity to have formal qualifications. It is possible that in the future managers will be accredited and have to register in the same way as nurses and doctors. General practitioners are able to access the Postgraduate Education Allowance if they fulfil the criteria for attendance at postgraduate training sessions. Nurses are obliged to undertake a required amount of training to re-register with the UKCC. Some Health Authorities reimburse staff salaries or set budgets taking into account the level at which staff are trained. This may become more widespread. Many managers recognise the need for formal qualifications to ensure that they are not left behind in the expansion of their role in the primary care led NHS or to achieve promotion either within the primary sector, or, as some are choosing, in Health Authorities

There is a number of training programmes that carry qualifications suitable for practice staff and managers. However, the selection of a suitable course requires that certain considerations should be taken into account:

- the delivery of the programme: taught course, distance learning, open learning;
- the amount of time involved: time away from the practice, personal commitment, time in practice, travelling time;
- the venue: distance to travel, convenience of access;
- the cost of the programme;
- the qualification: national recognition; leading to further qualifications; part of an undergraduate or postgraduate degree course. Does it carry Credit Accumulation Transfer Scheme points (CATS points);
- the syllabus content: is it appropriate?
- method of teaching: didactic, group work, role play, interactive discussions;
- method of assessment: essay, multiple choice questions, modified essay questions, oral presentation;
- How much self-directed learning is involved: reading, researching,
- attending learning sets or 'self-help' groups, completing assignments, writing papers;
- the tutors: are they from within primary care to give a specific slant to the topics, are they from outside to give a broad view and promote lateral thinking?

You must decide which of the above are most important in making your choice, whether for yourself or for a member of your team. It may be useful to make a list of the priorities and check them off against what is on offer.

The Association of Managers in General Practice (AMGP), the only organisation that specialises solely in the support of all managers working in primary care, offers three different paths to qualifications which aim to meet a variety of learning needs and styles: taught course programme, distance learning programme and NVQ assessment.

### Taught course programme

The Professional Certificate and Diploma in Primary Health Care Management is based on the four key roles of the Management Charter Initiative (MCI) Management Standards at Levels I and II: Managing People, Managing Finances, Managing Services and Managing Information and Technology. This programme is being delivered via universities and colleges throughout the UK. Some programmes have been accredited by the universities and carry CATS points.

AMGP accredits the postgraduate Diploma in the Management of Purchasing and Commissioning in Primary Care that is delivered by the Institute of Health Policy Studies, University of Southampton, and La Sainte Union College, Southampton.

### Distance learning programme

The postgraduate Diploma in Practice Management is based on the Rainbow III materials that were developed by a consortium of NHS organisations in conjunction with Greenhalgh & Company Limited. This material is a comprehensive pack of reading and activities on using information in practice management. There are six weekend tutorials to support the programme, which is supported and sponsored by BUPA.

### NVQ Assessment Centre

The AMGP NVQ Assessment Centre is accredited by the Institute of Health Care and Development in conjunction with the Open University. This Centre offers the opportunity for managers and staff to prove their competence by qualifying for NVQ awards using national standards. These are mentioned in more detail in the section 'Evidence-based management'.

## Development opportunities

There is an increasing awareness of the benefits of inter-professional learning and the need for groups to work effectively together. 'Away

## THE SOCIETY OF CHIROPODISTS AND PODIATRISTS

The Society of Chiropodists and Podiatrists, founded in 1945, is the professional body for the state registered chiropodists in the United Kingdom.

In order to become state registered, a chiropodist must complete a three year full time degree course at one of 14 schools, all of which are attached to, or part of, a higher education establishment. The degree is recognised by the statutory Chiropodists Board of the Council for Professional Supplementary to Medicine (CPSM) for the purpose of UK state registration. It is necessary to be state registered in order to work in the National Health Service.

Approximately half the Society's members work full time in the NHS. Others are employed in industry and in private hospitals, but most non-NHS members are in private practice, and it is most important to ensure that any chiropodist whom a GP employs, associates with or refers to is State Registered. This is denoted by the designatory letters SRCh. Over 80% of state registered chiropodists are members of the Society of Chiropodists and Podiatrists, and this is denoted by letters FChS (Fellow) and MChS (Member). As at 31/12/96, the Society has 6458 members. There were 1487 students in training.

The State Registered Chiropodist is qualified to provide a wide range of treatments. Some will specialise in, for example, biomechanics, sports medicine or diabetology; some will be able to perform bone surgery; and most will be able to carry out painless treatments using local injected anaesthesia.

More specifically, the state registered chiropodist can offer the following services for your patients, depending upon facilities available and the scope of practice/specialisms of the individual practitioner.

- The removal of callous and corns
- The treatment of nails: their general management, including total or partial nail avulsion
- The eradication of ingrowing toenails
- The effective treatment of verrucae and warts
- Biochemical examination and gait analysis
- The provision of orthotics
- The treatment of sports injuries
- Massage and Strapping
- Advice on the choice of footwear, and on modifications to footwear
- Minor foot surgery

The Society publishes foot leaflets with the following titles: Verrucae, Children's Feet, Ingrowing Toenails, Corns and Callous, Care of your Feet, Bunions and other Toe Deformities, Sporting Feet, Sweaty Feet, Ageing Feet, Diabetic Feet, Walking Feet, Chilblains, Arthritic Feet, Working Feet, Fungal Infections, Choosing the Best Shoes, Heel Pain.

These are available from the offices of the Society, from which the Society's monthly "Journal of British Podiatric Medicine" is published.

Advertisements for premises, practices, equipment and job vacancies appear in each issue. A Directory of Members is published annually, and publications on Standards of Practice and Health and Safety are also available.

The Society is a TUC affiliated trade union for its members employed in the National Health Service. Lists of state registered chiropodists in private practice are available from the Society's offices.

*The Society of Chiropodists and Podiatrists, 53 Welbeck Street, London W1M 7HE Tel: 0171 486 3381 Fax: 0171 935 6359.*

days' for the whole or sections of the primary healthcare team are becoming increasingly popular. These are often more successful using an external facilitator. The Institute of General Practice, Exeter University, is well-known for its small groups skills courses. They are provided at a number of levels, starting with an introduction course, and are delivered nationwide. They can also be tailored to meet a practice's specific needs. These courses enable and encourage an understanding of one's own personality, attitude and behaviour, as well as that of others.

At a personal level, apart from obtaining relevant qualifications, it is necessary to continue to keep up to date. At its most simplistic this can involve reading relevant publications. Short courses and seminars on specific topics and current issues will ensure further development, as will attendance at relevant meetings and conferences. Involvement in appropriate committees, steering and development groups related to primary care will provide further opportunities to develop knowledge, exchange ideas and views and to put forward one's opinion.

## Conclusion

If managers in primary care wish to be taken seriously by their medical and nursing colleagues, both in the primary and secondary care sectors, they need to take a professional approach to their training and development. This should include membership of their professional association. The Association of Managers in General Practice, through its Code of Principles, will enable and support them in the effective management of their practices and in their contribution to the provision of a high quality of patient care.

# Evidence-based Management

*Clare Landymore*
*Institute of General Practice*
*Exeter University*

## Introduction

The continuing evolution within the National Health Service has given general practice a new impetus to develop its clinical and business skills as primary care is heading towards the millennium. It has become evident that practices must address the management of the business of general practice. This is vitally important to the functioning and future of each individual practice, whether single-handed, a group practice, fundholding or a member of a commissioning group, to give just a few examples.

Within this context, the opportunity to develop all members of the primary healthcare team in this business and clinical setting has given the team the chance to improve their working skills, no matter if the member of staff is an established part of the team or has come into the field of general practice from the outside working environment.

There are now many diverse educational opportunities for teams to address the necessary skills and gain recognisable qualifications which can be used to enhance their job competence and improve the business aspect of the practices in which they work.

## The basic principles of evidence-based management

Evidence-based management has been developed to provide managers within business settings with an alternative opportunity to gain relevant and meaningful qualifications. These are not necessarily based on the conventional, formal academic routes of study, but are related to the gathering of workplace evidence, measured and assessed against proven business standards. This gathering and assessment of evidence enables managers to report on their own individual current workplace tasks and to build a portfolio of evidence which is guided by a predefined set of standards.

The length of time that managers take to complete the reports and portfolio can be flexible and managed to suit their own workplace requirements. The pressure of time is well recognised by all managers working in primary care at present and the gathering of evidence and writing of these reports can be integrated into the working day. Each manager embarking on an evidence-based management course has access to a supporting tutor and peer group managers who are all working with the same standards and towards the same qualifications. This is a particularly useful source of inspiration for managers who are often working in general practice in a degree of isolation. Great motivation is provided by the opportunity to discuss the principles of general practice business with those working in industry. The discovery that it is possible to take the business aspects of primary care and correlate the work against a set of standards developed for industry in the widest sense is a challenging one which gives a great deal of confidence and security to the practice managers who have reached these goals and to the partners who employ them.

The achievement for the managers and their practices are threefold:

1. There is the personal achievement for managers in having their portfolios assessed against a nationally recognised set of standards and achieving a professional qualification.
2. The practice has the opportunity to use this portfolio work to develop aspects within the business area of the practice.
3. The process cannot be carried out in isolation. Therefore, various members of the team will be involved in the standards report and evidence gathering. This becomes a team effort and can lead to a more united policy in the delivery of the business part of general practice and the services offered to patients.

## The structure of standards

There are several standards available for managers to use within their working environment. These standards are in the first instance developed by an industry lead body, such as a professional association or employers group.

The standards might then be linked to a framework for qualifications such as a National Vocational Qualification (NVQ). The Occupational Standards for Managers (MCI) developed at Levels One and Two are particularly suited for use by practice managers (these are equated to NVQs at Levels Four and Five). The standards are divided into four main categories:

- Operations;
- Finance;
- People;
- Information.

These four headings are then subdivided further into Units, with titles such as:

- Recruitment and Personnel Selection;
- Exchange Information to Solve Problems and Make Decisions.

The final division of the standard is the Element, against which candidates provide examples from their own work setting, together with a written report detailing their own methodology for tackling these topics. The reports are cross-referenced to the portfolio of evidence. Throughout the process there are comprehensive guidelines to ensure that the portfolio is progressing along the correct path. These have titles such as:

- Performance Criteria;
- Range Indicators.

The evidence gathered throughout this work must be valid, authentic, sufficient and current. It can come from a variety of sources within the practice workbase. Detailed below are just a few examples that have been used in a practice management portfolio:

- practice team discussion – workloads;
- patients' newsletter – development and implementation;
- patients' complaints – practice protocol;
- surgery costings;
- health and safety policy – general review;
- staff planning meetings – relevant topics for the agendas;
- staff study day – planning the programme and writing up the action list.

## Evidence of management competence

The following summary of the four main sources of assessment evidence is taken from the booklet *Guidance on the Collection of Evidence for the NHS Management Standards in General Medical Practice Context.*

*Direct Evidence*
– Performance of management functions in a current work role: this is by far the most appropriate source of evidence, and should be given the most attention. The Examples of Performance Evidence

provided for each Element of Competence clearly show that Practice Managers perform many management activities, especially if they are team leaders. What you do in your present job may well provide you with enough evidence to demonstrate your management competence.

*Indirect Evidence*
— Performance of management functions in a past work role: this is historical evidence relating from management activities which you might have undertaken in the past. You might have held a post where you undertook some of the elements of competence more often than your current work role allows. You can use this experience to generate evidence of competence. The main problem with this source of evidence is that you may well have problems generating this evidence now.

While you may be able to provide a personal report of what you did and account for the thinking behind your actions, you might not be able to provide the documents to support your claim of competence. You not only have to show you did something, but that you met the requirements of the performance criteria when you did it.

— Performance in a simulation/test or special assignment: these can be skills/proficiency/competency tests or projects and assignments. Skill tests are normally subject to fairly tight controls, and are usually designed to provide the individual with the tools necessary to be competent. It is the application, not the possession, of these skills in real work situations that is assessed when making a judgement of your management competence, so the fact of passing a skill test is not sufficient in itself. Simulations such as role play and training exercises are more acceptable, as they seek to reflect real life conditions and can be tailored to provide evidence of competence. Projects and assignments allow for more freedom of action and are usually work based, and as such more fully demonstrate the extent of management competence. They are usually designed to achieve real management objectives, and therefore have as much if not more evidence value than normal management activities. All these types of evidence can be useful, but is must be remembered that simulations can be costly and they do not always fully reflect the real work situation.

— Responding to questioning: this is a valuable source of evidence in that it is the means by which you can provide the assessor with further information on your ability to handle a range of variables (including some that are unforeseen), as well as demonstrating your understanding of the principles and appropriate knowledge required to underpin each element.

It is also useful in establishing your ability to apply the element across the range statements. The questions can be in an oral or written form, and can be asked during observation of your activity, or in separate sessions after the event. The amount of questioning will depend on the assessment system being used, and on the individual assessor.

Assessment Evidence can be provided in the following ways:

— Performance evidence: this is the actual performance or the products of performance of management functions within the work role. Actual performance activities might include briefing other team members, allocating work or recruiting people. The products of performance are the outcomes of this activity, such as a new team member recruited, or the practice working effectively. This is evidence that needs to be:
— observed directly by an assessor (possible where the assessor is working with the manager in a situation that does not disrupt normal procedures)
— personal report
— witness testimony (oral or written report by independent colleagues or line manager which needs supporting by other evidence)

— Documentary evidence: this can be the outcome of your own performance, but could also be generated by others eg: hospital policies. Care should be taken to respect the confidentiality of certain types of information.
Such evidence may include:
Reports, Schedules, Proposals, Financial Information, Articles, Letters etc.

— Knowledge evidence: This is evidence that you have sufficient knowledge and understanding of your area of responsibility to perform effectively, and can demonstrate the thinking behind your actions. It should be demonstrated via other evidence and particularly in:
Personal report
Responding to questioning.

> (IHCD, *Guidance on the Collection of Evidence*
> *for the NHS Management Standards in*
> *General Medical Practice Context*)

Note, revised standards are being phased in from 1 April 1997 over a three-year period.
As detailed above, the manager has an opportunity at this point to add their own personal report to the evidence gathered from their

working experiences. These reports are your description of how a task is undertaken and the process used to obtain a satisfactory conclusion. Detailed below is an actual working report from an NVQ portfolio at Level Five using the MCI Standards at Level 2. The Element in this example is dealing with: The Control of Costs and Enhancing Value.

---

**Report**

Since the practice moved into a new building in 1991, I have monitored the costs of the day-to-day running of the building. These have remained under certain specific headings (as detailed in Portfolio Evidence 3.1).

I review these quarterly to see if there are costs which might be exceeding the budgets which have been set.

If there are costs exceeding budgets – I would discuss the relevant problem with the appropriate members of staff.

These items would usually be an agenda item on the next monthly staff meeting.

We would discuss the various ideas and re-assess in a set period of time.

I had noted from (Evidence 3.1) that the practice electricity bills had increased from accounting year 1994 to 1995 – I therefore requested that all members of staff attempted to be more vigilant with regard to heaters/lighting, etc.

As a result of the agenda item the electricity bill was reduced by approximately £300 by the end of the next assessment period. This information was fed back to the staff in a very positive manner. A good team effort.

The next expense to be tackled along the same pattern was the use of the telephone system within the practice and again this was a project tackled by the whole team. A date was agreed to review after a three-month period.

---

This is a very simple report which illustrates clearly the positive benefits of all members of the practice team working together. The report is referenced to the relevant work evidence listed in the portfolio. It also details the contribution made by all members of the primary care team and their work towards the reduction in costs is noted in a positive way — giving good examples of motivation, effective team work, task definition, raising of standards of performance, and ability to work within a set timescale.

**The benefits of evidence-based management for the primary healthcare team**

Within evidence-based management the use of these standards can be of positive use in the raising of team performance in the delivery of healthcare to the patients. The standards can help to develop the following:

- **A practice business plan**. Much has been written about this topic, but the need for the partners and manager to decide on a format and work towards the development of a meaningful and user-friendly document cannot be emphasised enough. It forms the basis for innovation and standard setting within the team.
- **Job descriptions/specifications/appraisals**. These documents are necessary for new members of staff and are equally valuable for those who have been in post for a number of years – often it is these jobs which are changed and modified as the practice has developed. Staff in post appreciate a regular review of their work and recognition of their skills. The use of appraisal in this context is of great value to managers in the monitoring of staff development and workloads.
- **Identification of training needs**. There are now many opportunities for practice staff to pursue training opportunities offered by government and National Health Service development bodies. The use of evidence-based management firmly encourages all primary care team members to recognise the need for training.
- **Training programmes**. Following the identification of the training needs for the practice team, practices may decide to tackle the topics which are to be covered for staff, on an inhouse basis or by buying in the services of relevant local training bodies. Training programmes may become staff driven and led. For example, if there are no local courses which meet the team requirements, the staff may devise and organise their own training days/courses. They could subsequently be advertised for other practice staff in the area to attend.
- **A benchmark for practice development**. The practice has the opportunity to take the evidence produced by the standards as a starting-point to work on areas within the business which might be in need of review of as a discussion point for innovation. Topics such as audit, practice reports, the practice complaints procedure, the development of IT, the monitoring of items of service claims, and development of team-building skills are just a few examples of the diverse subjects which might be addressed.

## Summary

The use of evidence-based management within the primary care setting has given managers the opportunity to develop and check their working skills with a national set of management working standards – they have shown that practice managers cover the whole spectrum of management techniques. They have multiple skills which are employed each day.

The evidence-based management portfolios can be used by the primary care team further to develop the team skills on a number of topics such as decision-making, innovation, motivation, and time management. It may be that from the start of portfolio work the practice will decide to develop their own standards.

The standards provide a measurable base from which to work and for managers to develop not only their own skills but those of the whole team.

## References

*Managers Working for Patients – Guidance on the Collection of Evidence for the NHS Management Standards in General Medical Practice Context*, NHS Training Directorate (now the IHCD), Association of Managers in Practice and Ciba Pharmaceuticals, Bristol, March 1994.

Occupational Standards for Managers, Management II and Assessment Guidance, sponsored and funded by the National Forum for Management Education and Development, and the Department of Employment, September 1991.

# Research General Practices in Primary Care

*Philip Evans and Timothy Smith*
*St Leonard's Medical Practice*

---

Over the last two years a new breed of general practice has arisen — the research general practice. This exciting and innovative concept has important implications for those doctors interested in research in primary care and inevitably their practices and practice managers. These practices also provide a substantial opportunity to improve the quality of research in primary care and to facilitate multidisciplinary research.

The Department of Health has recently committed itself to a primary care led National Health Service. In *Primary Care: The Future* (Dorrell, 1996) the Department states that 'it seems self evident that to research better patient care in general practice, the research ought to take place there, on general practice populations'. This is precisely the role of the new research general practices which are a timely addition to the NHS research and development strategic plan.

## Background

The development of research general practices was initially promoted by the Royal College of General Practitioners and their Chairman of Research, Denis Pereira Gray. In October 1994 the college appointed the first two such practices after national advertisements. Subsequently the South and West Regional Research Directorate appointed ten practices in their region in April 1995 and then seven in the second tranche in April 1996. Five appointments are imminent in Scotland and six are already established in the North and West region. Currently there are 27 such practices in the UK, one of which is our own in Exeter, Devon.

Research in general practice extends back over 200 years to Edward Jenner. University departments of general practice have been established in the UK and there are now 35 general practitioners in the country who currently hold chairs of one kind or another (Pereira Gray, 1996). In 1991 Pereira Gray outlined what he called 'the law of inverse opportunity' in that the educational and research opportunities were available at least to the branch of medicine which needed them most, namely general practice. He defined several reasons for this paradox including historical precedents, methodological difficulties in primary care research, the relatively short time spent in vocational training, and the absence of research opportunities once a general practitioner principal was established in post. He contrasted the educational and research opportunities of senior registrars in hospital who have protected study to complete theses, with the self-employed general practitioner principal whose NHS contract is research free.

Many of the departments of general practice have linked academic practices yet excellent research has been performed by individual practitioners or small groups of enthusiasts, away from these academic centres, and often without appreciable support. These practices have always provided an NHS service commitment to their registered population as well as producing research output, a potential conflict which may well until recently have proved untenable without adequate funding. The costs incurred in such practices have been underestimated and not realistically separated from service costs until the arrival of the concept of research general practices.

It is really too early to evaluate fully the success or otherwise of the research general practices but these data should be available in the near future. One can however envisage a steady increase in research general practices over the next decade paralleling that of training practices in the 1970s and 1980s.

## What are research practices?

Pereira Gray (1995) defined a research general practice as an 'ordinary general practice offering at least one practice partner, preferably two, with a real interest in research and a current research capability'. They must have good practice management, computer systems and preferably a definitive computer database from which to research the important questions in primary care. They are *not*:

- necessarily training practices, although they may be;
- necessarily attached to academic departments, although they are encouraged to do so;

- necessarily part of a research network, although they may join up with other practices to encourage each other and facilitate research.

The award is *not* given as a:

- training fellowship to an individual, but as a grant paid to the practice with a lead researcher in charge;
- research grant to perform a single research project but as a grant to cover infrastructure costs incurred by the practice in conducting research.

### Selection criteria

Thus far the research general practices have been intended to 'rescue', as Pereira Gray put it (1996), those able and experienced researchers who have an established track record in research with at least two publications in the peer-reviewed literature. The principle was to set up a system whereby practitioners would be protected from the personal financial burden imposed on them by paying for research time and facilities from their own or their partnership funds. The other criteria are detailed in Table 3.3.1.

**Table 3.3.1**  *Selection criteria for research general practices*

> - Enthusiasm
> - Previous research courses/training
> - Desktop computing
> - Age-sex and diagnostic registers in use
> - Practice team, nurses and manager
> - MRCGP/FRCGP/FRCGP by assessment
>
> and
>
> - Two previous publications in the peer-reviewed literature
>
> **Reproduced with permission**

*Source:*   Pereira Gray (1996)

### What is the aim of a research general practice?

The aim of a research general practice is the production of high quality research from within the practice. As in any other branch of science the quality of such research will be gauged by the number of publications in the peer-reviewed literature. The grant, currently £12,500 per annum, could be used by the practice to contribute towards a single research project or alternatively the practice may decide to run several smaller projects. In many of the practices the grant is used as 'pump priming' in that it enables the lead researcher and his team to take quality time out of the practice to consider new ideas for research and to produce protocols. These protocols can then be submitted to other bodies in search of funding, which in turn draws money into the practice.

Another equally valid use of the research general practice grant is the development side of research and development (R&D). Individual practices are well placed to assess the impact of new ideas, new treatments or new ways of working on the patients in their care. These studies too can be formalised into papers and published. Our own practice, for example, has recently considered the impact on patient care of anticoagulation for atrial fibrillation (Sweeney et al., 1995) and the possible risk of breast cancer on hormone replacement therapy (Pereira Gray et al., 1996).

## Funding

The funding in the south and west region is currently £12,500 per year. This is paid to the practice after their successful application to the regional NHS Research and Development Directorate. The money is paid as a block award in monthly instalments once the research contract has been signed by the lead researcher of the practice. This money is then managed by the lead researcher and the practice manager at their discretion.

The funding is for three years in the first instance and is renewable annually on production of an acceptable annual report. In the South and West region this summarises the research and development achievements of the practice during the year. It includes a detailed description of current research studies in progress and details of those studies successfully published. The practice will also be asked to outline any work towards higher degrees by members of the primary healthcare team; grant income obtained by the practice; visitors to the practice and details of the dissemination of the results of the research that has been performed in the practice. It is suggested in this region that the funding is used to cover the elements in Table 3.3.2.

## Implications for the practice of becoming a research general practice

Becoming a research practice influences the practice in at least two ways. It has an effect on the doctors and also on the staff, notably the practice manager.

**Table 3.3.2**  *Possible uses of the research practice block award*

- General practitioner's time. The award provides for the equivalent of one partner's time for one day a week.
- Research assistant's time for one half-day a week.
- Administrative and secretarial support for half a day per week.
- Running costs, e.g. miscellaneous stationery, postage, computer supplies, etc.

## Implications for the doctors

Much of the responsibility for organising the research general practice will fall to the lead researcher. He will have to satisfy himself that the practice and the doctors fulfil the criteria for inclusion and then complete the application. It will be his job to facilitate research within the practice as well as carrying out the other roles expected of a lead researcher (Table 3.3.3).

**Table 3.3.3**  *The role of the lead researcher*

- Leadership of, and responsibility for, the research team within the research general practice.
- Choice of which research projects to run and subsequent project management.
- Writing up and submission for publication of research and development projects.
- Responsibility for research staff skills assessment and training needs.
- Accountability for spending the award.
- Advice to the practice manager on software and hardware essential for research.
- Preparation of each year's annual report and an annual research plan for the practice.
- Presentation of research at scientific meetings.
- Liaison with interested researchers in secondary care or in other disciplines such as psychology or sociology.

Personally the lead researcher may have training needs of his own, for example, training for statistical packages on his computer or perhaps qualitative research methodology if one of the research projects includes such an approach. The award can be used to offset any costs that may arise from such training needs. He or she will also be required to head up the public face of the research general practice in terms of receiving visitors and also being available to staff and patients alike if they are interested in the practice research.

## Implications for the practice manager

A research practice has its own identity that combines general service provision typical of most general practices with general practitioners undertaking research programmes which seek to improve patient care of the future. This combination brings its own unique features that affect those practices involved in research.

Research may lead to reduced availability of general practitioners in the practice, resulting in fewer appointments provided by them and therefore increased pressures on the practice. Locum bills will also increase due to absence. The practice needs a balanced approach to taking time away from the practice, ensuring that all are happy with the arrangement and acknowledge its financial implications.

How then does recognition as an NHS Research in General Practice help to alleviate these issues? Recognition involves the appointment of a lead general practitioner taking overall responsibility, funding of £12,500 for three years and an increasing profile of research within the management of the practice.

## Reorganisation

This falls into four areas namely staff requirements, staff review and development, finance and resources (see Tables 3.3.4, 3.3.5, 3.3.6, 3.3.7).

## The future

This research general practice is ideal for multidisciplinary working within the primary healthcare team. These practices are encouraged to involve other members of the team, including the practice manager, in the production of new ideas for research and in the studies themselves. There now exists the exciting opportunity of establishing an evaluative culture across the whole of the practice, allowing all professionals to question current practice, to produce ideas for research and to gain research skills themselves.

**Table 3.3.4**  *Possible staff requirements*

---

*Research assistant and secretarial support*
- Employed on a fixed term contract for the duration of NHS agreement.
- Employed on a separate basis from the practice with clearly defined job descriptions.
- Secretarial support may only be needed on an *ad hoc* basis.

*External short-term researchers*
- For specific projects.

*Management of the research practice*
- This may fall to practice managers incorporating such duties into their daily routine. They must ensure that time spent on research management is costed through the research budget.

---

**Table 3.3.5**  *Staff review and development*

---

*Review*
- Annual appraisals of key roles are essential to a productive research unit from which personal development and training needs are identified.

*Training*
- Individual training needs will differ but word processing, spreadsheets, graphical software, statistics and audit skills are key needs for research staff.

*Practice team*
- Regular research meetings between the lead GP, practice manager, research assistant and the practice team leaders provide an opportunity for feedback on progress and addressing concerns arising from research.
- Communication throughout the practice on research projects is important to ensure that staff are informed of what the practice is seeking to achieve and the successes that it has had.

---

**Table 3.3.6** *Finance*

*Budget*
All matters relating to research may now be identified, costed and financed through the research practice. Set and agree the budget with lead GP. The following accounts may be required:

- Lead GP salary
- Staff wages
- Research equipment
- Stationery
- Sundries
- Partners' drawings

*Research account*
It is advisable to operate a bank account separate from the practice one. The accounts should be managed on a similar basis as the practice account with a cashbook, monthly reconciliation and year end account.

**Table 3.3.7** *Resources*

*Immediate need*
- Office space. Thoughtful consideration within the practice as to where the lead GP and research assistant are going to work, timings agreed and planned with GPs and staff.
- Research computer. A computer with sufficient capacity to meet software developments of the future, a *Windows* operating system and a suite such as *Microsoft Office* are recommended incorporating word processing, spreadsheets and graphical presentation in one. Statistical software such as *SPSS* may also be needed.
- Equipment. Basic necessities include the use of a photocopier, telephone and fax which will probably be shared with the practice.

*Future needs*
- A modem, e-mail, the Internet and *Medline*. These all provide useful facilities for researchers across the globe.
- Consider office space. What requirements will be needed for the future? Are current working arrangements satisfactory? Developments may lead to a fully separate and fully resourced research unit within or detached from the practice.

## References

Dorrell, S (1996) *Primary Care: The Future*, NHSE, London.

Pereira Gray, D (1991) 'Research in general practice: law of inverse opportunity', *British Medical Journal*, **302**: 1380–82.

Pereira Gray, D (1995) 'Research general practices', Editorial, *British Journal of General Practice*, **45**: 516–7.

Pereira Gray, D (1996) 'Research general practices', in *RCGP Members' Reference Book 1996*, Sterling Publications, London.

Pereira Gray, D, Evans P, Sweeney, K and Steele, R (1996) 'HRT – a paradigm for the complexity of prescribing in general practice', in *RCGP Members' Reference Book 1996*, Sterling Publications, London.

Sweeney, K, Pereira Gray, D, Steele, R and Evans, P (1995) 'Use of warfarin in non-rheumatic atrial fibrillation: a commentary from general practice', *British Journal of General Practice*, **45**: 153–8.

# Fellowship by Assessment

*Professor Mike Pringle*
*Royal College of General Practitioners*

## Introduction

Fellowship by Assessment (FBA) of the Royal College of General Practitioners is the premier clinically-based assessment of general practitioner performance in Britain, and perhaps the world. It offers a way in which general practitioners who are also members of the College can demonstrate at least once in their professional career that they can achieve the highest levels of patient care.

Under the traditional system — which continues in parallel to FBA — a member is nominated by local Fellows as a suitable person to enter fellowship. This nomination happens without the nominee's knowledge and the Committee on Fellowship considers the merits of each case. Only if the committee is unanimous will a name go forward and the member be notified. This system works well in small colleges where everybody knows everybody.

In general practice, however, there are two real dangers. One is that high quality general practitioners are not recognised because they are not known to local Fellows. This is particularly liable to happen to those in small practices, but also to those who do not attend committees, teach or do research — in other words to the bedrock of primary care. The second problem lies with the fact that some nominees may be well known for their political activism, but their clinical care may not be well-known to the nominators; this can lead to issues of credibility for Fellowship.

In response to these problems, the College decided in the second half of the 1980s to institute a second route to Fellowship — Fellowship by Assessment. In 1989 the first four FBAs were installed at the College's AGM. By 1996, 107 Fellows by Assessment had been awarded this honour and it can be said to have established its place alongside Fellowship by Nomination as a legitimate route to Fellowship.

## Why is Fellowship by Assessment important for practice managers?

Fellowship by Assessment only exists to identify and reward individual members of the RCGP who are delivering high quality patient care. It is not a method for offering accolades to practice teams or to practice managers, so why should you be interested?

When doctors do FBA, they must have efficient and effective systems behind them. The practice must be well organised, operating as a real team in good premises with excellent information systems. Clearly a single-handed GP without a practice manager can do this; but for most of us, co-operative and committed partners and managers are an essential pre-requisite for success. If a practice contains an FBA this reflects credit on the whole team, including the manager.

Second, the alternatives must be considered. While BS5750, ISO9000, The King's Fund Organisational Audit and other schemes offer a methodology for measuring good management, none directly concerns patient care. While health and safety at work and minutes of meetings are important, they are no substitute for the main purpose of general practice – to deliver high quality care to a defined population.

FBA can be a great catalyst to team development. Almost all the practices that have undertaken this assessment report that the process of application has increased clinical and managerial group cohesion. So, although perhaps not the applicant and direct recipient of the award, a wise practice manager sees the implications of such a system for the practice as a whole.

The last point is a pragmatic one. A GP will find doing FBA really difficult without a lot of administrative back-up. We all rely on our support teams to prepare and succeed, and the manager's role as the co-ordinator of the application can be invaluable. It is for all these reasons that you should be considering whether you have a plausible candidate within your practice and whether you should be encouraging them to apply. If you are approached by a doctor considering FBA, you should offer your support and encouragement – the potential for the whole practice is substantial.

## The principles

Fellowship by Assessment is based on the following principles:

1. **It is by self-nomination.** A general practitioner does not have to wait to be recognised; if he or she believes that they are delivering

high standard care, then they can test themselves against the FBA criteria.

2. **It is criterion based.** There are 56 criteria, each of which is a clear statement of what must be achieved. Nobody should ever 'fail' because if they cannot meet the criteria it should be apparent before they apply.

3. **All criteria must be achieved.** There is no discretion — each of the 56 criteria must be passed.

4. **The criteria are based on care for patients.** As already said, the criteria have been written to identify good patient care. Serving on committees, teaching or undertaking research is not necessary for Fellowship by Assessment, and makes no contribution to the assessment.

5. **The criteria are published and freely available.** There is no secrecy or hidden route. There is only one extra hurdle, and this is the same as for Fellows by Nomination. Every applicant is asked about breaches of terms and conditions, court cases and litigation. If a member has satisfied all the criteria but has a major problem with a complaint, then the Committee on Fellowship may decide that their recommendation for Fellowship is not appropriate.

6. **The criteria are reviewed and updated every year.** A set of criteria such as these cannot be set in tablets of stone. On 1 October each year a new set — basically amendments to the previous set — of criteria is published and applies throughout the next twelve months. The changes reflect the evolving context of primary care, experience from visits, and increased expertise in formulating criteria in new areas. The new criteria are formulated by a working party in the Vale of Trent Faculty and have to be approved by the Council of the College.

7. **Notification of 'intention to apply' freezes the criteria for one year.** This is to avoid a member being prejudiced by changes in criteria while preparing an application. As soon as a member formally notifies their faculty that they intend to apply, they have a year in which to do so under the existing criteria. If that year elapses, then they must re-register their intention to apply and be assessed on the criteria existing on that second occasion.

8. **The assessment is done by Fellows on a practice visit.** The principle of peer review is integral to FBA. Other respected general practitioners assess the general practitioner in his or her place of work.

9. **The visit serves to confirm that criteria are met.** The applicant should know that almost all the criteria are met before the visit takes place. The task of the visitors is to confirm that the application is accurate and to assess those criteria that require discussion.

10. **Fellowship by Assessment has equivalence to Fellowship by the traditional route.** Fellowship by Assessment costs the same (twice the annual membership fee), and is awarded at the Annual General Meeting.

## The criteria on which the assessment is based

In a chapter such as this it is impossible to give all the criteria verbatim; I can only give a flavour of the breadth of them. The full criteria are available from:

Mrs J Baily
The Faculty Office
The Vale of Trent Faculty of the RCGP
Department of General Practice
The Medical School
Queen's Medical Centre
Nottingham NG7 2UH
TEL: 01159   709391
FAX: 01159   709389

'Fellowship by Assessment: Occasional Paper 50'[1] is available from the Royal College of General Practitioners. The 56 criteria are grouped into sections which cover the important areas for assessment and the following text gives an indication of the requirements.

The first section covers the basic qualifications of an applicant who must have been a member of the College for five years and a principal in general practice for five years – and in the current practice for at least two years. This often causes some angst when a young partner wishes to do FBA with more established partners and does not quite qualify, but these are the minimum requirements.

The candidate is asked to describe the development of the practice and his or her contribution to it. We also ask for two publications which have influenced the applicant's care. This is to look for a positive attitude to the application of standards and evidence-based medicine. In the third section on availability the candidate must describe standards for appointment availability which must have been published to the patients, and must supply an audit to show these are being met.

The continuity of care section requires a description of arrangements for holiday, day off and out-of-hours cover, with clear guidelines which ensure that a candidate's quality of care is maintained in his or her absence. In the fifth section – the consultation and organisation of care – the average consultation time for a routinely booked patient must be over seven and a half minutes; the repeat prescribing system and its safeguards must be described and audited; consultation and visiting rates must be given; and a foolproof system for handling letters and results must be demonstrated.

Under health promotion, the candidate must show that levels of immunisation and cervical cytology meet the specified standards, that child health surveillance is being carried out to a high level, and that pre-conception and contraceptive care is of a high quality. In the next section, the member must describe arrangements for out-of-hours care and must do significant event audits[2] on a number of patients who have experienced an important event within the previous two years.

If a prospective candidate is getting complacent when reading through to this point, the real googly occurs in section eight on clinical care. This starts with an audit of the presentation to management intervals for patients with malignant and non-malignant diagnoses. A recent case of terminal care must be discussed, and then there must be ten management plans with each audited (which means the audit cycle must have been completed with a re-audit) to show evidence of improvement. This is a major requirement and often takes some time to prepare.

To demonstrate consultation skills the doctor must video tape ten consecutive consultations with consenting patients and then analyse them in a consultation workbook. A number of key skills must be shown, most of which have been designed to identify a patient-centred doctor. A video-camera with a wide-angle lens will be required and this should be available from a vocational training scheme.

The consultation skills section is demanding both in terms of the skills required, the self-revelation involved in sharing a surgery with visitors, and in terms of the complexity of the workbook. However, it is a fair test of a general practitioner and any with above average skills should be successful.

The tenth section deals with resources and their use. This includes prescribing, referring and investigating, and requires evidence of effectiveness and efficiency. Under teamwork, the candidate must demonstrate the organisation of the primary care team and how communications work. Next, a list of housebound patients must be known and systems for accessing social care must be shown.

The premises and the systems for securing controlled drugs must be adequate. The medical records — manual, computer or both — must reach defined levels and the information systems of the practice such as disease registers must be complete, accurate and functional. The systems for communicating with patients must be in place. In the last section, section 16, the member must demonstrate that their education is sufficient for personal development and that they are using the techniques of business planning to develop the practice.

All these criteria are set out in the documentation. They have been placed at a level to which any general practitioner delivering high quality care in a supportive practice should aspire. The criteria have been examined for bias against special groups such as rural or inner city doctors, part-time or female doctors, or ethnic minority doctors. Some criteria have then been refined to eliminate any bias and we now believe them to be tough but fair.

## Preparing to apply

If you and a partner in your practice decide to explore Fellowship by Assessment, you should start by going through the criteria very carefully, identifying those that cause no real anxiety and those that need work and preparation. Timetabling is important since some, such as the clinical management plans and their audit, will take up to two years to get sorted out.

You should contact your local faculty of the RCGP soon into the process and make contact with the local FBA adviser. This will be someone experienced in the system – often a successful FBA candidate – who can offer support and guidance through the preparation. There are regular FBA study days nationally and regionally and you might wish to attend one of these. At least get in touch with a practice manager in an FBA practice and ask for advice.

The general practitioner who is applying might wish to join an FBA group where candidates share experience and support each other. Some practice managers also attend these groups and find them very helpful in ensuring that criteria are not over-, under- or misinterpreted.

A key element of success lies in getting the whole practice team involved. Where multiple partners are eligible, collaborative applications dramatically reduce the individual workload involved. If, say, three partners are applying together, then one can do the description of the repeat prescribing system while another is looking at teamwork. Clinical audits can be shared. Some criteria, such as the consultation skills, significant event auditing and presentation to management intervals, are personal to the applicant. These are submitted in a personal folder and the common material can be submitted in a practice folder.

It is important to note that each candidate elects to be assessed on a personal list or a practice list. If the former, some standards, for example in medical records quality, are higher; if the latter then often the candidate needs to identify patients that they have dealt with, for assessment.

A good practice manager can be invaluable in helping an applicant to keep up morale and to maintain progress. Some candidates take four months to prepare, while others take several years. The average is about one year, and it can be difficult to keep progressing towards what seems like a distant goal throughout the period.

In particular it must be emphasised that much of the material can be prepared using clerical and secretarial staff. There is no sadistic requirement that the candidate should type their submission, nor that they should pull all the records that they audit. The only requirement is that the candidate is delivering high quality care and that the submission shows this to be the case.

## The visit

When a candidate is sure that every criterion is met, and the documentation shows them to be met, you will be asked to arrange the visit. This entails three Fellows coming to the practice for a day. One will be the local adviser; a second will be another local Fellow; and the team leader will be nominated by us in Nottingham from outside the area. As you can imagine, organising such a visit is no mean feat – getting three busy professionals to your practice on a day that suits you is a formidable undertaking and you must give a least two months' notice.

The visit is inevitably stressful for the candidate, you and your staff. It is not every day that three colleagues examine every aspect of your care and organisation. However, if the material has been honestly and well prepared, it is, in fact, an opportunity to enjoy a rare educational experience. After the visit the team will say what impressed them, but they will also offer personal advice to the candidate and feedback for the practice.

For the candidate the worst part is usually the consultation session. He or she will choose one consultation to show the assessors and they will choose two consultations which they will play through. This is a nerve-racking experience for even the most experienced doctor – and worse the more experienced the doctor is – but will be handled with great sensitivity by the visitors.

You will no doubt be concerned to get the hospitality right. Copious cups of coffee are welcome; the lunch should be enjoyable without being ostentatious (a finger buffet is ideal); alcohol is unnecessary (but may be required by the candidate after the visit); and the possible need to cater for vegetarian assessors should be covered by enquiries in advance of the visit.

At the end of the visit there are only three possible outcomes. Hopefully the assessors will announce that they are entirely satisfied and will be recommending the member for Fellowship. Very occasionally visits have been made where the doctor has not taken advice and has not believed that we really mean that every criterion should be met. Under these circumstances the candidate is invited to re-apply when ready. In between is the possibility that one or two minor problems have been identified which can be easily rectified.

Under these circumstances the assessors agree with the member a timescale for getting the evidence right; only when they are convinced that it is satisfactory will they then recommend Fellowship.

## Conclusion

Fellowship by Assessment is designed for individual members of the College to achieve higher status through the demonstration of highest standards of clinical care. However, I hope that this chapter has shown how it requires a team effort and team skills. A practice manager may not be rewarded directly, but should be able to see how an application within the practice can stimulate higher standards — in protocols, in audit, in prevention, in organisation, in information systems, and most importantly in care for patients.

## References

1  Pringle, M (ed.) (1995) *Fellowship by Assessment*, Occasional Paper 50, 2nd edn, London, Royal College of General Practitioners.
2  Pringle, M, Bradley, C, Carmichael, C, Wallis, H, Moore A (1995) *Significant Event Auditing*, Occasional Paper 70, London, Royal College of General Practitioners.

# PART FOUR

# MANAGING RELATIONSHIPS

# AMGP Code of Principles

*Sandra E A Gower*
*Fellow of Association of Managers in*
*General Practice*

---

## Introduction

As defined by the *Oxford Dictionary* 'a principle is a personal code of right conduct by which we live'. The manager of today's primary care will need both a personal and professional code of principles. Managers are just as accountable for their personal and professional practice as all other professionals working within this environment. General practitioners are accountable through the General Medical Council (GMC); nurses, midwives and health visitors through the United Kingdom Central Council (UKCC); and chiropodists, dieticians and physiotherapists are among the professions regulated by the Professions Supplementary to Medicine. There is no doubt that the primary care manager of the future will be subject to mandatory codes of both conduct and competency. The Association of Managers in General Practice (AMGP) has developed the Code of Principles for managers in primary care.[1]

## The need for a code of principles

It is the Association's purpose of its 21 years' existence which provides the backbone for members' professional practice and, thus, this Code: 'To enhance the standard of professional management's contribution to patient care'. The White Paper published by the Government on 13 November 1996 *The NHS: A Service with Ambitions*[2] recognises 'the professional basis of the NHS workforce is one of its strength. The combination of professional self-regulation and public accountability ensures that the professions are committed

89

to the health and well-being of their patients, and to the development of the NHS as a whole'. The Association is a professional organisation with ambitions. Ambitions to raise standards of primary care management; to demonstrate fitness to practise; and to become the preferred choice for practice management so all managers subscribe to the Code of Principles.

With these ambitions in mind, and in response to the pressing demands for demonstrating competence on a continuing basis across all professions, the Code of Principles was developed by the AMGP membership and colleagues. It was designed, also, to support and complement the codes adopted by other professional colleagues in primary care. Knowing what is expected of us as professionals helps us meet the challenges ahead and it is anticipation which is crucial for the professional managers in primary care. Anticipating the future pressures on managers is a key role for the Association and it has adopted the Code of Principles which set out the standards of personal and professional conduct to which members can and do subscribe. The Code, at the same time, provides a comprehensive framework for professional support for all managers in primary care.

In recognition of the rapidly changing profession and in anticipation of what was to come, the Association's 19th Annual Course held in 1994 at the University of Warwick, took 'Ethical Dilemmas in General Practice' as its theme. This forum enabled the extensive (and intensive) discussion, debate and sharing of views between managers and healthcare colleagues. It was this forum which reinforced the belief that ethics and ethical behaviour has everything to do with management, and that ethics is as much a professional organisational issue as a personal issue. And, it was at this forum that the incredible depth of feeling to 'do something' for the profession of practice management was felt so strongly by the Association. Views put forward at Warwick gave the green light for further work, and a period of thorough consultation led to the drafting of the Association's first Code of Principles. This Code was agreed by Council, presented to the members and adopted at the AGM in 1995 at Ashridge Management College.

The work was developed alongside the increasing public debate on professional accountability and public accountability within the NHS. The key documents which influenced this agenda included:

- 'The Cadbury Report'[3] which reviews the corporate governance framework;
- The NHSTD/AMGP Guidance on the collection of evidence for the NHS Management Standards for General Medical Practice Managers[4] which sets out 163 specific criteria which the competent manager should meet;

- *The Code of Conduct for NHS Boards*[5] which itemises public service values of probity, openness and professional accountability;
- *The Code of Practice on Openness in the NHS*[6] which sets out the principles underlying public access to information;
- *The Patient's Charter* which sets out clear and specific performance standards on which the NHS is expected to deliver;
- *The Accountability Framework for GP Fundholding: Towards a Primary Care Led NHS*[7] which provides key requirements for demonstrating accountability for NHS resources in the four areas of:
  1. management accountability;
  2. accountability to patients and the wider public;
  3. financial accountability;
  4. clinical and professional accountability.

## The Code of Principles – the context

To put the Code in context, that is the business environment within which primary care managers work, and the Association's increasing professional responsibility remit of anticipating the future pressures on managers, it is essential to comprehend the extended powers of the General Medical Council – powers which impact on the profession as a whole, and not only the doctors. It is here that professional accountability shifts from being solely an individual responsibility to a collective responsibility. It is this change to medical policy which has become one of the most important external influences to *the Code of Principles* for managers in primary care. The Medical (Professional Performance) Act received Royal Assent in November 1995. The new Act amended The Medical Act 1983, to include the new professional performance procedures. The aim is to protect the public on the rare occasions when doctors' performance is seriously deficient, and will do so by ensuring professional assessment and remedial action is taken where necessary. It also extended the General Medical Council's existing powers to impose conditions on, or suspend, a doctor's registration, where it finds the standard of the doctor's professional performance to have been seriously deficient. The GMC's Position Paper No 2 of June 1996 provides further guidance and interpretation:

'A doctor's registration may be called into question by repeated or persistent failure to comply with the professional standards appropriate to the work being done by the doctors, particularly where this places patients, or members of the public, in jeopardy. This may include repeated or persistent failure to comply with the GMC's guidance in *Good Medical Practice*.'

In anticipation of the future the GMC produced guidance of what is expected of doctors. The booklet *Good Medical Practice* is one of four booklets which forms the 'Duties of a Doctor' – guidance from the GMC[8] prefaced with the words 'Patients must be able to trust doctors with their lives and well-being. To justify that trust, we as a profession have a duty to maintain a good standard of practice and care and to show respect for human life'. The other booklets provide guidance on *Advertising, HIV and AIDS: the ethical considerations,* and *confidentiality.*

*Good Medical Practice* sets out the basic principles of good practice that are expected of doctors. In particular as a doctor you must:

- make the care of your patient your first concern;
- treat every patient politely and considerately;
- respect patients' dignity and privacy;
- listen to patients and respect their views;
- give patients information in a way they can understand;
- respect the rights of patients to be fully involved in decisions about their care;
- keep your professional knowledge and skills up to date;
- recognise the limits of your professional competence;
- to be honest and trustworthy;
- respect and protect confidential information;
- make sure that your personal beliefs do not prejudice your patients' care;
- act quickly to protect patients from risk if you have good reason to believe that you or a colleague may not be fit to practise;
- avoid abusing your position as a doctor;
- work with colleagues in the ways that best serve patients' interests.

The new President of the GMC, Sir Donald Irvine, is the first general practitioner to be elected to this position and it is he who leads on the development of the new procedures to assess a doctor's performance. The GMC has affirmed the basis for its performance procedures which are to be introduced in about September 1997. According to the GMC's Position Paper No 3 of June 1996, the form that the assessment programme might take could include a visit to the practice where the practice documentation, systems and management would be verified and audited, and colleagues who work with the doctor interviewed, exploring in particular the doctor's performance in relation to the qualities expected of registered doctors as set out in *Good Medical Practice.* In anticipation of such a scenario, a manager subscribing to AMGP's Code of Principles would take a personal responsibility to provide a 'safety net' – a supporting framework of organisational fitness and sound management systems to facilitate good practice, as well as the leadership and challenge if performance gives cause for concern. Professional accountability is now a collective responsibility, as well as a personal responsibility, which empowers each professional group to work within their own and each other's professions standards.

## What is the Code?

The principles are intended as self-regulatory guidelines to personal and professional conduct and are indicators of good practice, in line with the new guidance from the GMC. In carrying out their responsibilities, members of AMGP will seek to demonstrate good practice through their personal and professional competence specifically through a:

- patient focus;
- team and primary care organisation focus;
- personal focus.

The Code followed the introduction of full membership to the Association by qualification. Full membership is only gained either by the academic or portfolio route at National Vocational Qualification (NVQ) level 4 or Management Charter Initiative (MCI) level 1 or via Accreditation of Prior Learning. Management standards recognised at these levels were identified, agreed and published in 1994 in conjunction with the NHS Training Division.[4] Thus, full members of the association can stand alongside their primary care colleagues having gained professional entry.

## The focus

The Code of Principles has three sections: patient focus, team and primary care organisation focus, and personal focus.
**Patient focus** entails:

- making decisions to serve the best interests of patient care;
- taking responsibility for promoting service improvements beneficial to patients and the practice;
- maintaining confidentiality;
- respecting individual rights and applying statutory regulations fairly;
- promoting openness of information and effective communication.

**Team and primary care organisation focus** entails:

- respecting colleagues, working in co-operation with them to enhance the quality of care;
- working with colleagues to assist them actively with their continuing professional development;
- recognising employment rights of staff within the primary care

team and applying statutory regulations fairly;
- acting with probity to correct, prevent or report unprofessional, unlawful or unethical conduct;
- being accountable for using all resources effectively.

**Personal focus** entails:

- taking personal responsibility for own continuing professional development;
- adopting a strategic approach to the needs of the practice;
- recognising the need to seek help and guidance for matters beyond current competence;
- acting with honesty and integrity, and by not abusing any privilege or position of power for personal gain.

As an aid to continuing professional development the Code is intended to encourage development at three levels:

1. personal knowledge and skills;
2. professional attitudes and behaviour;
3. the management competencies for primary care 'business' development.

It is intended that individuals should be able to review each of the broad areas on which the Code focuses (i.e. patients, team and primary care organisation, and personal) and identify appropriate development activities at any or all of the three levels listed above which would, once successfully undertaken, improve the functioning of the primary care facility.

### What does the Code mean?

By subscribing to the Code of Principles the manager joins the Association of Managers in General Practice, and it is the Association which provides the professional fitness to practise framework. In the event of a challenge to fitness to practise it is the Association which will provide the appropriate assessment and re-training programme. Having gained full membership of AMGP, personal and professional fitness are demonstrated through the commitment to life-long learning. Principle 2.7 states 'working with colleagues and other healthcare professionals to assist them actively with their continuing professional development'. As well as committing to one's own development, this principle encourages active involvement in the continuing professional development of colleagues and other healthcare professionals e.g. the implementation of clinical supervision for nurses. As identified by Christine Beasley, Regional Director of Nursing, North Thames, in her foreword to the *Clinical Supervision*

*Resource Pack*[9] there is no single way of implementing clinical supervision. However, 'one of the most effective ways to generate an individualised model is for clinical staff and managers to discuss the issues and agree their own solution'.

Questions to consider here include: 'Are our procedures for planning continuous professional development in line with recognised recommendations?' – UKCC, GMC, AMGP; and 'How well prepared are we to take action on any shortcomings we discover?' Each of the 14 principles will raise questions in the minds of those reviewing current practice. It is the questioning which facilitates the ongoing personal and professional development. The questioning, too, provides the challenge to the status quo and checks out the 'what if' scenario.

The Code imparts a different meaning for each focus.

## Patient focus

For patients it is a public demonstration and commitment to continuing competence and life-long learning. It is a demonstration of our fitness to practise and furnishes public confidence and credibility for the provision of optimum patient care and services. Principle 2.5 promotes openness of information, effective communication processes and responsiveness. Questions to consider here include: 'Do appropriate individuals and bodies e.g. patients, health authorities, and CHCs have access to our local resolution procedures, Practice Charter and performance/service plans and reports?'; and 'How can they best be involved in these agendas?'

## Team and primary care organisation focus

For other colleague professions it provides the security that good employment practice, including the early identification of health problems, will be on the management agenda. The UKCC report of November 1996 on 'Issues arising from professional conduct complaints' illustrates that, although an individual practitioner may be reported to the UKCC for misconduct, some cases have demonstrated poor management processes and a lack of effective staff supervision. 'An agenda for action – issues for management' has been put forward by the UKCC; thankfully, AMGP is one step ahead for managers in primary care and the Code offers support and guidance.

For general practitioners, as the current employers of practice managers, it signals the preferred choice of provider and the many benefits this beings in terms of success in partnerships, from profitability to optimum patient care. For other organisations, especially the new organisations as health authorities, it means a contribution to their performance management framework and primary care indicators.

*Personal focus*

For the practising practice manager in primary care the Code provides the backdrop for personal, professional and organisational fitness. it encourages good practice, ethical behaviour and competent, professional management. It promotes the framework for effective management and managing for quality. It is about making a difference; continuing professional development is not about keeping up to date, but being one step ahead, positively moving forward and leading others. And, on the way, anticipating the risks of the 'what if' scenario. It provides the opportunity for really understanding the environment within which managers work, the pressures facing all professionals in a primary care led NHS, thus enabling personal, professional and team development for optimum patient care. As management troubleshooter Sir John Harvey Jones identifies, there is a misunderstanding about what management is in such places as the NHS: 'It is not about maintaining the status quo; it is about going somewhere. Managers have to look ahead and decide where they want the organisation to be.' Never a truer word with the challenges facing the NHS and the opportunities for development and flexibility in the new White Papers *Choice and Opportunity*[10], *A Service with Ambitions*[3] and *Delivering the Future.*[11]

## Conclusion

The *Code of Principles* published in 1995 anticipated a future need for further development of these principles. It was designed to be a beginning and *Code of Principles II* was published in the autumn of 1996. This provides a comprehensive framework for professional support and continuing professional development which brings success in partnerships.

The relevance and value of the 14 principles were reaffirmed and it was noted by the Minister of Health, Gerry Malone, in his keynote speech at the Association's 21st Annual Course addressing 'Choices, Choices, and Yet More Choices' at Glasgow in November 1996 that AMGP has tackled the very difficult subject of priority setting. He wondered whether at the end of the course the principle 2.12 would be widened to include a greater public view on priority setting. This states 'being accountable for using, and influencing the use of, all resources as effectively, efficiently and economically as possible for the consistent delivery of service quality, through the setting and attainment of performance standards and targets'. When reviewing current practice within our own organisations having attended such a course as part of our continuing professional development, the questions this principle raises, along with those within the patient focus, will most certainly widen as primary care develops. Hence, the importance of questioning within the Code – as a medium to challenge, stimulate and lead primary care development. Ambitious? Yes. Managers subscribing to the Code are ambitious to 'enhance the standard of professional management's contribution to patient care'.

## References

1 Association of Managers in General Practice (1995) *Code of Principles*, London.
2 Department of health (1996) *The National Health Service; A Service with Ambitions*, Department of Health, Leeds.
3 Cadbury A (1992) Report of the Committee on the Financial Aspects of Corporate Governance (Chair: Sir Adrian Cadbury), Gee and Co Ltd, London.
4 NHS Training Division/AMGP (1994) Guidance on the collection of evidence for the NHS Management Standards for General Medical Practice Managers, Bristol.
5 Department of Health (1994) *Code of Conduct. Code of Accountability*, Department of Health, London.
6 Department of Health (1995) *Code of Practice on Openness in the NHS*, Department of Health, Leeds.
7 Department of Health (1995) *Accountability Framework for GP Fundholding; Towards a Primary Care Led NHS*, Department of Health, Leeds.
8 Guidance from the General Medical Council – Duties of a Doctor (1995) GMC, London.
9 Department of Health (1995) *Clinical Supervision – a Resource Pack*; special edition for London practice nurses, Department of Health, London.
10 Department of Health (1996) *Choice and Opportunity; Primary Care: The Future*, Department of Health, Leeds.
11 Department of Health (1996) *Primary Care: Delivering the Future*, Department of Health, Leeds.

# AMGP Code of Principles and Whistle-blowing

*Rosey Foster*
*Association of Managers in*
*General Practice*

---

The Association's hallmark has been its commitment to raising standards in primary care management. No other organisation has grasped the nettle as the Association has in explicitly stating the minimum standards expected of a manager to become a full member of AMGP (agreed at National Vocational Qualification level 4/Management Charter Initiative level 1) or how those standards should be achieved or the managers supported if they underperform.

In developing Stage II of the Code of Principles[1] the Association was conscious of the growing concern surrounding accountability in public life, the wider powers of the General Medical Council and performance procedures for doctors due to come into force in 1997 and the 'clinical supervision' pilot projects for nurses. Specifically it was noted that:

> Demands for accreditation and for demonstrating competence on a continuing basis is increasing across all the professions. The profession of management is no exception. The primary care manager of the future will almost certainly be the subject of mandatory codes of both competence and conduct, occupy a pivotal role in both determining objectives and delivering results through the coordination of a wider spectrum of health care colleagues and require increasing technical, legal, social and financial skills.

Stage II represents the drawing together of a number of ongoing initiatives by the Association in response to these needs. It provides a comprehensive framework for professional support, enabling practice managers to develop knowledge and competence, to assume responsibility for the effectiveness of their own practice and to further their personal professional development.

It is expected that the preferred choice for entrants to the profession of practice management will be those who meet the membership standards and subscribe to the Code of Principles.

### Environmental links

It is important to fit the Code of Principles Stage II into context with the drive on accreditation and certification models by other professions working within the NHS and outside. The Association identified nine stakeholders who would have a vested interest and a part to play in the success of Stage II (see Figure 4.2.1). In particular, we paid attention to the changes and developments of the two regulatory bodies of our professional colleagues.

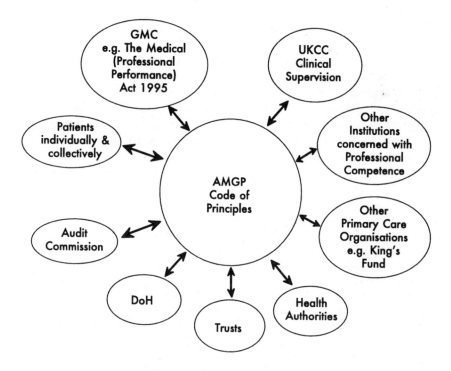

**Figure 4.2.1** *Environmental links*

### General Medical Council (GMC)

In 1995 the GMC issued a publication entitled *Good Medical Practice*[2] including 'The Duties of a Doctor' which gave specific guidance to all doctors on maintaining a good standard of practice and care. In November 1995 the GMC was given wider powers following the Royal Assent to the Medical (Professional Performance) Bill. The aim of the Act is to protect the public – and it will do so by ensuring that:

- doctors whose pattern of professional performance is alleged to be seriously deficient are professionally assessed;
- that remedial action is taken where necessary;
- where required, conditions of the doctor's registration are imposed or the doctor removed from practice.

It is anticipated that the new assessment referral and the professional performance will be in place by September 1997.

### United Kingdom Central Council (UKCC)

The UKCC is the regulatory body for nurses, health visitors and midwives. Recently guidance has been given on clinical supervision. Clinical supervision has been defined as 'a term used to describe a formal process of professional support and learning which enables individual practitioners to develop knowledge and competence'. It was first identified as a target in the 1993 *Vision for the Future* document.[3] Pilot schemes are in progress around the country and we recognised the importance of this work, and to highlight to managers that their nursing colleagues should have similar opportunities to access peer support.

### Other institutions

Other institutions concerned with professional competence include the Royal College of General Practitioners (RCGP) and the British Medical Association (BMA). Membership of the RCGP is becoming a prerequisite for new GP principals and Fellowship by Assessment for the College[4] has gained the subtitle of the 'ultimate audit', endorsing the College's drive on quality and standards within general practice.

Proposals and a model for a practice accreditation system have also been drawn up in consultation with a multi-disciplinary team and is ready for pilot.

The General Medical Services Committee of the BMA have drafted proposals for the recertification of doctors.

During 1996 a review was commissioned by the Department of Health to consider new legislation and a new statutory body and powers to provide 'a state of the art regulatory system for health and related professions'.[5]

Outside the NHS, it is interesting to note that Robert Smith, President of the Institute of Chartered Accountants, wrote in *The Times* that 'any true professional would acknowledge the need for continuing education and most would accept the need for active encouragement from their professional body'.[6] A new regime of mandatory post-qualification professional development is being introduced in Scotland by the Institute in 1997.

## Other primary care organisations

Other primary care organisations that have played a major role in shaping the future of standards and have been supportive of AMGP initiatives, include the King's Fund with its organisational audit programme.[7]

## Health authorities and trusts

Health authorities and trusts are playing an increasingly important role. Individually they have a vested interest to ensure that a practice is well managed, that the funding and resources allocated in primary care are properly accounted for and that patient services are more than just adequate. The National Association of Health Authorities and Trusts (NAHAT) was reported in *General Practitioner* as suggesting that all practices should be accredited and re-accredited to ensure 'minimum standards'.[8]

Under NAHAT proposals, areas such as 'organisational competence, management and teamwork' would be examined as well as 'qualifications and experience of staff.'

## Department of Health

Two documents published by the Department have relevance in primary care, *Code of Practice on Openness in the NHS*[9] and the *Code of Conduct: Code of Accountability*.[10] Without doubt accreditation is very high on the Department's agenda. It is, however, best summed up by a quotation from the Secretary of State, Stephen Dorrell: 'One of the key issues is the gap between good quality general practice ... and the trailing edge. Re-accreditation is one way of addressing the problem.'

**Figure 4.2.2** *The AMGP professional support process – applying the Code of Principles*

### The Audit Commission

The Commission's report *What the Doctor Ordered*[11] identified that the 'best managed and outward looking practices tend to achieve more benefits for their patients'. Patients and carers, individually and collectively, are finally the most important stakeholders. It is very much in their interest that the manager is competent and fit to practice.

### Applying the Code of Principles

The AMGP professional support process to applying the Code is best viewed as a continuum (see Figure 4.2.2). This process involves entry into the profession through to achieving the goal or target of a successful practice or partnership with patients and carers, and success in partnership with professional colleagues both within and beyond the practice.

By taking the first steps to join the Association, a manager signals to the NHS and the world at large that he or she subscribes to the Code of Principles and continuing professional development to prove competency. Full membership of AMGP, or as an associate working towards full membership, is the first essential step to accreditation and professional status. Having gained it, we must work together to ensure that managers continue to be professionally fit to practice – through a commitment to lifelong learning. By continuing their professional development the spectre of re-accreditation will be less threatening. Taking part in quality initiatives such as the King's Fund Organisational Audit, Investors in People, Fellowship by Assessment, or similar nationally recognised schemes, will enable the manager to provide strong evidence of competence. However, should a manager be challenged over fitness to practice, the Association will provide the necessary framework to appeal, support, counsel and advise on a retraining or further education programme where necessary.

'Whistle-blowing' in the public sector has been widely publicised under 'sleaze' headlines. Public Concern at Work is a charity which is totally independent of government with the stated objectives 'to promote good practice and compliance with the law in public, private and voluntary sectors by focusing on the accountability of those in charge and the responsibility of those at work'. Their second annual report stated that 'there is a growing recognition that those who do sound the alarm on serious malpractice are not being disloyal, but deserve public thanks and support, rather than punishment and humiliation'.[12] Challenging professional conduct or competence in the Health Service is a highly sensitive topic. 'Sick' doctors, nurses or managers need the trust and support of their fellow professionals and their patients certainly need protection. No whistle-blowers should feel victimised and indeed the Nolan Committee Report into standards of public life promised to make life safer for them.[13]

A useful fourteen-point checklist entitled *Do the Right Thing*[14] is available from Public Concern at Work and has been recommended by the Audit Commission as good practice for the NHS and local government. The time has come when very clear messages need to be sent out that fraud and other forms of serious malpractice, and unethical behaviour or professional misconduct will no longer be tolerated or overlooked. This is in the best interests of patients, practitioners and managers. Not taking action can result in costly legal proceedings, if not death.

The new GMC performance procedures have been drawn up to prevent a doctor from ever reaching the point of being found incompetent. This is also true for the Association's Code of Principles. By taking heed of professional support and peer review and by accessing and participating in continuing professional development, no manager should be found to be underperforming.

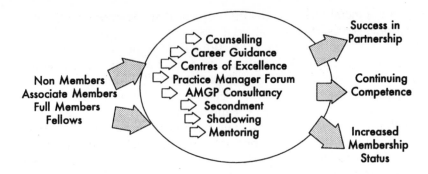

**Figure 4.2.3** *Continuing Professional Development framework*

## AMGP Continuing Professional Development framework

The Association plans to have the following mechanisms and activities in place for its members, with access for all managers in primary care (see Figure 4.2.3).

### Counselling

Already undertaken informally, we consider it essential that managers should have access to professional counselling if required.

### Career guidance

Personal assessment of development and placement within the wider context of the NHS or parallel environment should be available.

### AMGP Centres of Excellence

There are two Centres of Excellence currently established at Exeter and Newcastle, with the aim of one in each NHS region. Essential criteria are access to AMGP Certificate and Diploma modules, to provide multi-disciplinary resource facilities and a helpline. Each centre may have additional facilities dependent upon their expertise, as, for example, at Exeter where there are leadership and interpersonal skills courses and specific post-graduate education such as an MSc.

### Practice manager forums

The holding of practice manager forums is another essential criterion for a Centre of Excellence, but also available in other regions and areas, providing a vital communication and discussion point on local and national issues.

## AMGP Consultancy Service

Launched in 1996, the service provides AMGP accredited consultants to help GPs, managers and their practices who become overwhelmed by personnel, development or organisational problems. The consultants diagnose the issues and provide practical action plans on how to move the organisation forward.

## Secondment, shadowing and mentoring

These three separate and vital activites are available in industry and occasionally in secondary care but never given priority in primary care. If managers are to be encouraged and developed these basic activities can and should be available. Secondment could include a vocational training scheme for practice manager 'registrars' with placements in accredited practices similar to the criteria for the GP vocational training scheme.

It is a well-quoted fact that the people, or human resources, are the most valuable asset in an organisation. The NHS is the largest employer in Europe and it has taken nearly 50 years for primary care and its people to be recognised as 'the jewel in the crown" of the NHS. The Association is determined to ensure that managers gain the support and recognition they need and deserve. The Code of Principles – Stage II offers the strategic framework essential to take primary care beyond the year 2000.

## References

1 Association of Managers in General Practice (1995/1996) *Code of Principles: Code of Principles – Stage II*, AMGP, London.
2 General Medical Council (1995) *Good Medical Practice*, GMC, London.
3 Dept of Health (1993) *Vision for the Future*, HMSO, London.
4 Royal College of General Practitioners (1996) *Occasional Paper 50: Fellowship by Assessment*, RCGP, London.
5 Dept of Health (1996) *The Regulation of Health Professions: Report of a Review of the Professions Supplementary to Medicine Act (1960) with Recommendations for New Legislation*, HMSO, London.
6 Smith, R 'Duty-bound to keep up to date', *The Times*, 3 October.
7 King's Fund (1996) *Primary Care Organisation and Commissioning Standards*, King's Fund, London.
8 *General Practitioner* (1996) 18 October.

9 Dept of Health (1995) *Code of Practice on Openness in the NHS*, HMSO, London.
10 Dept of Health (1994) *Code of Conduct: Code of Accountability*, HMSO, London.
11 Audit Commission (1996) *What the Doctor Ordered: A Study of GP Fundholding in England and Wales*, HMSO, London.
12 Public Concern at Work (1996) *Second Annual Report*, Public Concern at Work, London.
13 Nolan Committee (1995) *Standards in Public Life*, HMSO, London.
14 Public Concern at Work (1996) *Do the Right Thing*, Public Concern at Work, London.

# Consumer Issues in General Practice

*Bob Gann*
*The Help for Health Trust*

Over the past decade patients in general practice have had increasing expectations of access to information and involvement in their own healthcare. There are least four good reasons why this should be the case.

- It is ethical to do so.
- People want it.
- Research shows it works.
- Legislation requires it.

## It is ethical to do so

Honesty is an ethical imperative which is fundamental to any social contract. Truth telling is not only a moral absolute but also produces the best kind of social relationship, one based on mutual trust. Doctors sometimes argue that withholding information from patients is necessary because of another important principle – that of doing the patient no harm. But it is difficult to justify doctors being the one group in society exempt from this fundamental role in human relationships. Any deception infringes the autonomy of the patient – the patient's right to know.

## People want it

There is abundant evidence that people want more information and involvement in their own healthcare and treatment. In a 1988 Consumers Association survey 91 per cent of patients wanted to see their own health records. In another public survey 63 per cent of people said they would prefer an honest answer to whether they had cancer. Patients continue with this wish when they have a serious diagnosis. In studies with cancer patients most wanted to be given a considerable amount of information (Deber, 1994). Patients particularly want to know more about drug therapy, as well as cause, diagnosis, reasons for and results of tests, and prognosis.

## Research shows it works

In clinical trials it has been demonstrated that better functional and physiological health status is closely connected to good doctor-patient communication and shared responsibility (Kaplan *et al.*, 1989). In studies of patients with hypertension those with higher 'active patient orientation' had better treatment outcomes. Patients who seek and use information have been shown to experience less stress. Reviews (Ley, 1988) have identified benefits of information, including shorter hospital stays, less pain and lower use of drugs.

## Legislation requires it

Patient's rights in the UK have, since 1991, been set out in the *Patient's Charter*. There has not been specific legislation to implement the *Patient's Charter*. Rather the Charter summarises a collection of rights and standards based on both legislation and common law. Rights to clear information on treatment and research are based on the fundamental common law principle of informed consent. The right of access to health records was established by two Acts of Parliament, the Data Protection Act 1984 and the Access to Health Records Act 1990. The rights to information on local health services, guaranteed admission within 18 months and investigation of complaints have no basis in law, but depend for their implementation on managerial incentives and sanctions, including published performance tables.

## New imperatives: openness, partnership and effectiveness

More recently new NHS agendas have emphasised the need for increased patient communication and involvement. These include:

- NHS Code of Openness;
- Patient Partnership Strategy;
- Promoting Clinical Effectiveness;
- NHS Research and Development.

Health service managers and practitioners are increasingly aware that sharing information with consumers (patients, carers and the wider public) can be a significant factor in:

- encouraging informed and discerning use of health services;
- creating public awareness of the concepts of effectiveness and uncertainty when considering treatment options;
- helping set priorities which reflect consumer values;
- encouraging professionals to develop skills in communicating with patients.

## Openness

Published in 1995, the NHS Code of Openness encourages health services to enable public access to information about NHS services, costs, quality and performance; proposed service changes and how to influence decisions; decisions and actions affecting their own treatment; and what information is available and how to get it.

There is a number of implications for general practice in the Code of Openness. Health authorities are required to ensure mechanisms for public access to information on availability of GPs, dentists, pharmacists, optometrists, including late opening for family health services. Information about the number of complaints and response times must also be communicated. Although general practitioners are self-employed independent contractors and cannot therefore be required to publish sensitive information about their 'business', general practice contracts specify information which must be available to patients. Practice leaflets must be published and obtainable either from the practice or the health authority. These must contain information including names, sex and qualifications of practitioners, appointment systems, clinics and services available, geographical area covered, and details of complaints systems.

The NHS Performance Tables now contain information about achievement against primary care targets including:

- number of practices with practice charters;
- vaccination and immunisation rates;
- cervical cytology screening.

The Performance Tables are published in the summer of each year as a booklet, on the Internet, and in summary form in many newspapers.

## Complaints

For many years there has been dissatisfaction with the NHS complaints system which was seen as fragmented and confusing for both patients and staff. This criticism led to the government setting up a review of the complaints system in 1993, which provided a basis for the new system which was introduced on 1 April 1996. Key features of the new scheme are:

- a unified system for all services provided under the NHS, whether from hospitals, community health services, health authorities, or family health services;
- greater emphasis on most complaints being handled by staff or practitioners through a local resolution process;
- resource to an independent review panel for those who remain dissatisfied with local resolution (if a panel convenor agrees it is appropriate);
- extended role for the Health Service Ombudsman who will for the first time be able to consider complaints about family health services and issues of clinical judgement.

General practices must have practice-based complaints procedures, with one person responsible for their administration and publicity for their existence and operation.

### Patient partnership

NHS Executive medium-term priorities as set out in *Priorities and Planning Guidance 1997–98* include the need for 'giving greater voice and influence to users of NHS services and their carers in their own care, the development and definition of standards set for NHS services locally, and the development of NHS policy both locally and nationally'.

Achieving this in practice is not easy. Patient surveys and Health Service Ombudsman reports repeatedly highlight concern about lack of information, poor communication and absence of real partnership in decision-making. As a first step towards remedying this at all levels within the NHS, the NHS Executive in 1996 published the first comprehensive *Patient Partnership Strategy*. The strategy, with points for action at local and national level, focuses on the work that needs to be done in four main areas:

- production and dissemination of information for health service users and representatives;
- structural, organisational and resourcing requirements for patient partnership and involvement including skills development and support for users;
- supporting staff in achieving active partnership and user involvement in service development;
- research and evaluation into effective mechanisms for patient partnership and involvement.

### Effectiveness and research-based evidence

Sound information is an essential prerequisite for promoting clinical effectiveness and supporting decision-making by patients as well as professionals. There is now a number of information gathering and dissemination initiatives funded as part of the NHS R&D programme, including the NHS Centre for Reviews and Dissemination, the UK Cochrane Centre and the Health Technology Assessment programme. The *Promoting Clinical Effectiveness* framework for action recognises the importance of patients and carers having access to this information alongside clinicians and managers. A number of projects (e.g. King's Fund and NHS CRD) are developing evidence-based patient information materials to support informed treatment choices. Furthermore, a Standing Advisory Group on Consumer Involvement in NHS Research and Development has now been established, beginning its work advising the Central Research and Development Committee (CRDC) in 1996.

## Health information services

In response to these changes in public expectation and driven by explicit NHS policy, there has been a major growth in information services for patients and the public over the past ten to fifteen years (Gann, 1991).

There are now specialist health information services for the public in many settings including health shops, hospital enquiry points, health information mobiles, patient libraries, etc. The first services were established in Stevenage and Wessex in the late 1970s, with a gradual and patchy development of information centres during the 1980s. The *Patient's Charter* in 1992 and the accompanying Health Service Guidelines on health information services (HSG(92)21) have been a major boost to development of services in the 1990s.

Under the *Patient's Charter* a single national freephone number for health information was established. Callers dial 0800 665544 and are automatically routed to their nearest health information centre. The local centres operate under an umbrella service name: the NHS Health Information Service (HIS). The *Health Service Guidelines* require these centres to provide information on:

- common illnesses and treatments;
- self-help groups;
- healthcare services;
- waiting times;
- keeping healthy;
- patients' rights and how to complain;
- Patient's Charter standards.

The information centres linked to the freephone number were originally based at regional level. With the abolition of NHS regions in 1996, new Health Service Guidelines (HSG(95)44) devolved responsibility for securing HIS provision to local commissioning authorities from April 1996. Some health authorities have continued to buy into the former regional service providers; others have set up their own services. As a result there is now an increased number of HIS providers, with 23 health information centres in all.

As well as introducing new purchasing responsibilities for HIS, HSG(95)44 also require for the first time provision through the HIS of information on 'outcomes and effectiveness: evidence-based information to enable users to make informed choices on treatments'.

Health information services can be expected to have a range of information to offer in the area of clinical effectiveness. This might include:

- contacts for self-help groups to enable shared experiences, support for decision-making, and provision of experiential evidence as a complement to more conventional evidence from RCTs, etc.;
- consumer health information in a variety of formats, including books, leaflets, magazines, videos, Internet, etc.;
- reviews of evidence, including access to the databases of the Cochrane Collaboration, NHS Centre for Reviews and Dissemination, *Effective Health Care* bulletins, etc.;
- information on how to get access to treatments, including referral mechanisms and waiting times;
- intelligence on enquiries received to inform purchasing and research agendas.

## Health information in general practice

Despite the existence of health information services and helplines for the public research, Buckland (1994) demonstrates that most people's preferred setting for information giving is within general practice – although there is also a good deal of dissatisfaction with the information actually provided.

We are now beginning to see the development of a number of public access information systems in general practice, using touch screen computer terminals to give access to databases of self-help and health promotion information. Examples include the In Touch With Health system developed by Brann and the Healthpoint system.

In 1995 The Help for Health Trust carried out an evaluation of public access via health information terminals in four Dorset general practices which were supplied with the Trust's database of self-help information (Helpbox) and the Dorset County Council's DORIS community information system (Buckland, 1995). A fifth of patients used the system in a month, a quarter of these more than once. Twice as many women as men used the system. The most used information related to leisure, sport and what's on, and there was in fact low use of health information (although, of course, the sport and leisure information had a health promoting role).

Increasingly we can expect patients to have access to an enormous range of health-related information via the Internet. A recent study published on the Internet (Consumer health & medical information on the Internet: supply & demand http://etrg.findsvp.com/health/mktginfo.html) identified some of the characteristics of Internet health information users and suppliers:

- Health information users are more likely to be women, married, with children, college educated, than the average Internet user.
- They are sophisticated users, using search engines and visiting sites in depth.
- There is a good deal of diet information available, adequate illness information and little treatment information.
- Most health sites are links to others rather than original in content.
- More than half of health information sites are owned by organisations 'likely to be biased or inaccurate'.

Of British homes 40 per cent now have a PC and a recent MORI poll indicated that 2 million people use Internet (at home, work, school, etc.). Development of 'smart' TVs accessing Internet via cable TV network are likely to extend this usage even more.

General practitioners and other members of the primary care team are realising that the patient of the new millennium is likely to be more assertive, more questioning and in some cases more sophisticated in understanding of risks and benefits, clinical uncertainty and effectiveness. This consumer demand, underpinned by policy imperatives, and enabled by technological advances, will produce a very different 21st-century patient.

## References and further reading

Blaxter, M (1995) *Consumers and Research in the NHS*, Department of Health, London.

Buckland, S (1994) *Unmet Needs for Health Information: Report to the Nuffield Provincial Hospitals Trust*, The Help for Health Trust, Winchester.

Buckland, S (1995) *Evaluation of DORIS in Four GP Surgeries: Report to the Dorset Health Commission* The Help for Health Trust, Winchester.

Deber, R (1994) 'The patient physician relationship: changing roles and the desire for information', *Canadian Medical Association Journal*, 151: 171–6.

Department of Health (1992) *The Patient's Charter*, Department of Health, London.

Gann, R (1991) 'Consumer health information: the growth of an information specialism', *Journal of Documentation*, 47(3): 284–308.

Gann, R (1995) 'Consumers and evidence based health care', *Evidence Based Purchasing*, 9.

Kaplan, S H *et al.* (1989) 'Assessing the effects of physician–patient interactions on the outcomes of chronic disease', *Medical Care*, 27(3 Supplement): 110–27.

Ley, P (1988) *Communicating with Patients*, Croom Helm, London.

NHS Executive (1992) *Local Voices: The Views of Local People in Purchasing for Health*, NHS Management Executive, London.

NHS Executive (1995) *Code of Practice on Openness in the NHS*, NHS Executive, London.

NHS Executive (1996) *Patient Partnership: Building a Collaborative Strategy*, NHS Executive, London.

NHS Executive (1996) *Promoting Clinical Effectiveness: A Framework for Action in and through the NHS*, NHS Executive, London.

# The New Health Authorities and the Primary Care Led NHS

*Andrea J Jones*
*North Staffordshire Health*
*Authority**

From my experience as a practice manager, a manager with an FHSA and from 1 April 1996 an associate director with a new health authority, I offer readers a view of the new health authorities and how they are coping with the primary care led NHS six months after the final stage of the government's NHS reform process has been completed.

In this chapter I focus only on the role of the health authorities in relation to general practice. However, it must be recognised that the agenda for the new health authorities is much broader than primary care, and that the primary care agenda also includes working with the dental, pharmaceutical and optical contractors. However, in acknowledgement of general practice's co-ordinator role in the primary care led NHS, this review has focused specifically on this area.

It is some five years since I worked as a manager in general practice. My work since then has been to facilitate, enable and develop primary care while working in both a Family Health Service Authority (FHSA) and currently with a new health authority. It is important to acknowledge that my views have been developed through experiences at both general practice and health authority

---

* The views and opinions of the author, as expressed in this chapter, are personal and do not attribute to North Staffordshire Health Authority.

level and that this chapter offers readers very much a personal perspective of the subject.

## Introduction

### A primary care led NHS

From the first time that I heard the expression 'a primary care led NHS', which must have been sometime in 1992, I remember thinking rather naively at the time that at last the importance of primary care has been recognised and acknowledged by the centre. I was working as a primary care manager with an FHSA at the time and I have to admit that I did not have a comprehensive view of exactly what a primary care led NHS meant. But the concept fitted with my belief that there was a need for the NHS to refocus the service that was provided so as to match more closely patients' needs. A crucial part of this process was to continue to redress the balance of power between primary care and secondary care practitioners.

The earlier comment of 'rather naively' is made as, in developing my understanding of the wider NHS and the implications of a primary care led service, I now consider my enthusiasm was somewhat impetuous. I did not take full account of the associated responsibilities that have to accompany such a policy change. The more that we develop our understanding of a concept and translate this into actions, the more potential differences between the interests of the various stakeholders become apparent.

The responsibilities of a primary care led service are concisely captured by Geoff Meads[1] in his statement that these are the convergence of the clinical referral powers, the financial controls and service planning responsibilities. The challenge for those of us who believe in the vision and who want to make it a reality, is to work truly in partnership, to accept and manage the constraints, to value and respect each other's perspective and acknowledge that there will have to be compromises within a tax-based, cash-limited system that has to provide services which have been shaped from both a population and patient basis.

### The policy context

The central aim of the 1990 programme of health service reform, has been to build a NHS that is more responsible both to the individual patient needs and to the health needs of a population as a whole. The key changes of the past five years have been:

- separation of the purchasing and providing function;

- development of purchasing, health authority and GP fundholding;
- improving health through specific targets, Health of the Nation;
- increased users' awareness of the service availability, Patient's Charter;
- integration of the FHSA and DHA functions, and devolution of central responsibility.

The policy documents setting out these changes include: *Working for atients*[2], *Caring for People*,[3] *Health of the Nation*,[4] the *Patient's Charter*[5] and EL(95)24, *The Creation of the New Health Authorities*.[6]

The other major national debate that has an influence on primary care today is the report documenting the outcome of the primary care listening exercise. This national programme was announced by Stephen Dorrell, the Secretary of State for Health, on 18 October 1995 during his address to the National Association of Fundholders conference. The outcome of the 'Listening programme', the first stage of the debate on primary care, has been captured and published in the document *Primary Care: The Future*.[7]

## The new health authorities

### The differences between their functions and their 'evolving role'

The new health authorities created on 1 April 1996 have taken over the responsibility for all of the statutory functions previously exercised by district health authorities, family health services authorities, and also a number of functions that have been transferred from regional health authorities. Guidance in the form of EL(96)34 *Changing Statutory Functions of Health Authorities* describes the changing statutory functions and covers in detail those which are either new to the health authorities or limited in the way they may be carried out. This guidance deliberately does not set out how these functions are to be carried out.

The style and manner in which the new health authorities carry out the statutory functions is described as their 'evolving role', and has been described in a number of policy documents, namely, EL(94)79 *Developing NHS Purchasing and GP Fundholding – Towards a Primary Care-Led NHS*;[8] EL(95)24 *The Creation of the New Health Authorities*; and EL(95)54 *Accountability Framework for GP Fundholding*.[9] The way in which the new health authorities are developing this role is one of the areas of change that presents both the most challenging agenda for the new authorities and the one that theoretically creates the most opportunity for facilitating change in primary care.

## Practical challenges for the new health authorities

The latest reforms offer considerable practical challenges to the new health authorities. These challenges are very similar to those experienced by FHSA personnel in 1990, the start of the reform process and the first stage of the reorganisation of health authorities. Family Practitioner Committees were given different statutory functions and responsibilities as well as a new evolving role with primary care. Does any of this sound familiar?

The major differences between the two stages of the development are first that the Department of Health has now put in place the policy framework which will enable new health authorities and primary care teams to progress towards a primary care led service. The second difference is that the latest changes are taking place in an environment of increasing pressures on administrative budgets. For health authorities this takes the form of continually reducing management cost targets; for all purchasers (fundholders, locality commissioning groups and health authorities), there is the requirement to secure a challenging 3 per cent efficiency target for activity return on investment. Alongside this the NHS continues to face an increasing demand for services.

It is also important to recognise that the pace of change in the development of health authorities has varied considerably in different areas of the UK. For instance, some health authorities and FHSAs had joint executive appointments for a couple of years before the legislative changes in April 1996 and some have worked as commissions with a joint chief executive. These organisations are generally at a different evolutionary stage than those that only came together on 1 April 1996. Lack of co-terminosity between DHAs and FHSAs and the restructuring of local authorities during 1995–6 have also proved additional restraining factors in terms of the pace at which health authorities have been able to develop.

The restructuring of health authorities in England is generally recorded as having been seamless.[10] I doubt that many of the personnel who have been through the recent changes would agree with this and I imagine that the NAHAT report which quoted this was reporting senior commissioning managers' opinion. Health authorities that did not have joint executive appointments prior to 1 April 1996, and which have experienced some of the other complexities detailed above, are still sorting out such internal issues as what the new organisation means and how the different components can work together.

## Challenges of the 'evolving role' of health authorities

In full consideration of the practical constraints outlined above, the main challenges that health authorities face in the evolution of their role may be considered under four key headings:

- management style;
- the purchaser and provider role of the new organisation;
- support versus monitoring role in primary care;
- communication.

### Management style

In the majority of cases, the new health authority chief executives have previously held DHA posts, although there is also a small number of ex-FHSA and trust chief executives in these positions. Staff previously employed by FHSAs have in many cases been subsumed by their DHA counterparts, as illustrated by former FHSA chief executives now being employed as directors of the new authorities.

The new health authorities have a predominance of senior staff with considerable experience of managing secondary care, a very small number of senior staff (usually one at board level) with family health service experience, and rarely more than one with actual primary care provider experience. I recently found a brilliant illustration of the possible consequences of the new health authorities having many senior staff from DHA backgrounds at a conference in September 1996. The conference subject was primary care led purchasing. The speaker, an executive director of a new health authority, spoke continually about the district health authority's role in developing primary care led purchasing. You may think 'what's in a name', but I have to say in this case everything. We are some six months into the new organisations and this particular individual appeared to have no concept of the need to acknowledge the change in the role of their own authority. This provides a perfect illustration that changing the structure of an organisation does not change the values and way of thinking of the employees; this takes considerably longer.

In developing the primary care led NHS, the new health authorities have to support a primary care provider role and enable primary care teams to meet the challenges of the new strategy. In order to manage this role effectively it is essential that executives and managers have an understanding of and empathy with the primary care environment. Dr June Huntingdon has explained the organisational characteristics of general practice as a human service organisation and explores the need for health authorities to understand the differences between general practice and health authorities in relation to the different cultures and complexities.[11] At its basic this translates into an understanding of the complexities of the mixture of the health and business aspects of general practice. To the more enlightened, this will be an understanding of the psychological conflicts of interest that practitioners experience and manage daily, i.e. being an advocate for the patient while considering the cost of alternative treatments and prioritising care.

The management style and culture of the new organisation is very different to that of the command and control model of the DHAs. Changing style and culture is exceedingly difficult and takes time. Changing the values and developing a new paradigm (common mindset) that fits the new organisation can only be achieved by illustrating these through behaviour. This most importantly demands change from the chief executive, as leadership is required to embrace and continually demonstrate and reinforce the change in approach and values. An ongoing programme of organisational and personnel development is also an essential component of a developing or learning organisation.

### Purchaser and provider role

In the early development of the purchasing role and separation of the provider function, the purchaser culture that was encouraged within DHAs was one that actively legislated against taking the interests of the provider into account when making purchasing decisions. As purchasers and providers have matured, on the whole so has their relationship.

The dual role of the new authorities, i.e. that of purchasing and providing, should theoretically facilitate a holistic approach to patient services. It is accepted that potential difficulties have been introduced in having to manage the conflicting demands of, on the one hand, facilitating and enabling primary care providers and, on the other hand, of operating a market management approach when working with trusts. For senior staff appropriately to manage this potential conflict there first needs to be a commitment from them to wear both hats.

The main challenges created by this situation are that managers will need to switch between both ways of working, depending on which situation they are in. It has taken DHA staff five years to separate and develop a purchaser perspective. The provider function of the new authority could be viewed by them as a step backwards. FHSA staff, on the other hand, will have less experience of the purchaser role. They may find that the predominance of senior staff with secondary care experience leads to a continuing strong purchaser culture that does not accept the need to consider and support provider interests. In order for the new organisations to develop there is a need for all staff to accept the values of the other and learn different ways of thinking and working if the organisations are to function as intended. This can only be achieved through a considered and planned process of personal development.

Having spent some time in the commercial private sector, I have to admit to feeling considerable confusion over the benefits of the purist NHS purchaser perspective that legislates against seeing a provider of healthcare as an essential component of a purchasers' business. This approach has been encouraged through the terminology of the internal market. I believe a macho interpretation of the purchaser-provider split is critically flawed. The commercial sector has realised this and has developed strategic alliances with both competitors and suppliers. The NHS has much to learn from the private sector in terms of getting the best from the supplier and competitor, so as to offer the best quality of product or service.

*Monitoring performance versus supporting role*
The challenges of having the responsibility for ensuring the quality and accessibility of primary care services could potentially be seen to conflict with having the responsibility to support the delivery of primary care in one area only, that of patient advocacy. Health authorities now have the challenging role of being advocates for the patient in primary care, and also of being enablers of primary care delivery. In order to avoid any potential conflict of interest, most organisations have separated out the responsibilities for these two roles, usually each having different executive directors. The challenge here is to ensure that the separation of responsibilities does not hinder communications and learning between the staff involved.

Performance management in primary care has been successfully introduced over the last few years by several authorities or commissions through the use of practice annual planning and review. The important factors in successful introduction and participation are:

- the process must have proven benefits for practices;
- the process must focus on the issues that are important for both parties;
- the debate must be adult to adult;
- the debate must be based on agreed performance data.

It is essential that there is trust and empathy between the two parties if constructive dialogue and development are to be achieved.

*Communications*
Some new health authorities have employed communications experts in their management structure. The most enlightened of these are developing a communications strategy that includes communications

with primary care. It is unreasonable to consider that health authorities can just forward on to primary care all of the directives that they receive, copies of their strategies and business plans, etc. and expect that GPs and the primary care team members will read and use them. From the government scrutiny *Patients Not Paper*,[12] this approach is shown to be ineffective. Again an awareness of the way in which practitioners operate and their time-limited environment suggests that there is a need to précis documents, offering full documents if requested.

## How are the new health authorities coping?

### Indictors of the evolutionary stage of health authorities

Primary care practitioners and managers are in the best position to measure the development of their own health authority in relation to the management style and approach that they have taken to primary care. In considering how the new health authorities are coping with the evolving role, I have identified some indicators that primary care teams might use to assess the development.

*Examples of a basic stage of development - seamless integration of authorities*

- No adverse change in the processing and timing of contractor payments during and since 1 April 1996 − surely if health authorities value their contractors then this has to be acknowledged as the most important indicator of a successful 'creation'.
- The new health authority's organisational structure and named contacts have been shared with primary care practitioners and their teams − in some instances where health commissions were in place prior to 1 April 1996, this could be a communication of no change.
- New organisational arrangements are seen by the primary care team to have been built on the knowledge and networks that existed within the FHSA or commission prior to 1 April 1996 − there is the risk that primary care teams will feel that they have lost an advocate in the FHSA staff and gained more managers from the new organisation.
- Practice staff are made to feel equal partners in their interactions with the new health authority − invariably there will have been some staff and job changes at the new health authority. It is possible therefore for new appointees to have little empathy with primary care teams and their support requirements, as well as having their own development needs. This should be transparent to the primary care team.

*Examples of an intermediate stage of development*

- Primary care teams will have information about the health authority strategy and business/investment plan in an appropriate format for them to use – this assumes that the new health authority has an overall health strategy. This indicator acknowledges the need for documentation that is to be shared with practice teams to meet the readers' needs.
- Many primary care practitioners are working with the health authority in developing the strategy/ies and forward plan – the local characteristics and heterogeneity of general practice make it essential for the health authority to have a number of mechanisms for engaging practitioners and their teams in developing the plan.
- Practice teams are participating in an agreed annual planning and review process with health authority staff, not only fundholding practices – for practice teams to agree to participate in this process there has to be a shared understanding and trust.
- Practice staff use health authority staff to advise and facilitate innovative practice developments, some of which may be at the boundaries of the current legislative framework. Much has been written on the need for different models of primary care organisation. The early piloting and development of such models has only been achieved where health authorities and practitioners have worked together to agree an appropriate way forward.

*Examples of an advanced stage of development*

- The health authority and practitioners participate in a formal process of performance management – this would be an extension of the current annual reviews moving the debate on to a more adult basis where both organisations tackle the jointly agreed agenda in an environment of comprehensive information relating to practice-based GMS, HCHS and Social Care (financial and activity information).
- The health authority provides an information service to practices. This would support primary care led commissioning and interpretation of local and national policies – the health authority would act as a trusted interpreter and provider to primary care teams.
- Practitioners' experience of working with the health authority is one of 'steering rather than rowing', as Osbourne and Gaebler (1992) put it.[13] This assumes that both activities are essential if forward progress is required. In practical terms the roles of steering and rowing interchange depending on the work.
- Different models of primary care provision are being developed that are based on patient and practitioner needs – this assumes that the health authority has compiled a comprehensive baseline of

information which has identified the needs and the current level of service provision and has devised a method which can evaluate and measure the success of different organisational models.

I trust that all managers in general practice can identify some indicators from those listed above with the actions of their own health authority, accepting that this list is in no way exhaustive.

## Conclusion

The primary care led NHS is with us today and in certain parts of the UK innovators are making the policy real – either through fundholding, total purchasing or agency approaches such as the Lyme Community Care Unit. I believe that rapid changes have to be driven by primary care and supported with adequate training and development for those who are delivering care in a new innovative environment.

The new authorities are changing much more slowly – the term evolution means 'a gradual change in the characteristics of a population'. The difficulty that the new organisations face is to be able to get ahead of the potential developments in primary care. As their role in the long term has to be that of pure commissioners of service, the provider role will and must disappear due to the transfer of management costs to primary care providers. For health authorities to be good commissioners of primary care, they must first have the information stated in the last indicator above. The role of health authorities is to ensure that whatever developments they support meet patient needs, lead to health gain and are cost effective. My belief is that so far the health authorities' support has too often been a leap of faith as they do not have the information to know what the long-term outcomes will be. This approach is acceptable for the odd pilot project, but not when managing in a strictly cash-limited environment, ensuring equity and quality healthcare services.

If we are successfully to implement and achieve a primary care led NHS, then the critical word for practitioners and health authorities is partnership. Both parties will have to work at developing the comprehension and empathy with their new partners. The good news is that some vehicles already exist for developing these partnerships – total purchasing projects being the main opportunity.

## References

1 Meads, G A (1996) *Primary Care-Led NHS Putting it into Practice*, Churchill Livingstone, Edinburgh.
2 Department of Health and Social Services (1989) *Working for Patients*, HMSO, London.

3 Department of Health and Social Services (1990) *Caring for People: Community Care in the Next Decade and Beyond*, HMSO, London.

4 Department of Health and Social Services (1992) *Health of the Nation*, HMSO, London.

5 Department of Health (1992) *The Patient's Charter*, Department of Health, London.

6 NHSE (1995) *The Creation of the New Health Authorities*, NHSE, London.

7 Dorrell, S (1996) *Primary Care: The Future*, NHSE, London.

8 EL(94)79 *Developing NHS Purchasing and GP Fundholding – Towards a Primary Care-Led NHS*.

9 EL(95)54 *Accountability Framework for GP Fundholding*.

10 NAHAT (1996) *The 1996/97 Contracting Round*, NAHAT, Birmingham.

11 Huntingdon, J (1996) 'Future relationships between health authorities and general practices', *Primary Care Management*, 6 (7/8).

12 Meads, G (1996) *Future Options for General Practice*, Radcliffe Medical Press, Abingdon.

13 NHSE (1995) *Patients not Paper: Report into the Efficiency Scrutiny into Bureaucracy in General Practice*, NHSE, London.

14 Osbourne, D and Gaebler, T (1992) *Re-inventing Government*, Addison-Westley, Harlow.

PART FIVE

# MANAGING INFORMATION

# 5.1

# The Paperless Surgery

*Bill Edwards*
*Hillsborough Medical Practice*

One of the biggest challenges to managers in general practice during the next couple of years will be integrating information technology into the surgery. In fact, this process started for most practices when they bought their first typewriter, then came the photocopier, personal computers and surgery networked clinical systems and then we had lots of paper — all over the place! The irony is that this technological development that brought us all the printed information will also, so we are led to believe, remove it one day. But it is going to be a painful and trying time for us all and the sooner we accept the inevitable the better.

Contingencies have to be put in place now to ease ourselves into the so called 'paperless' surgery. By that I mean protocols for recording information on our clinical systems, agreed formats for the computerised consultations and establishing electronic links with laboratories, health boards and providers. All these 'computer' functions can be implemented now and in parallel to our paper systems. The trouble is that there is a frustrating amount of duplication and for a while, during the transition from paper to paperless, there is going to be even more paper or at least information about our patients. This may be confusing to those dealing with patients, there will be some information on the computer, some in the chart, some on both, and so on, but I'm not sure that this situation can be avoided.

Not everyone is going to accept the inevitability of going paperless, some will accept it but equally will say 'not in my time'. If that happens to be the practice manager in the first instance then there are problems because our role is fundamental in implementing any change in the surgery. If we remain uncommitted and unconvinced, it is going to be extremely difficult to allay the fears and doubts of the rest of staff and the doctors, the latter being particularly concerned about medico-legal aspects. Although still a big problem, a conversion is possible, but the arguments for, and an acknowledgement of the drawbacks, will have to be presented clearly. Therefore, if the practice manager is required to move towards a paperless surgery – or just less paper – the following will have to be engraved on the minds of all those technophobes in the rest of the building! However, just to remind ourselves of one very important thing – this is all about creating the right conditions for the general practitioner to practice medicine. Let us not forget we are talking about human patients and not a car with a plug-in diagnostic attachment allowing the engineer to carry out a foolproof fault finding check on the engine.

The first and greatest obstacle to overcome is to recognise that we all feel comfortable with a piece of paper in our hand – it doesn't disappear off the screen accidentally when a jacket brushes over a critical combination of keyboard buttons. We can tear it up, write extra notes on it, photocopy it and post or fax it to someone else. A pen in the hand of a skilled writer can be very expressive and precise and with just a few well chosen words will impart a considerable amount of information. Even the odd bit of punctuation can mean a lot ... !!??

The trouble is, paper is bulky, it is very susceptible to damage by the elements and can easily be mislaid. Copying (backing up) paper is not very practical and in any case if the building burns down the whole lot goes anyway. Conversely, computer records, although just as vulnerable to damage, are more easily protected and certainly copying a vast amount of records is extremely simple and fast. In fact, several copies can be made for added security with at least one back-up tape off site in case the building is raised to the ground. Office copies can also be kept in a small fireproof box claimed to protect computer tapes and disks for greater convenience.

Possibly the greatest argument for the computer record is the fast and direct access to records or more especially parts of records and the ability to maintain their integrity. The programmers of all the accredited clinical software suppliers have incorporated measures to prevent falsifying records. Once an entry has been made and filed e.g. a diagnosis or drug issue, a subsequent audit trail will reveal any changes that have been made, by whom and on what date. This audit cannot be altered by practice staff and from a legal point of view – paradoxically – it does strengthen argument for computer records because they cannot be tampered with as can paper records. One final word on the legal aspect is that we are of course required to keep records 'on the forms provided' and I believe that health authorities have challenged some 'paperless Doctors' for failing to do this. That said, no one has been struck off or penalised for this technical point provided of course that adequate records are being kept and one would presume pre-computer notes remain accessible.

Nevertheless, it has to be recognised that it is easy enough scanning through paper charts but if you are looking for something very specific and during a particular time frame then nothing can beat the power, speed and versatility of a computer search. However, those doctors keen on writing detailed notes for every consultation will need to be convinced that the limitations of computerised note taking – short, brief and general – are acceptable. The advantages will have to be explained; by adopting a protocol of recording problem title and diagnosis using Read Codes with limited free text the practice will be able to audit much more easily.

Many doctors are already convinced and appear to be glad to rid themselves of all the confusing notes and information that paper seems to demand. However, perhaps an even more powerful argument is that for reception tasks: making appointments; checking patients in; charts out; the doctor calling for next patient; notes delivered to the right doctor; chasing un-filed letters or results; and finally putting the chart back on the shelf in the correct place, can be achieved with so much less fuss. Thus allowing more time for other pressing matters, not least being pleasant and amenable to the public. How often does one see a receptionist who is under pressure from all directions, appearing a little difficult with the patients?

It is difficult to argue against the logic of this – isn't it? Well, I suspect it is going to be, simply because we all have a tendency to be reactionary and in any case we are coping without it at the moment. The question is, for how long will we cope without using information technology to assist us with our tried, tested and conventional systems? Most people will grudgingly admit that it will come but the transfer will not be possible overnight and the preparations referred to earlier will need to be in place well in advance. I am sure that just getting started is the major barrier to cross, thereafter many other technological aids will suddenly become available and with them no end of time saving and more efficient applications. Access to the Internet and Email is already commonplace for many and is a powerful research tool and will facilitate rapid and convenient communications with anyone in the world with access to a telephone line.

It may be a little optimistic in hoping for 'paperless surgery' but the thought of a 'considerably less paper surgery' must surely be appealing to all primary healthcare professionals. None of us can really afford to ignore the technological advances but they have to be managed carefully. The scope for generating problems, not least complying with patient confidentiality and data protection rules, will be at least commensurate with the potential benefits. We all need to decide where we stand and if, as I suspect, most people will say we accept the concept of a paperless surgery, we need to start preparing and educating others now.

Disadvantages:

- dependency on complex electrical equipment, e.g. power failure could be very disruptive if contingencies are not in place;
- additional training burden on all users;
- expense — but reimbursements are available for hardware and software;
- security — especially if records are transmitted electronically or are accessible via modems without adequate security measures in place.

Advantages:

- easy to back up/copy computer records;
- quick and easy search of records;
- audit;
- difficulty in altering records for illegal purposes;
- consultations with full access to records anywhere where there is access to a telephone line and modem link to the surgeries main computer;
- administrative and reception duties stream lined;
- rapid exchange of information with outside agencies e.g. health authorities and laboratories.

# The Future for Managing Information

*Kathie Applebee*
*Practice Consultancy Services*

Writing about the future is both difficult and easy. Difficult, because none of us can guarantee even a minute of the future, and easy, because the pace of change and innovation makes errors understandable and, at times, even forgivable.

The future is an elusive concept which beckons us with promises of a better life. We have learned that our Western world is a fast developing environment, and we now expect a steady stream of new gadgets and aids to enable us to realise its tantalising promises. Unfortunately, all of this bounty comes at a price, some of which can be measured in human as well as financial terms. The price of the information revolution is sensory overload, known as Information Fatigue Syndrome.

## The current position

One definition of information is that it is knowledge which you do not yet possess. Some of it is factual and objective, such as laboratory test results and income tax tables. However, even when information is apparently factual, its significance will depend on the recipient. The meaning attributed to the above test results may vary according to the approach and the expertise of those involved in interpreting them.

Other items are speculative or subjective, with varying degrees of reliability. The importance of an article on staff appraisals, for example, may depend on your opinion of appraisals and the reputation of the author of the article.

The major difficulties facing us now in general practice with managing information are access, retrieval and storage. There are known problems both with identifying data and gaining access to them. Once accessed, they then have to be handled, assimilated, interpreted and stored.

Much of our information management is focused on these problems, and we assume that future developments will ease these by facilitating data access and handling. Technically, this assumption is reasonable, and already there are clear signs that the situation is improving. However, we may also look back wistfully at the good old days when we had less information and consequently fewer problems in understanding and absorbing it.

Information overload reduces our ability to make decisions without feeling the need to check every possible type and source of data. While this may improve diagnostic facilities in clinical areas, paradoxically it may cause delays while previously inaccessible avenues are explored. Information technology has advanced sufficiently for us to feel dissatisfied with the present situation. We now know that there are few, if any, limits to the ways in which data can be trapped, manipulated, stored, transmitted, translated and projected. They can go anywhere, anytime. But general practice, like the rest of the Health Service, appears to be trapped in the slow lane of the Information Superhighway.

## The pace of change

Most doctors, nurses, therapists, managers and administrative staff are struggling with growing mountains of paper and cumbersome computer systems. Each practice employs an army of helpers who feed information from the former into the latter, often producing more paper in the process.

Practices need room for their hated paper and cardboard records, photocopiers, shredders, files and filing cabinets. Although the technology exists for these to become obsolete, barriers of Himalayan-sized proportions stand between practices and the final solutions to their paperwork problems.

A major hurdle is funding constraints, both for individual practices and for the general practice computing market at large. Those practices which are committed to ridding themselves of paper records, both clinical and administrative, are willing to invest GPs' personal funds as well as health authority and fundholding money (where available) in improving their systems. Others will not make this investment, refusing to spend any money on information technology unless it is fully funded.

However, an equally significant barrier is caused by the attitudes of many doctors and staff who yearn desperately to stay with the past, and who reject the picture that is painted of the future. They are happy to use a car instead of a horse and trap, a biro instead of a quill pen, and a credit card instead of a pile of gold sovereigns, but want to limit the introduction of computers as a tool for information management.

In fairness, some hide behind the cumbersome nature of the present systems. Doctors may refuse to use keyboards, promising that they will dictate consultation records onto a computer once voice-recognition systems become cheaper. Reception staff may fight against the introduction of computerised appointments systems, insisting that they are too slow and difficult to use.

Because the general practice computer market is so small, the suppliers are limited in their ability to make best use of the frequent advances in system design tools. Software produced for mass markets can be redesigned at regular intervals because the volume of sales will pay for the upgrades. Redesigning software for a specialist 'vertical' market, particularly one which is funded through the public sector, does not produce a fraction of the returns enjoyed by general commercial software houses. This will limit the speed at which new developments can be introduced.

## The future of general practice

Anticipated changes to general practice may force the pace of change for any reluctant individuals. Practice members, along with their colleagues elsewhere in the Health Service, are frustrated by an ever-increasing amount of duplication and cross-referencing. This is caused by having to use manual systems to inform others in and beyond the primary healthcare team (PHCT) of information which could be transmitted electronically.

As general practice surgeries give way to primary care centres, and the practice population comes to expect an increasingly sophisticated range of services, PHCT members will find that their roles are becoming increasingly complex. Their need for fast, accurate, comprehensive and well-presented information will increase, as will the requirements to communicate this to a variety of other organisations and individuals.

As these problems are resolved by technological advances, team members will find themselves with fewer reasons to delay decision-making. They will have access to all that they need — and the pressure then will be to make sense of all the data and use them to deliver improved healthcare. Constant decision-making is a tiring and difficult process, and unless decision support services are there to provide help, stress levels are likely to rise rather than decrease.

Clinical decision support systems are being developed, but again are being hampered by lack of funding and the misapprehension that they belong in the unspecified future. There may also be a prevailing attitude that such systems, like voice-activated computers, will be used when they become widely available. Unfortunately this availability is dependent on a clear demand being shown, and the associated willingness to pay the asking price.

## The practice manager

The practice manager currently has a pivotal role within general practice. As ringmaster, he or she should be responsible for monitoring practicalities, such as systems, premises and finance; managing personnel, including clinicians and administrative support workers; and ensuring the provision of the all-pervading information which underpins the work of the practice.

Managing and facilitating the flow of information through the practice requires more than a knowledge of the various clinical and administrative computer systems, although this is an important element. It also needs an understanding of the practice's information requirements, the present and potential sources of this information, and its storage requirements.

The information flowing through a practice or other medical establishment is like that of a news desk, or a command centre in wartime. The practice manager, like an editor or general, has the responsibility of ensuring that each individual has access to the information that is required for accurate decision-making.

## Information needs

In order to provide the necessary infrastructure, the practice manager needs a clear view of the information which is going to be required. Although medicine and administration are changing rapidly, the pace of change is less frenetic than that within the information technology market, and it may be easier to make predictions.

The clinicians of the practice require comprehensive but easily accessible information on conditions, therapies, procedures, sources of expertise and advice, and alternative solutions. The patient needs to know how the clinician reached their diagnosis or conclusion, and be provided with background information and practical advice.

Giving patients advice (in the format of the day) and links to treatment centres and support groups will not only reassure them that everything possible is being done, but may also improve the efficacy of their care. Many problems occur at present because patients either do not understand or forget information and advice which they are given verbally, or fail to benefit from fact sheets which are designed for general rather than specific purposes.

The present role of administrative staff as paper handlers is going to change dramatically as computers facilitate increasingly direct links between patients and clinicians. They will change from servicing paperwork to servicing (in the non-technical sense) information systems and those who use them. Redundancies are inevitable, not necessarily in the numeric sense (although this is likely) but because there will no place for technophobic staff who cannot adapt to the paperless practice.

## The future of GP computers

The future of computer hardware is particularly optimistic, with processor speeds and storage capabilities rising in staggering leaps. Fortunately these are directly linked to diminishing container sizes and falling prices, a happy combination which should enable every computer to have access to every other computer, just as every phone now has access to every other phone, within certain restrictions.

While this state of affairs has its drawbacks in human terms, it does mean that the current problems, such as lack of speed, storage limitations, cost and desktop space, should be overcome, even within the cash-strapped NHS.

The future of software is equally exciting, with an apparently endless flow of clever and useful programs among a plethora of badly designed and unnecessary ones. Better still is the concept that owning programs will no longer be necessary as you will simply rent one, via a link to a software provider, whenever you need it. This will enable those who wish to take advantage of frequent innovations to experiment with new software without having to purchase it.

## Connectivity

The key to using master copies of software, stored on some distant system, is connectivity. Much of the hardware and software which is available at the present time would combine to meet the bulk of general practice's needs, if only it could be linked to hospitals, other practices, health authorities, universities, libraries, support services and a host of other institutions and organisations.

We now have everything available in terms of hardware, software and technical knowhow but we still lack the coherent structure that will blend it into a seamless information sharing service. Once this linkage is fast, affordable and secure, practices will cease to have good reasons for electing to remain isolated and out of touch.

A foundation of this service is the mechanism for transmitting data. At present we are relying on an overloaded phone service but that too will be resolved, as have all the other technical challenges encountered along the way. The so-called Information Superhighway may resemble the M25 at rush hour but, unlike the motorway system in Britain, it is not limited to a single medium when seeking solutions and improvements.

## Problems with attitudes and expectations

Although the information technology problems are being tackled, the human issues are lagging behind. School children are growing up at ease with the concept of electronic communications and data sharing, but their parents and grandparents may still feel uneasy at this apparent breakdown in formal systems.

In general practice, it is sometimes easy to hide behind medicine and the patients. Change has to be guaranteed and well tested before it can be adapted because risks are unacceptable. This implies that the current paper-based systems are foolproof, and that we do not experience problems with missing or incorrect documentation and delays in land mail systems.

Human error can never be erased, but it can be safeguarded against. If testing and examination readings are entered automatically by two machines communicating, the possibility of human error is reduced. Machine error exists but is often drastic and noticeable whereas human error can be subtle and convincing. Also, machines are easier to monitor as they do not become offended by regular system checks.

In addition to reducing the potential for data entry errors, the machines will also be faster, sending the results to all relevant computers without the types of delays which bedevil human systems. In addition, responses can be checked. If you send a tax return to the Inland Revenue or a letter to a patient, you have no way of knowing that this was received, even if it was sent by recorded delivery. An electronic delivery system can tell you that it has been received and also that it has been read or stored in an in-tray for reading later.

It is this latter concept that disturbs those who seek to hold back the pace of change. These are the people who bemoan the advent of mobile phones because they can never escape, ignoring the fact that these may actually give them greater freedom by enabling them to deal with queries at a distance.

## Funding and practicalities

The financing of the developments that will change general practice and all other businesses, as well as our personal lives, is an uncertainty. The price of systems should continue to plummet but we may yet encounter the IT equivalent of the oil crisis, and find ourselves scrambling in cupboards for old 286 processors.

General practice is suffering badly at the present time because of an inability to pass on IT costs to its customers. Although some funding is available from the NHS, it is inadequate for proper development. This results in the enthusiasts having to fund new systems personally, either fully or partially, and also limits the potential development of these systems, the suppliers being cash starved in a comparatively penurious market.

Apart from lack of finance, practices are also having difficulty with space constraints and security. Present-day systems are large and clumsy, with keyboards and big processors. Until practices are able to benefit from the miniaturisation that is sweeping the IT world, they are going to struggle to accommodate and, in high crime areas, store their systems.

These problems will be overcome in time by screens with voice recognition systems being built into furniture or walls, and the absence of processors which will be based at remote service providers and accessed as needed.

## Working methods and people

In order to prepare for this brave new world of endless information flowing in all directions, the practice needs to begin reviewing its present-day approaches to data and information.

It is traumatic for practice members when new systems are introduced in a radical manner. For example, many practices at the current time are waiting to obtain links with their pathology labs before starting to use the computer system for accessing results. Once the details start arriving electronically, everyone involved with test results, from doctors to receptionists, will have to be able to access the required screens quickly and efficiently – and this takes training and practice.

Those practices which are already entering them manually are finding the transition to direct electronic links much simpler because they only have to adapt to the new method of data entry. Access itself is relatively unchanged, although more data may be stored in some practices than previously. The changeover is thus less traumatic for them.

Many practices have dual systems, using a 'belt and braces' approach because the computer system is regarded as untrustworthy, too slow, liable to be stolen or beset by other problems. These parallel systems double the workload and increase the potential for errors. Time which could be spent understanding and using information is spent duplicating data entry, filing pieces of paper and hunting for missing records.

If the majority of data and information handling problems in general practice could be removed at one fell stroke, stress and workload levels would fall dramatically. However, the thought of this change, so alien to many doctors and staff, may seem to cause more stress than it would save.

The future of managing information in general practice lies not with the hardware and software producers and those who are linking systems together. Nor does it lie with the civil servants who make the regulations and set the budgets, nor the patients who want better and quicker services. It depends on the members of the PHCT being willing to shed the old shackles of cumbersome systems and pointless paper shuffling, and seeking a paperless future.

If, as a manager, you are unable or unwilling to accept these concepts, you should reconsider your future in general practice because you will not enjoy it.

# PART SIX

# MANAGING FINANCES

# Planning Health for the Future: Business and Financial Issues

*Lorna M G McMillan*
*Abington Health Complex*

During the last decade general practice has radically changed in all areas and will continue to do so in the future if it is to keep pace with the ever-changing world in which we live. Will the National Health Service (NHS) survive or will private medicine overtake it? In all probability the future will be a mixture of the two.

The future direction of the NHS was the subject of a debate by the partners at the Abington Medical Centre. The reason for this debate, which took place in 1987, was to try to predict the general trend of the future direction of the NHS and in some to way pre-empt those changes. If this could be achieved the practice could plan its future ensuring that it had sufficient facilities and resources to meet the challenges of the 1990s and beyond. From this debate the concept of a 'one-stop health complex' was evolved.

In order for this concept to become a reality the practice needed to relocate and, as a precursor to this, the partners met with the then Family Health Services Authority (FHSA) to negotiate reimbursement for a new practice under the cost rent scheme. When the FHSA agreed in principle to the new practice, the compilation of a business plan and the hunt for an area of land sufficient to accommodate a one-stop health complex commenced. With the completion of the business plan the project came one step closer to reality. To finance it the partners needed a large amount of capital. Discussions were held with several financial institutions which were prepared to lend the partners the funding they required. Eventually they decided on the General Practice Finance Corporation (GPFC) as their lender. The financial package was based on an endowment mortgage with the policy on two of the younger partners.

The search for the land also started to look promising. An area within easy distance of the current practice became available. Northampton Borough Council had redesignated this land, previously used as allotments, for 'health purposes'. Without hesitation the partners put in a successful bid for the land. Their pleasure soon soured when, shortly after contracts were signed, land prices fell significantly leaving them with the problem of owning land worth significantly less than the half million pounds they had just paid for it. Nevertheless they remained undaunted, still believing in the viability of the 'one-stop health complex'. It was decided that the medical centre would comprise:

- five consulting rooms;
- two GP registrar rooms;
- two treatment rooms;
- midwife room;
- health visitor suite incorporating office accommodation and health education room;
- reception and patient records area;
- waiting area incorporating a large children's play area.

This accommodation was arranged in a circular configuration surrounding the patient waiting area. The following areas were also included:

- district nurse room;
- four administrative offices;
- library;
- staff common room/meeting room;
- small kitchen;
- patient and staff toilets.

The provision of a library may seem superfluous but the practice operates as a training practice and therefore the library was deemed essential, both to provide much needed accommodation for tutorials and as a repository for the large quantity of reference material required to support this role. The facilities would be of benefit both to trainees and regular staff.

Full reimbursement for all the accommodation was not possible under the terms of the cost rent scheme operated by the FHSA. However the partners were adamant that the additional space not covered by this scheme was essential to the future running of the medical centre. Once completed, the planned centre and car park would only occupy approximately two-thirds of the total site, A scheme was needed for the remaining one-third that could finance itself and hopefully provide a sound investment for the future. The partners developed a proposal that required the GPFC to lend them additional funds so that they could extend the site with the addition of a dentist, an optician and a pharmacy. They calculated that the revenue from the rental of these units would cover the additional borrowing. The GPFC saw the viability of this scheme and agreed to lend the additional funds. With advice from their accountant and solicitor regarding tax advantages, the partners transferred ownership of the undeveloped portion of the site to a separate partnership formed by their wives. This partnership was named the Abington Health Complex.

The final design of the surgery was agreed with the architect and resulted in a uniquely shaped complex which, when viewed from above, resembled a musical note, with the main portion of the Medical Centre forming the bulbous body and the administrative offices, optician, dentist and pharmacy forming the stem. The site was still not fully occupied and ways of attracting further occupants were examined.

Northampton was one of the first areas in the UK to operate an out-of-hours extended rota system (NORMED) for general practitioners. The Northampton GPs provided the funding for an administrative office from which to operate this service but the accommodation was deeply inadequate and car parking was a major problem. The partners entered into negotiations with the NORMED committee to provide, for an agreed rental, a small office complete with toilet, kitchen and a bedroom from which to operate the service. A deal was struck and this office was planned to be built adjoining the administrative offices.

The first building to be completed on the new site was the medical centre, which was occupied in July 1991. The out-of-hours extended service office became operational shortly after. The partners felt that finding the additional tenants could prove difficult so they enlisted the help of an estate agent to find suitable occupants for the proposed dentist and optician suites. The task proved to be extremely simple and in hindsight it would have been more cost effective to have advertised for tenants directly in local journals and newspapers. As it transpired the estate agent had to carry out very little work for the fee which was based on a percentage of the annual rent of each suite.

Next to be completed was the dental unit, with the dentist taking up residence in autumn 1991, followed by the optician in the spring of 1992. Originally it was planned that the pharmacy located next to the old surgery would relocate to the new site. Unfortunately a chemist in the locality of the new complex, who was initially offered the tenancy but refused it, objected to this pharmacy in the vicinity. Four years of legal hearings and negotiations followed, eventually ending with a judicial review in 1995. The ruling of this review was that the prospective chemist could not relocate to the new site. However, at this point, the objecting chemist now indicated that he would like to reverse his previous decision, providing that acceptable terms could be negotiated, and relocate to the site.

With the future occupancy of the pharmacy finally resolved, only one piece of undeveloped land remained. Many discussions and brain storming sessions took place to try to formulate ideas on the use of this space. The ideas ranged far and wide and even included such uses as a café and a pet shop. Eventually it was decided that since there was a deficit of small consulting rooms within the area, a suite would be developed. This suite would also include a fully equipped physio unit. During design discussions with the architect the theme expanded until this suite became a sports medicine clinic with consulting rooms available for rent, on a sessional basis, to specialists in this field. Fortunately for the partnership, the GPFC could see the potential of this new venture and agreed a further loan to cover the building costs of the clinic. However, a condition of this loan required that an additional endowment policy had to be taken out on the lives of two additional partners.

Work commenced on the building of the pharmacy and the sports medicine clinic in the autumn of 1995 while in January 1996 changes were underway to the out-of-hours service. The government was to provide additional cash to encourage the extension and streamlining of this service which would take the form of the provision of a centrally located facility where patients requiring out-of-hours treatment could, if their illness allowed, visit the duty doctor rather than the doctor having to go to the patient's home. With the current location of the Northampton out-of-hours service being totally unsuitable for this purpose it seemed like an ideal opportunity for the partnership to underpin some of the needed income for the new clinic by offering larger premises for rent to the out-of-hours service within the new sports medicine clinic. Following the submission of proposals to the NORMED committee, their business was secured and the design of five rooms within the new clinic was slightly modified to accommodate the NORMED requirements. NORMED relocated to the rooms in the new clinic in April 1996 and to date the service has proved to be immensely popular with Northampton patients. For the partners the income from their rental has underpinned the running costs of the clinic during its start-up period.

For my own part, I joined the practice in July 1991 just one week prior to its relocation in the newly built medical centre and unfortunately had no part in the design of the premises. The surgery building works extremely well at a functional level and is light, spacious and relaxing for patients and their families. However, I would recommend that anyone involved in the design of a new health centre or surgery should think very carefully about the question of storage space. One average size walk-in storage cupboard is certainly not sufficient.

My involvement with the total 'one-stop health' complex began in earnest during the final construction phase of the dentist and optician units, following the bedding down of the medical centre. One of my major tasks was to ensure that the occupancy by the new tenants went as smoothly as possible and to rectify quickly and efficiently any of the inevitable problems associated with a new building.

The 'one-stop health complex' now comprises three distinct sections: the medical centre, the sports medicine clinic and the allied health services. The medical centre is effectively a completely separate autonomous unit that is financed, in the main, through the GP's cost rent scheme. The remainder of the land and buildings on the site are owned by the doctors' wives' partnership, the Abington Health Complex, which operates as a property company.

I operate in a dual role as practice manager of the medical centre and as general manager of the Abington Health Complex. In my general manager role I manage the whole site and act as landlord to the tenants. My responsibilities include site maintenance, resolution of tenants' problems, marketing of private services and financial management. In this latter role I have learned very rapidly about VAT and company financial regulations.

The sports medicine clinic was formed into a limited company on the advice of the partners' solicitor and I was appointed company secretary. As a reward for the work I had put into the project I was also offered a profit share partnership. At the outset I was very much involved in the establishment of the sports medicine clinic and in the building design, including the colour scheme and furnishings. The sports medicine clinic is run purely as a business enterprise and has attracted chiropractors, osteopaths, chiropodists, podiatrists, psychotherapists, hypnotherapists, reflexologists, aromatherapists and an audiologist. These professionals rent rooms on a sessional basis, which includes full secretarial services.

Currently there are three physiotherapists working at the clinic, two are part-time, self-employed and one on a full-time basis. The clinic is open twelve hours a day, Monday to Friday, as well for four hours on Saturday and Sunday mornings. Although officially company secretary, my role in the clinic is to manage the total business function. This includes meeting prospective tenants and agreeing suitable rents, developing a marketing strategy for corporate clients, advertising and keeping a tight rein on the finances. Most of my 'normal' working time is spent managing the medical centre, while the remainder of my 48-hour week is used in promoting the sports clinic.

When the out-of-hours service moved to its new location in the clinic, its previous office became available for use by the practice. Following protracted discussions it was decided to convert this space into a physiology laboratory and equip it with 'high tech' equipment. The purpose of this laboratory would be to test the fitness levels of athletes, provide a service to corporate clients with stressed out executives and managers and also offer pre-employment medicals to local companies. To staff this unit the sports clinic employed a young physiologist, currently on the England basketball squad, who is very enthusiastic about her job.

Over the five years I have been with the practice my role has changed and expanded quite dramatically. I have taken part in and passed an NVQ Assessors Award. In addition I have learnt new skills and my previous financial knowledge has been put to good use and expanded. The whole of the site is financed through an endowment mortgage with Norwich Union. The cost rent reimbursement covers some 70 per cent of the cost of the medical centre. The partners are therefore required to be quite innovative in earning money to finance the cost of the whole site. This has been achieved through very careful housekeeping, with every aspect of the NHS income being examined and maximised. The practice has also become a yellow fever centre and travel clinic. The income from this service is quite lucrative providing that efficient systems are in place to ensure that:

- you get a discount on your vaccine;
- people know about the clinic;
- patients are charged the appropriate fee;
- the prescription is correctly written out.

In addition each winter there is a big drive on 'flu vaccinations, targeting all those deemed to be at risk. They are either invited to visit the surgery or are visited at home by a doctor or district nurse. Again, an efficient system has been put into place to ensure that all vaccinations given to patients are recorded and subsequently reclaimed.

Every doctor knows that one of the ways of increasing the NHS income is to enlarge the practice population, and this we did. Over the past five years the list size has risen by approximately 2,500 overall. On the downside, this has put tremendous pressures on both doctors and staff and the decision had to be made to close the list to all except first degree relatives to ensure that facilities and services were not overstretched and that the patients received a good standard of care.

Several years ago the practice took part in a total quality management (TQM) initiative run by Oxford Region, with one of the areas under review being the doctor's availability to patients. The outcome of this activity, which analysed the requirements of patients,

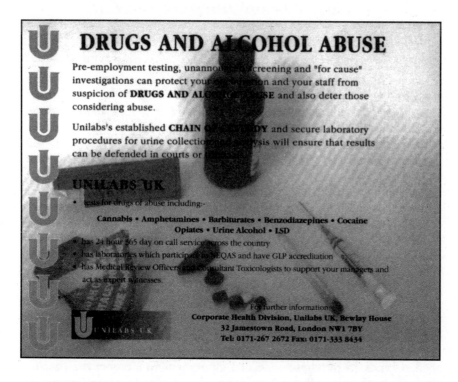
Drug and alcohol abuse in the workplace is a major challenge for all employers. The effects on safety and staff costs be very damaging to <u>any</u> business, with increasing public awareness of legal rights and litigation.

Alcohol, illicit drugs and the illegal use of prescribed drugs require regulation in the workplace. An effective company policy will contain measures to identify and deter the use of prohibited substances.

Their identification is most efficiently achieved by the detection of the drugs and their metabolites in body fluids. Urine is the most acceptable medium for employee testing, since samples can be obtained by non-invasive methods. Breath can be used for the detection of alcohol using portable breathalyser equipment.

A drug testing programme is straightforward to implement but requires careful attention to detail. It should be seen to be fair and reasonable, important considerations if judged by a Court of Law or Industrial Tribunal. When implementing a drug testing programme, employers must remember that the majority of their employees will not be drug users. They must also be prepared for challenges to positive results.

To help employers establish policies to minimise drug abuse and maintain patient, public and staff safety, Unilabs UK have developed a dedicated Customer Service Programme, the quality and effectiveness of which has been proven time and again by our major blue-chip clients.

*For further information please contact:*
## Unilabs UK, *Bewlay House,*
*32 Jamestown Road, London NW1 7BY*
*Tel: 0171 267 2672    Fax: 0171 333 8437*

doctors and staff, was the establishment of an open access clinic at the medical centre for two hours every morning and afternoon. Doctors cover these sessions on a rota basis and although patients do have to wait they seem pleased with the service. One result of the open access clinic is a reduction of the 'extras' at the end of a scheduled surgery, which could be as many as 12 for the duty doctor to see at the end of normal surgery.

The medical centre is not just about healing the sick but has become an integral part of the local community. This can be clearly illustrated by an organisation known as 'The Happy Hour Group'. Operated entirely by volunteers, this group organises local people to visit the housebound, the lonely and the elderly of the community. The service is not forced on patients but operates on a 'by request' basis. In addition, the group hosts a two-hour meeting once a month where, apart from the obligatory cup of tea and a chat, planned activities take place including talks by guest speakers on wide-ranging topics such as eligible benefits from the DSS, gentle exercising, keeping warm in winter, cookery. At Christmas there is a party, complete with Father Christmas and presents.

A patient participation group is also very active and raises much needed funds to purchase specialist equipment to support the patient care. Financial support for the Happy Hour Group comes from the patient participation group which organises raffles, draws and car boot sales to raise the money. The group is run as a charity with patients as trustees.

Private medicine is also at the forefront of our endeavours and a conscious effort has been made to ensure that patients are not kept waiting for appointments for medicals. We employ a highly skilled medical secretary who completes the PMA reports and passes them to the doctors for checking; this achieves a faster turn around time. One of the doctors also carries out police medicals for the local constabulary. Another has passed the Diploma of Occupational Medicine and is in negotiation with several companies to act as their medical officer. Sadly it is a reflection of our times that GPs can no longer depend on their NHS income to finance their premises and to ensure that they have an adequate life style.

What the future will hold we cannot really tell but I feel that the Abington Medical Centre is ready and willing to face it.

# Value from Resources in Primary Care

*Lindley Owen, Cornwall & Isles of
Scilly Health Authority, and Graham
Dover, Shirley Health Centre
Southampton\**

## Beliefs and values

The single greatest obstacle to achieving better value in the NHS is
the belief, widely and sincerely held by many people at all levels in the
service, that the government is getting its health service 'on the cheap',
compared with other developed countries, and that further investment
will therefore automatically solve many of its problems. NHS
managers and clinicians are. thus split between those who are
convinced that it is their duty to make this shortage evident, and
the rest, who believe that by demonstrating economy and efficiency
they will be given more to spend as a result. If the directors of an NHS
trust, or GP principals in a practice believe the first hypothesis, they
will not be interested in value from resources, but will see it as doing
the Treasury's dirty work. On the other hand, if effort is made to
ensure that funds currently received are used as effectively as possible,
then, when a government decides to bring its spending on health into
line with other 'developed' countries, a system will be in place to
ensure that such additional investment brings commensurate benefits
to patients.

A cursory glance at any GP's in-tray shows a heap of literature with
headlines which bode ill for those interested in 'home grown' savings.

---

\* The opinions expressed in this chapter are personal and should not be construed
as representing the policy of C&IoSHA.

GP magazines such as *Financial Pulse* and *Medeconomics* reveal that, despite being 'financially conscious' when dealing with their own businesses, GPs still invest considerable energy on central funding. The incessant appeals for solutions from the government to problems such as rising workloads, out-of-hours payments and the current recruitment crisis suggest a leaning towards a 'want more to get more' culture. Nor has the Fundholding Scheme, which gives practitioners real power to use devolved budgets to effect changes in resources, been the unqualified success which its architects hoped for. The Audit Commission's recent report[1] on the Scheme's progress shows that, while some, particularly first wave, fundholders have used the Scheme to introduce substantial improvements to all aspects of patient care, the typical approach has been more cautious.

However, a closer look at relationships within primary care reveals a more complicated situation than a simple debate about financial responsibility. A series of conferences run by the King's Fund on the core values in general practice identified two sets of values.[2] Those which are central to the practitioner, for whom a one-to-one relationship with the patient is paramount; and the contrasting, practice values which are held by a wide range of health professionals if they intend to focus on maximising the health of the practice population within available resources. As such, tension can exist not only between central government and primary care but within primary care itself.

## VFR and VFM

History is not on the side of those who advocate traditional 'value-for-money' methods in the NHS. All too often resources saved are seen to be diverted away from the thrifty to prop up or bail out the profligate. There is no guarantee that virtue in the form of better economy, efficiency and effectiveness brings rewards in the shape of additional resources. What a Value from Resources (VFR) approach can achieve, however, is the identification and unlocking of those hidden resources which may be under-used; a process which can become self-generating as savings, in whole or in part, are continuously reinvested.

The phrase 'value for money' (VFM) brings to mind penny pinching, and scrimping − managers' and accountants' work, beneath the concern of doctors. 'Resources', on the other hand, draws attention to the importance of people's time, (especially that scarcest and most expensive resource − professional time), of premises, equipment, materials and ideas. For example, software firms with few tangible assets can be highly valued because of the intellectual power they represent. Patients can also be a vital resource to a practice, by virtue of their collective wisdom; about the aetiology of their disease and their enormous range of skills and knowledge of other aspects of life.[3]

On the one hand patients have become specialised 'experts' in clinical areas, often encouraged by general practitioners, and on the other practices are seeing the value of involving patients in delivering different models of community care.

An example of this can be seen at the Marylebone Health Centre in central London,[4] where patients run a participation programme which ensures that volunteer activities such as befriending, practical support, crèche, telephone advice service and a practice newsletter are available to the local community. Nor is this limited to the UK. On a recent trip with the King's Fund to Toronto in Canada, a local hospital manager spoke of a community where many people were presenting at A&E with dog bites. The local residents' response was to round up all the stray dogs, resulting in a dramatic reduction in A&E attendances. Then they negotiated a percentage of the savings from their local hospital.

## Resources tend to be invisible

From 1948 until the late 1970s (when Labour Chancellor Dennis Healey introduced cash limits), the NHS enjoyed continuous real growth and regional hospital boards used this extra money to fund new developments, without upsetting people who provided and received existing services. Old habits die hard and the cry continually goes up from a service which today receives £35 billion annually: 'We've no money to do these new, desirable, nay essential, drugs/investigations/treatments.' Unless, for the first time in two decades, the government has a change of heart, it will continue to expect the NHS essentially to fund new care from internal efficiencies, which means stopping doing those things which no longer work,[5] and finding smarter, more economical ways of doing those which do.

In primary care an example is drug prescribing. A conservative estimate is that up to £100 million of prescribed medicines a year are not being used, and one HA found that £800,000 worth of medicines were wasted across the county each year. In the instance of a single condition, diabetes, a recent survey (of specific patient conditions) by the British Diabetic Association demonstrated that the NHS spends £2 billion per annum on non-insulin dependant patients. The Association believes that significant savings can be made by preventative care and tighter monitoring.

One response to making resources more invisible is the 'evidence-based medicine' movement which requires clinical evidence and outcome to inform decision-making. The Cochrane Collaboration Centre, which produces reviews on CD-ROM, the NHS R&D Directorate and the Centre for Reviews and Dissemination at York University, are several of the prime sources of information. At the local level it is worth investigating 'Bandolier', a monthly evidence-

based newsletter which now has a paper circulation of over 2C
not including those visiting its web site on the Internet.

## Look for quality, not savings

A sure way to lower morale in the GP surgery is to get the
together and tell them 'we've got to save 5 per cent of our bu
Staff know that the lion's share of health budgets is staff cos
only saints would propose pay and/or job cuts for themselves o
colleagues. On the non-pay front, drugs are likely to feature l ~ .
This is an emotive area where savings, at least in non-fundholding
practices, are notoriously difficult to achieve. Besides, in non-
fundholding practices the strict demarcation between GMS[6] drugs
and staffing funds effectively stops any savings from prescribing being
retained locally.

The VFR approach defines quality as 'fit for the purpose' – any less
or any more is, by this definition, wasteful. Similarly, a quality
treatment is that which resolves a condition with the minimum
intervention and therefore the least risk of adverse side effects. If an
operation can be done equally well with a local anaesthetic instead of a
general, then the former is the optimum quality, the latter being more
expensive and potentially riskier.

In primary care the least tapped resource is staff. For many practices
the primary healthcare team exists in name more than substance.
However, GPs may find that those around them are more 'fit for the
purpose' than perhaps was once thought.[7] As a by no means unique
example, the Grove Medical Practice in Southampton recently
experimented with a practice nurse assisting the duty doctor with
same-day appointments. Urgent cases for the day were seen initially
by the nurse; patients who wanted to saw the doctor. In 14 days they
saw 161 patients and a subsequent audit showed that 52 per cent did
not reattend in the following month. There is an ongoing study
elsewhere in Southampton which is examining the value of practice
nurse screening of out-of-hours calls.

Quality can be improved by expanding the team to integrate health
and social care schemes. The South West Region of the NHS has
shown improved local user access to community care; the then
Wiltshire and Bath Health Commission had nearly 50 per cent of GP
linkworkers attached to general practice in 1995. On a large housing
estate in Basingstoke a SSD linkworker for older people placed with a
GPFH practice provides integrated health and social care domiciliary
packages, stimulating and accessing the local voluntary sector, while
providing direct social services input.

In the area of prescribing, practices can employ pharmaceutical
advisers where the focus is on improving the quality of the individual

prescription and service to the patient, with the cost savings seen as secondary. They can analyse 'PACT' data, practice formulary and repeat prescribing patterns. Further developments include a full-time practice pharmacy manager (such as the model at Northgate Medical Centre in Walsall) where the role has been expanded to involve patient counselling, domiciliary visits and helping patients to manage their medication.[8]

GPs can also improve the quality of their service by reducing the number of inappropriate visits (which have risen steadily for decades, and more sharply since the introduction of the Patient's Charter) through offering more telephone advice. Early indications from out-of-hours co-operatives,[9] have found that, with clear protocols, between 40 per cent and 60 per cent of calls can be dealt with by telephone advice. The ability to offer immediate consultations has led to increased patient satisfaction, while reducing pressure on GPs.

## Look for less

Constantly search for simplicity, because it is strongly linked to value. Tenner[10] vividly describes the 'revenge effect' where complex systems, often designed by the ablest minds, nevertheless can result in unanticipated adverse consequences. He explains why, despite computers heralding a paper-free dawn, they have instead proliferated a paper storm. In seeking to simplify what have become over-complex and costly systems, some NHS trust managers are applying the principles of 'business process re-engineering'.[12] They often avoid the BPR tag, for fear of frightening the staff, because it amounts to applied commonsense and excellent VFR.

Modern healthcare organisations are complex, with a strong tendency gradually to become more labyrinthine as the years go by. The need for new activities occurs sporadically, while change is required urgently. As a result, new roles tend to be grafted on to what already exists, rather than replacing or being fully integrated at the time. For example, a new duty is as likely to be allocated to the person or department with free capacity, as to the one to which it most appropriately belongs. Hence the perceived importance of being 'seen to be busy' at all times. The NHS tends to be both the most complex and the most professionally dominated of organisations. Those charged with responsibility for costs, the managers, have lower status and less influence than those who commit resources, the clinicians. It is not the best recipe for economy in operation. Resource saving ideas, in this climate, can only succeed where they have the active support of the organisation's clinical leaders (as seems to be the case at BPR pilot site, Leicester Royal Infirmary).[13] It is essential to create an opportunity, and permission for those who daily do the job,

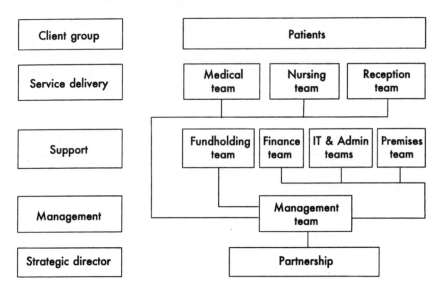

**Figure 6.2.1** *The Grove Medical Practice organisational profile*

mentally to deconstruct their own organisation and to reassemble it from first principles – in short, to seek fitness for purpose.

One way to approach this at the practice level is to turn traditional organisational structure on its head. Despite the fact that many primary care teams often reveal a degree of informality not found in other clinical settings, the old restrictive hierarchy is often evident. By redrawing the chart it is possible to demonstrate a change in emphasis – the focus becomes patient orientated, with management systems there only where necessary to support those at the front line (see Figure 6.2.1).

This approach can lead to a number of benefits:

• recognition of the dual roles of partners as directors and workers on the shop floor. In practice, it means that the day-to-day operations are left to the management team, allowing what were weekly business meetings to become clinical ones. The quarterly partnership meeting is to discuss strategic direction.
• Allowing the people who are the organisation to walk in the 'shoes of the patient' around the practice. This has led to improvements being targeted on areas that really matter to patients such as access, reception, waiting, consultations and referrals. The business plan uses each of these headings to select projects – such as redesigning appointment slots, standardising patient literature and appointment of a 'waiting list initiative' nurse.

## Seek the cost not just the performance benefit in innovation

Yet such innovation can be risky and the penalty of failure can both damage those involved while deterring them and many others from trying again. This tends to occur where an improvement has been introduced as self-financing or even a cost saver, but at the end of the day costs have risen.

The respected and time-honoured way of improving services, an approach adopted by many management consultants, the Audit Commission, National Audit Office and Department of Health, is to isolate one aspect of the NHS (such as day surgery or waiting times) and spend massive amounts of management time and ingenuity in redesigning the process and seeking improvements in outcome. It appears to work. Since the Audit Commission published *A Short Cut to Better Services* in 1990, the rates for elective procedures done as day cases have risen markedly. But why have those savings, clearly identified, not led to financial Nirvana for the trusts concerned? Why are some of the trusts with the highest rates of day surgery also those facing the biggest deficits?

Informal evidence from consultant surgeons in different specialties at a major hospital suggests that the move to day surgery has led in some cases to reduced thresholds at which the decision to operate is taken. The result is a simultaneous rise in admissions and in complaints from patients following surgery. This appears to be because more patients are being treated before their condition has reached the stage at which the benefits clearly outweigh the disadvantages.

Alan Butler, Director of Finance and Information at Southampton University Hospitals Trust, is one of the most forward thinking of his profession. When a manager comes to him with an imaginative business plan: 'if we invest in this new way of doing things, it will save twice that amount within three years', Butler's inclination is to back the project, but also to make sure that the planned level of saving is extracted through appropriate budget reduction. This makes the cost saving an imperative, rather than simply a bonus. In a cash limited service, to take performance benefits without ensuring the cost savings (on which so many innovations are sold) is irresponsible and self-defeating.

Some health authorities provide performance data on their primary care organisations, for example, a computerised package allowing practices to compare themselves with others on a wide range of indicators.[14] At the practice level partners can agree a budget which effectively sets their personal income at the start of the year. This means that innovative schemes may come along in the year, but if accepted may result in money being transferred away from other budgets or a drop in partners' income. Budgets also allow a devolution of resources to key staff to find efficiencies. For example, a group of staff complained about the speed of the medical system in producing results for audit. The solution was to purchase a fileserver, but not before agreeing with the IT team that they could improve on the practice claim rate to cover the costs of the investment. Any additional income would result in a bonus. Six months on they are well on their way to exceeding the target.

## To understand the whole, examine the smallest part

A study of the most basic interaction between a service and its customer can tell a great deal about the organisation as a whole.[15] What happens in a single consultation can have enormous significance because it is from such events, in aggregate, that most of the NHS total workload flows.

Studies of the dynamics of the consulting room experience reveal a power shift to the patient away from the practitioner. Rapid technological advance, especially in communications, gives patients increasing access not only to the most arcane of medical information, but also to medical decision-making facilities. It is possible to imagine patients in the near future, through their television at home, having direct access to self-diagnostic procedures. Patients will come to their doctors much more aware, with more ideas and a wish to negotiate the management of their condition from an informed viewpoint. The choice the GP faces is to welcome this and adapt to it, or to be stressed by it. The trend is irreversible.

## Incentives, intended and unintended

Many of today's problems have their origins in yesterday's 'solutions', which have turned out to have been merely 'fixes'. The most pernicious of these are where problems have historically been tackled by using payment to encourage behaviour which is seen as desirable. Primary care has many examples. As a result, a culture has grown up in which the first wholly understandable reaction to any proposed change tends to be 'make it worth my while'. Yet, the act of paying someone to do something they otherwise see as worthless demeans both the payer and the recipient. The recent attempt to encourage health promotion in primary care is just one example. If something is worth doing, it is worth selling as an idea. If those who work in primary care cannot see the intrinsic benefit, they are probably right. If change is worthwhile and seen to be so by all concerned then payment becomes less of an issue.

## References

1 Audit Commission (1996) *What the Doctor Ordered — A Study of Fundholders in England and Wales*, HMSO, London.
2 Practitioners & practices — a conflict of values? Julian Pratt, 1995.
3 Skerratt, D, personal communication.
4 Meads, G (1995) *Future Options for General Practice*, Radcliffe Medical Press, Abingdon.
5 See 'Bandolier' on the Internet for the latest on evidence-based medicine. (HTTP://WWW.JR2.OX.AC.UK/Bandolier)
6 General Medical Services
7 Marsh, G N (1991) *Efficient Care In General Practice*, Oxford University Press, New York.
8 *Pharmacy in Practice Journal*, July/August 1995; *The Health Service Journal*, April 1996.
9 For example, Kernowdoc, Cornwall.
10 Tenner, Edward (1989) *Why Things Bite Back*, Fourth Estate, London.
11 Primary care has seen a 300 per cent increase in computer operators since the 1990 contract and a 43 per cent increase in practice managers.
12 Popularised by Mike Hammer in the book of that name.
13 LRI has produced two excellent videos of its early experiences with BPR and experiment due to run until late 1997. What is already notable is the extent to which it has captured the enthusiasm of clinicians.
14 At Southampton & SW Hants HA.
15 Capra, F (1983) *The Turning Point*, Fontana, London.
16 The Grove, *op cit*.
17 Ibid.

## 6.3

# How do we Manage Self-Assessment?

*Valerie Martin, Partner, Pannell*
*Kerr Forster*

---

Self-assessment has been talked about for so long that it is hard to believe that it is now actually upon us and GPs need to ensure that they have taken the necessary steps to manage self-assessment both at the personal and partnership level.

Under the old tax regime there were different rules for different types of income and chargeable gains and different payment dates for the tax due on the various sources of income. This all changes under self-assessment which introduces the requirement that the taxpayer files returns by a fixed date and pays all income tax due on all sources of income, together with capital gains tax, by a fixed set of dates. For each tax year an initial payment on account of income tax will be due on 31 January in the tax year, a second payment will be due on the following 31 July, and a final balancing payment of any remaining income tax due will be payable, together with any capital gains tax due, on the following 31 January.

The tax liability will be based on the taxpayer's own calculation of the liability and this self-assessment is part of the tax return. As the personal and partnership tax returns will be required in order to calculate a GP's tax liability on total income and any chargeable gains, all tax returns will have to be submitted to the Inland Revenue by the due date. The date for both personal and partnership tax returns is 31 January following the end of the relevant tax year. As information is needed from the partnership tax return to go on the GP's personal tax return it is necessary for the partnership return to be completed some time before then to make this feasible.

## Partnership tax return

The information to be included on the partnership return is stipulated in Section 12AA of the Taxes Management Act 1970 as amended by Finance Acts 1994 and 1995. This states that the return must include the following:

- the names, addresses and tax references of each of the partners in the partnership;
- details of any capital disposals including the allocation of the disposal proceeds;
- details of the relevant accounting period;
- details of income and expenses comprising basically a summary of the accounts;
- tax computation to arrive at taxable profit;
- capital allowances claims;
- summary of the balance sheet;
- partnership investment income;
- the share of income, losses and tax credits and class 4 NIC for each partner;
- declaration – to be signed by one of the partners that the return is correct and complete.

### Partners' personal expenses

Partners' personal claims for expenses such as motoring costs which have not been included in the accounts must be included on the partnership tax return. The expenses must be aggregated in the relevant entry boxes with any similar expenses included in the accounts; for example, all the partners' motoring costs will be aggregated and included in the box under motor expenses. Similarly, the business proportion of any home telephone bills will be aggregated with partnership expenditure under general administrative expenses.

It will not be possible for an individual partner to claim relief for personal business expenditure on his personal tax return and, therefore, GPs will need to get accustomed to completing their personal expenses promptly after their practice's accounting year end, so that they can be combined with the information from the accounts on the return. If a practice prepares its accounts to 31 March then all of the claims will need to be included on the partnership return to be submitted by the following 31 January. However, if the practice prepares its accounts to, say, 30 June then the partners have 19 months to submit the information by 31 January following the end of the tax year in which the accounting year end falls.

Similarly any capital allowances on assets owned by the doctors personally, such as cars, home computers and medical equipment, must be aggregated with the partnership capital allowances on the return.The personal expenses and capital allowances can then be allocated to the relevant partner in the allocation of the profits included on the partnership return.

## Penalties

In order to ensure that practices file a partnership return on time, there is a system of penalties. These comprise:

- an initial penalty fixed at £100 per partner if the return is not filed on the due date;
- a further penalty of £100 per partner if it is 6 months late, unless the Commissioners of the Inland Revenue have given leave for a daily penalty of up to £60 per day per partner.

If a partnership tax return is found to be incorrect through fraud or negligence then each partner may be liable for penalties of up to 100 per cent of the tax found to be under-declared. If an honest mistake has been made then this can be reported to the inspector who will adjust the tax liabilities accordingly.

Partnerships will, therefore, need to take the completion of the partnership tax return very seriously and ensure that it is fully and accurately completed. This will, of course, normally be done by the practice accountants but the doctors will need to provide all the relevant information to the accountants in plenty of time.

## Personal tax returns

The deadline for submission of the GPs' personal tax returns is also 31 January following the end of the tax year, or 30 September following the end of the tax year if the GP wants the Inland Revenue to complete the tax calculations for him. This would, of course, necessitate the information regarding his share of the partnership taxable profits to be available from the partnership return before 30 September for it to be included on the personal return to be submitted to the Revenue.

All of the information on the personal tax return will need to be complete and it will no longer be possible to submit returns with items such as 'per accounts' or 'to follow' as fully detailed figures will be required.

An automatic penalty of £100 is imposed if the return is submitted late, and a further £100 is repayable if the return is more than 6 months late. This is in addition to interest and surcharges on the late payment of any tax.

The system is, therefore, deliberately tough to ensure compliance but this does mean that GPs must prepare themselves for the new tax system by getting their affairs totally up to date.

## Retention of records

Under self-assessment it is a requirement that all taxpayers keep and retain the records needed to make a complete and accurate return of their income. The requirement comes into effect for the tax year 1996–97, the first year of self-assessment. However, the profits assessable in 1996–97, for practices which existed prior to 5 April 1994, are based on the averaged profits from the two years' accounts falling between the old preceding year basis and the new current year basis. So, for example, a practice drawing up its accounts to 30 June will be assessed in 1996–97 on the average profits from the accounts for the year ended 30 June 1995 and 30 June 1996. This means that the requirement to retain records is effective from 1 July 1994 and not just from the tax year 1996–97.

Business records must be kept for five years from the annual filing date for the period covered by the return. So the records for 1996–97 must be kept until 31 January 2003 being five years after the filing date of 31 January 1998 and the records in the above example will need to be kept from 1 July 1994 until 31 January 2003. The records for 1997–98, based on say the accounts for the year ended 30 June 1997, will have to be retained until 31 January 2004.

In the case of a business the records which must be kept include:

- all receipts and expenses;
- all assets purchased and sold;
- all supporting documents relating to the transactions of the business, such as accounts, accounting records, deeds, contracts, vouchers and receipts.

Accordingly, GP practices will need to keep all quarterly statements from the Primary Care Agency; all invoices and any other documentation for other income; and all receipts for expenditure, as well as the manual or computerised accounting records of the practice. The same detail will need to be maintained for GPs' personal expenses.

For non-business income, taxpayers will need to retain documentation for at least one year after the relevant annual filing date. So documentation for 1997–98 will need to be retained until 31 January 2000. The relevant documentation will include evidence of the income received, such as bank statements or dividend vouchers. Doctors with hospital or other appointment income taxed under PAYE will need to keep their P60s and evidence of any taxable benefits received. Where there is a capital gain, or loss, it will be necessary to keep all the records relating to the asset sold and the calculation of the gain or loss on its disposal.

The penalties for failing to keep the records as required are quite severe with a maximum fine of £3,000 for each failure to keep or retain adequate evidence in support of a return. It is, therefore, essential to set up a clear and effective method of retaining your records so that all invoices and receipts are retained as well as documentation of the income and expense in the accounting records. This has always been good practice but is now crucial.

### Managing the tax payments in 1996–97

The introduction of self-assessment for GPs is confused by the fact that self-assessment for partnerships which were set up and commenced before 5 April 1994 does not begin until 1997–98, but self-assessment for personal tax is effective from 1996–97. It is, therefore, necessary to understand the interaction between the tax payable under the old style partnership assessment for 1996–97 and the tax payable by the individual partners under self-assessment for 1996–97.

The 1996–97 partnership tax assessment on profits will have been issued in the usual way, demanding tax payable by the partnership on 1 January and 1 July 1997. The normal appeal and postponement rules apply and the partnership will pay the tax, with interest running on any tax paid after 1 July 1997.

However, each individual partner with sufficiently high non-partnership income, will also receive a 'taxpayer statement' demanding payment of tax on account in two equal instalments due for payment on 31 January and 31 July 1997. This will be based on the known tax liability for 1995–96.

In April 1997 the partnership and each partner will receive a self-assessment tax return and these must be completed and submitted to the Inland Revenue by 31 January 1998.

Each partner's personal self-assessment tax return must include his share of partnership income, as well as all his other sources of taxable income to produce the calculation of the partner's total tax liability. Then the tax paid on his behalf by the partnership as part of the 1996–97 partnership tax liability in January and July 1997 is deducted from the total tax liability rather as though it were PAYE paid on account of an employee's income.

Then, after taking into account any personal tax payments made by the partner on 31 January and 31 July 1997, together with the partnership tax payments made by the practice on his behalf on 1 January and 1 July 1997, any balance of tax payable must be paid by the partner on 31 January 1998.

The position will be much simpler in 1997–98 and subsequent years as no partnership assessments will then be issued and the partnership will not be required to pay any tax. The tax liability will then be solely that of the individual GPs and there will be no joint and several liability for each other's tax.

Partners will receive taxpayer statements in December 1997 demanding the payment of tax due on 31 January and 31 July 1998 in respect of the 1997–98 liability. These amounts will be based on the total tax liability of partners, including tax on partnership profits, for 1996–97. When the self-assessment personal tax returns are completed and submitted, any balance of tax due for payment for 1997–98, based on the income actually assessable in that year, will be payable on 31 January 1999. This will coincide with the first payment on account for 1998–99.

## Choice of accounting date under the new tax system

The new current year basis tax system for the self-employed is being introduced from 1997–98 as part of the new self-assessment tax regime. Under this system a GP's profits assessable in a tax year will be based on the accounting period ending in the tax year. This means that the time span between earning profits and paying tax on those profits will still vary depending upon the choice of accounting year end. GPs will, therefore, need to consider which accounting year end will best suit them under the new self-assessment system. There are three main issues to consider in making this decision.

### Cashflow

Where profits are rising, a cashflow advantage can be gained by deferring the payment of tax based on a year's profits for as long as possible. In this case an accounting year end shortly after the end of the tax year is preferable to an accounting year end just before the end of the tax year. This is because the profits assessable in the tax year will be based on the accounting period ending in that tax year. Therefore, the tax year 1997–98 could be based on the profits earned in the year ended 30 June 1997 or 31 March 1998. In that case the 30 June year end would give a longer period between earning the profits and paying the tax on those profits.

### Deadlines for filing returns

As has already been mentioned, the penalties for the late filing of partnership and personal tax returns are potentially quite punitive, in order to act as an attempt to stop taxpayers failing to submit returns on time. As the deadlines for the submission of the returns relate to the tax year, a 30 June accounting year end will give GPs 19 months to complete their accounts and the relevant partnership tax return based on those accounts, whereas a 31 March year end will give GPs just 10 months to provide all the information and file the returns. As the returns have to include all the partners' personal expenses and capital allowances, practices with a 31 March year end will need to become accustomed to providing all the information to their accountants very promptly after the year end or this ten-month period will elapse all too quickly.

### Potential bunching of profits on retirement

Under the new tax system, GPs will pay tax on all the profits they earn to the date of retirement. This contrasts with the old tax system where, for example, a partner retiring on 30 June 1995 would be assessable for one quarter of the 1995–96 assessment in respect of the period from 6 April 1995 to 30 June 1995, which may have been based on the profits earned in the year ended 30 June 1994. The retiring partner would, therefore, not be taxed on their final profits earned in the practice and would effectively leave with a slice of tax free earnings.

Under the new tax system if a partner retires from a practice on say 30 June 2000 and the practice prepares its accounts to 30 June, then the partner would be taxed in 2000–01 on the whole of his share of the profits earned in the year ended 30 June 2000. If, alternatively, the partner were to retire on 31 March 2001 then his assessable profits in 2000–01 would be based on the whole of his profit share earned from 1 July 1999 to 31 March 2001 in order to tax all of the profits earned to retirement.

To compensate partners for this change in the tax system there will be an overlap relief but this will be based on the 1997–98 assessable profits and will not be adjusted for inflation. There is, therefore, a potential bunching of profits on retirement with any accounting date other than 31 March.

If accounts are drawn up to 31 March then the partners effectively pay the tax on their profits as they are earned and there is, therefore, no risk of any bunching of profits on retirement in order to bring the final profits into tax. However, it does mean that the tax has been paid on those profits as they are earned instead of deferring some of the tax until retirement.

Whichever year end is chosen all of the profits earned under the new tax system will be taxed and, therefore, it is important to remember that the choice of accounting date only affects when the tax is paid and does not alter the total profits to be taxed. However, of course the amount of the tax liability could vary if the rates of tax were to change.

Practices do, therefore, need to review their accounting date and ensure they have the date which best suits their temperament. On the whole, practices which have frequent partner changes (with some partners leaving possibly to return to a hospital appointment or to join another practice) may prefer to have a 31 March accounting date so that outgoing partners do not have to plan their retirement date to minimise their tax liability. Alternatively, fairly stable practices where partners generally leave at retirement age may prefer to have a 30 June accounting date in order to defer paying tax during their working lives and possibly have an additional liability on retirement.

## Provisions for tax

Whatever the choice of accounting date, GPs would be well advised to provide for tax either in the partnership or on a personal basis to ensure that they can meet their final tax liability. With the tax payment dates under self-assessment, tax continues to be payable for some time after leaving a practice. For example, if a GP retires on 30 June 1999, the final tax liability will be for 1999–2000. The tax will be payable on 31 January and 31 July 2000 and a final payment on 31 January 2001; the final tax is, therefore, payable 19 months after the GP has left the practice. If the GP has previously taken the view that he would always pay his tax out of the current year's profits, then he may find that he cannot afford to leave the practice as sufficient money has not been put aside to meet the final tax bill. This would be particularly relevant to a GP leaving before normal retirement age, perhaps to have a career break or just to change practice, when there would be no superannuation lump sum available to provide some funds.

Accordingly, tax provisions will form a very important part of managing the tax under self-assessment and even though the removal of joint and several liability for tax may initially seem to render the old partnership tax provisions no longer necessary, they may in fact form the easiest way of providing for tax and remove the temptation of dipping into a personal tax fund.

Self-assessment shifts the responsibility for the payment of tax entirely on to the taxpayer. Taxpayers will be totally responsible for declaring their income, calculating the tax liability on it and paying the tax over to the Inland Revenue without the Revenue having to do anything. Managing self-assessment is, therefore, essential and the key to this is to be up to date with your tax affairs now and to be fully aware of your responsibilities under the new tax regime.

PART SEVEN

# MANAGING THE PREMISES AND EQUIPMENT

# 7.1

# Waste Management

*David Barber*
*Environmental Resources Management*

---

## Wastes from primary healthcare

Primary healthcare, while not generating the range and quantities of waste materials resulting from hospitals, has the potential to produce a range of wastes. These wastes may be divided into two categories:

- clinical waste;
- domestic and similar waste.

The definition of clinical waste is provided by the Controlled Waste Regulations 1992, as follows:

(a) any waste which consists wholly or partly of human or animal tissue, blood or other body fluids, excretions, drugs or other pharmaceutical products, swabs or dressings, or syringes, needles or sharp instruments, being waste which unless rendered safe may prove hazardous to any person coming into contact with it; and

(b) any other waste arising from medical, nursing, dental, veterinary, pharmaceutical or similar practice, investigation, treatment, care, teaching or research, or the collection of blood for transfusion, being waste which may cause infection to any person coming into contact with it.

In addition, waste materials falling within this definition have been subdivided into five groups (Groups A to E) by the Health and Safety Commission (1992). Within these groups, certain types of wastes require special consideration, such as cytotoxic wastes, radioactive wastes and controlled drugs. The contents of each group are summarised in Table 7.1.1, and it is possible that certain wastes may

**Table 7.1.1** *Groupings of clinical waste based on Health and Safety Commission Guidelines (1992)*

| Group | Waste materials |
|---|---|
| **A**<br>Human tissue and infectious material | All human tissue, including blood (whether infected or not), animal carcasses and tissue from veterinary centres, hospitals or laboratories, and all related swabs and dressings.<br>Waste materials, where there is a risk to staff handling them, for example, from infectious disease cases.<br>Soiled surgical dressings, swabs and other soiled waste from treatment areas, including disposable protective clothing. |
| **B**<br>Sharps | Discarded syringe needles, cartridges, broken glass and any other contaminated disposable sharp instruments or items (which are capable of causing punctures). |
| **C**<br>Pathology and laboratory wastes | Microbiological cultures and any potentially infected waste, including disposable protective clothing, slides, culture dishes and blood or body fluids, from pathology departments (laboratory and post mortem rooms) and any other clinical or research laboratories. |
| **D**<br>Pharmaceutical wastes | Certain pharmaceutical products and chemical wastes, including out-of-date or redundant medicines.<br>Redundant, out-of-date or otherwise waste drugs which fall under the definition of controlled drugs given in the *Dangerous Drugs: Mis-use of Drugs Regulations 1985*. |
| **E**<br>Urine, faeces and hygiene products | Items used to dispose of urine, faeces and other bodily secretions or excretions, not falling within Group A, which carry a risk of infection due to their source or quantity of accumulation, including disposable bed pans and bed pan liners, incontinence pads, stoma bags, urine containers, disposable containers used to hold body fluids (i.e. suction bottles and apparatus), etc.[1] |

*Note:*
[1] Hygiene products such as sanitary towels, nappies, etc. are considered to be clinical waste if they arise from patients or they are accumulated into a sufficient quantity considered to pose a potential health risk.

fall into more than one of the clinical waste categories.

The main clinical wastes which arise from primary healthcare are as follows:

- sharps, particularly hypodermic needles from blood samples and inoculations;
- bandages and dressings which are contaminated with blood or other body fluids (although heavily soiled dressings are relatively rare, dressings used on, for example, ulcers may be highly contaminated with blood);
- out-of-date pharmaceuticals and medicines, some of which may be controlled drugs;
- soiled nappies, incontinence pads or other sanitary products derived from baby weighings or geriatric patients;
- disposable gloves and aprons used in conjunction with patient examinations or treatments;
- disposable hand towels used to clean hands and worktops between patients.

It should be noted that, although there is a case that many patients receiving healthcare do not pose an infection risk or hazard to other people, traditionally all wastes containing any bodily fluids or blood are considered potentially infectious and, therefore, clinical waste. In addition, there is currently no agreed de minimis (negligible) level of contamination — a single drop of blood within a large dressing renders the whole dressing as clinical waste, or if within a plastic bag the entire contents may, in principle, be contaminated and, therefore, clinical waste. This is the approach which is generally adopted in the UK to ensure that safety is given first priority.

Non-clinical waste can be termed 'domestic and similar waste', in that it resembles household waste in composition and the hazard which it may pose to public health and the environment. General practice typically produces the following types of non-clinical waste:

- waiting room waste, such as newspapers, magazines, drinks bottles, aluminium cans and sweet wrappers;
- kitchen waste, where a canteen or kitchen is available to staff;
- packaging waste, such as cardboard boxes, paper and plastic film wrappings;
- office waste, comprising waste paper and potentially confidential documents (for example, patient records).

Alongside these wastes will be building maintenance wastes, which comprise cleaning materials and empty containers, fluorescent light bulbs, etc., derived from the day-to-day maintenance of the healthcare premises.

## Health hazards and risks

Waste has the potential to cause harm to individuals and the environment and offence to the senses. The characteristics of clinical waste mean that it carries particular risks, but domestic type waste can also pose its own hazards.

The major problems which may arise from the generation and handling of waste in general practice are summarised in Table 7.1.2. These problems may occur during deposit, collection and storage at the general practice or during transport and disposal.

**Table 7.1.2**  *Health hazards and risks from waste generated in general practice*

| Hazard/risk | Type of waste |
| --- | --- |
| Puncture injuries and wounds ('needle stick') | Hypodermic needles |
| | Suture needles |
| | Broken glass |
| Cross-infection from contaminated waste materials | Hypodermic needles |
| | Suture needles |
| | Soiled dressings/bandages |
| | Hygiene products |
| Accidental intake and poisoning by drugs and other pharmaceuticals | Pharmaceuticals |
| | Out-of-date medicines |
| Odour | Body tissue or fluids |
| | Blood-containing wastes |
| | Hygiene products |
| | Food wastes |
| Encouragement of vermin, such as rats, flies and birds, and associated transmission of disease | Body tissue or fluids |
| | Blood-containing wastes |
| | Hygiene products |
| | Food wastes |
| Litter | Paper |
| | Plastic |
| | Packaging materials |
| Visual impact from unpleasant appearance | All wastes |
| Deliberate scavenging or theft | Hypodermic needles |
| | Pharmaceuticals |
| | Out-of-date medicines |
| Fire risk | All wastes |

These health and environmental hazards may affect staff, patients, visitors or the general public. The general practice will ultimately be liable for any harm which arises from failures to fulfil its responsibilities with respect to waste management. With higher standards of waste collection, handling and disposal being required by the Environment Agency and the Health and Safety Executive (HSE), the costs and liabilities of improper waste management are increasing and are expected to continue to rise. For example, in a recent case a trust in the north east of England was fined £15,000 when a child was found playing with a discarded, used hypodermic needle in a hospital.

Due to the proximity of primary healthcare establishments to local communities and typically the lack of 24-hour occupancy of the buildings, they are particularly vulnerable to accidental or deliberate interference with waste and vandalism. This presents a particular risk in that sharps boxes have been known to be stolen by drug abusers seeking to recover the hypodermics and, as a result, it can also lead to the exposure of the general public to risks as a consequence.

## Legislation

### Relevant acts and regulations

All healthcare managers have a duty to control waste and protect the health and safety of medical and support workers, patients, visitors and the general public. Waste management is essentially a health and safety issue and, therefore, falls within the remit of health and safety legislation. In addition, it is also subject to specific provisions and regulations whose primary focus is waste in particular. The key relevant legislation is as follows:

- *Health and Safety at Work etc Act 1974*: The Act and associated regulations place a duty on general practices to safeguard, so far as reasonably practicable, the health of workers and any other person who may be affected by work activities, i.e. patients, visitors and the general public. In-house waste management forms part of the work activities which the general practice has a duty to control and manage safely under the Act.
- *Control of Substances Hazardous to Health Regulations 1988 (COSHH)*: These regulations require that assessments are undertaken of all hazardous substances at work to which workers and others may be exposed, and that measures are implemented to protect their health and safety. Certain categories of clinical waste fall within the scope of these regulations, such as pharmaceuticals.
- *Environmental Protection Act 1990*: The Act and associated regulations place a responsibility on the general practice to protect

the environment from the unlawful depositing, handling or disposal of waste or the escape of waste from its control, known as the 'duty of care'. This duty includes requirements that the general practice ensures that:
- waste is only transferred to a person authorised to transport such material (a 'registered carrier');
- transfer of waste to another party is accompanied by an accurate written description of the waste and its hazards;
- disposal is carried out at a site holding an appropriate waste management licence.
- *Special Waste Regulations 1996*: These regulations provide a new definition of special wastes (equivalent to hazardous waste) and upgrade provisions for administering the transport and disposal of these wastes.

Hence, a general practice has a legal obligation to manage waste such that the potential risk to staff, patients, visitors, the public and the general environment is minimised so far as reasonably practicable. In turn, the staff working for the general practice also have legal obligations to ensure that any waste management procedures and facilities are implemented or used in a proper manner to protect their health and safety and that of others.

It should be noted that the failure to observe the requirements of any of the specific regulations is a criminal offence under the Acts referred to above (irrespective of there being any consequent harm or pollution).

### Special Waste Regulations 1996

The most recent legislation potentially affecting general practice is the Special Waste Regulations 1996, which came into force on 1 September 1996 and provide a new definition of special (hazardous) waste and provisions for the handling of such waste.

The Regulations have two direct and linked implications for general practices:

- definition of some categories of clinical waste as special waste;
- imposition of a consignment note system to record disposal of those categories of clinical waste defined as special.

The knock-on impacts of these implications are likely to be increased costs of disposal to cover the additional work in administering the consignment note system and increased penalties for failure to comply with the legal obligations on the general practice (since contravention will now be seen in the context of the special, i.e., hazardous, waste legislation).

Special waste is defined as any controlled waste (i.e. waste generated by households, commerce or industry, which includes healthcare) that is one of the following:

- identified in the Hazardous Waste List attached to Part I of Schedule 2 of the Regulations and displaying certain Hazardous Properties listed in Part II of Schedule 2 of the Regulations; or
- medicinal product, as defined in Section 130 of the Medicines Act 1968.

With respect to clinical waste, the Hazardous Waste List includes Waste Code 18, which is described as: 'Wastes from Human or Animal Health Care and/or Related Research'.

The key relevant Hazardous Properties which the above waste must exhibit to be classed as special waste, and which may be displayed by clinical waste materials, are the following:

- H5 'Harmful': substances and preparations which if inhaled, ingested or penetrate the skin may have a limited health risk;
- H6 'Toxic': substances and preparations which if inhaled, ingested or penetrate the skin may have an acute or chronic health risk;
- H7 'Carcinogenic': substances and preparations which if inhaled, ingested or penetrate the skin may induce or have an acute or chronic health risk;
- H9 'Infectious': substances which contain viable micro-organisms or their toxins which are known or believed to cause disease in humans;
- H10 'Teratogenic': substances and preparations which if inhaled, ingested or penetrate the skin may induce, or increase the incidence of, non-hereditary congenital malformations;
- H10 'Mutagenic': substances and preparations which if inhaled, ingested or penetrate the skin may induce, or increase the incidence of, hereditary genetic defects.

If a material within clinical waste has these properties, then it will fall under the definition of special waste provided by the Regulations. Pharmaceuticals, chemicals, cytotoxic and radioactive materials are expected to be classed as special waste, of which only redundant or out-of-date pharmaceuticals are likely to result from general practice. However, consultation with the Environment Agency has highlighted that other waste also typically regarded as 'clinical waste', for example, material contaminated with blood, has not yet been formally defined/categorised with respect to the definition of special waste, since the question arises whether or not the blood is potentially infectious and the magnitude of the risk. This highlights the difficulty in categorising blood contaminated material as a health risk on the grounds of risk of infection, and whether a de minimis (negligible) level of risk can be determined which may also allow some such wastes to be treated as non-clinical for waste management purposes. The Agency is currently debating this issue and thereafter it will issue guidelines for producers of clinical waste.

Any clinical waste materials which are defined as special waste will be required to follow a standard procedure for recording its transfer and disposal (a 'consignment note' system). This effectively builds upon the Waste Transfer Note system which is already in place via the duty of care in the Environmental Protection Act 1990, but with more onerous reporting of shipments to the Environment Agency. It should be noted that a fee is payable to the Environment Agency per consignment of special waste.

## Other regulations

Waste generated by general practice will also be subject to a range of other legislation which is typically the responsibility of the contractor employed to collect and dispose of the waste, but which (under the duty of care) the general practice should be aware of. These regulations cover the following:

- packaging and labelling;
- transport;
- transfrontier shipment;
- licensing and authorisation of the disposal facility.

Any contractor used for the collection, transport and/or disposal of waste should be obliged under contract to comply with relevant regulations in these areas.

## Essentials of implementing a waste management plan

### Objectives of a waste management plan

Due to the health risks and legislation controlling waste management, it is essential that a general practice implements a waste management plan to identify, collect, manage and consign for disposal of all wastes generated by its activities. The methods used for waste management should fulfil four objectives:

- protection of the health and safety of staff and others;
- protection of the environment;
- minimisation of the costs of waste disposal;
- avoidance of liabilities in the event of an accident or incident.

In all cases, it must be acknowledged that waste management is a support service and that healthcare is the first priority. However, waste is an unavoidable byproduct of healthcare and cannot be neglected or ignored.

## Key principles of a waste management plan

Any waste management plan developed for a general practice should implement the key principles indicated in Table 7.1.3 to be in accordance with UK best practice.

## Policies and procedures

A key component of a waste management plan is the establishment of policies and procedures. It is important not to confuse 'policies', which state the objectives and commitments of the general practice with respect to controlling waste, with 'procedures', which are the practical instructions for staff in order to achieve the policy statements.

Procedures, which may be in the form of local rules, instructions or a code of practice, should be designed to give direct guidance on the way different wastes should be managed. The scope which the procedures should include is summarised in Table 7.1.4.

There is a range of guidance available on clinical waste management, the most important of which is published by the Health and Safety Commission (1992) and Department of the Environment. Guidance can also be obtained from other sources, such as the London Waste Regulation Authority (1994), now part of the Environment Agency. However, the nature of the waste and wide variety of circumstances which occur in primary healthcare mean that prescriptive or standard approaches are often impractical. Therefore, the published guidance cannot provide all the answers and general practices need to look to apply their principles and recommendations in a customised fashion in their own local context.

## Equipment and facilities

An essential element, and often the root cause of problems in waste management, is the equipment and facilities used for collecting and storing waste. A waste management system will normally require the equipment listed in Table 7.1.5.

**Table 7.1.3**  *Key principles of a waste management plan*

| Issue | Key principle |
|---|---|
| Segregation | Clinical waste should never be mixed with non-clinical waste – if mixing inadvertently occurs, all the waste should be treated as clinical due to the risk of contamination and resorting should not be carried out. |
| | Sharps should be segregated from other clinical waste. |
| Packaging | Packaging should be designed to prevent spillage of waste or leakage of fluids contained in the waste. |
| | Plastic bags should be used for clinical waste (excluding sharps) and domestic and similar waste, with minimum gauges of 200 microns and 55 microns low density plastic, or equivalent, respectively. |
| | Sharps should be placed in puncture-proof and leak-proof hard plastic boxes, equipped with an integral closure device. |
| Bag holders | Bag holders should be designed to hold the size of plastic bags in use. |
| | Bag holders should preferably be metal sided and equipped with a pedal-operated flip lid. |
| Colour coding | Yellow should be used for all packaging and equipment used for clinical waste. |
| | Black/green should be used for all packaging and equipment used for domestic and similar wastes. |
| Labelling | All plastic bags and sharps boxes should be labelled clinical waste and be marked with the international symbol for biohazard. |
| Sealing | Plastic bags should be sealed at the neck when 75 per cent full with a tie, pull tag or clip (the selected mechanism can also incorporate a unique reference number to identify the source of the waste). |
| | Sharps boxes should be sealed when 75 per cent full by the proprietary mechanism integral with the box. |
| | Plastic bags and sharps boxes containing clinical waste should never be reopened or sorted without strict application of infection control procedures. |
| Handling | Plastic bags and sharps boxes containing waste should be carried by the neck or handles respectively. |
| | Plastic bags and sharps boxes should never be thrown, dropped or mistreated. |
| Central storage | Storage of waste should be in a secure (lockable), hygienic and accessible location, clearly labelled as containing waste. |

| Issue | Key principle |
| --- | --- |
| Administration | A single person should be given overall responsibility for supervising waste management.<br>All staff producing or handling waste should be trained.<br>Records should be maintained of the quantities of waste sent for disposal (and the costs). |

**Table 7.1.4** *Typical scope of waste management procedures*

| Aspect | Scope |
| --- | --- |
| Definitions | Types of waste generated by the general practice. |
| Segregation of different types of waste | Segregation of clinical waste from domestic and similar waste.<br>Segregation of sharps from other clinical wastes. |
| Packaging | Packaging systems. |
| Labelling and sealing | Labelling and sealing mechanisms. |
| Handling | Handling of waste. |
| Collection and storage | Collection and storage pending disposal. |
| Administration | Staff responsibilities.<br>Record keeping.<br>Training. |
| Accidents and incidents | Contingency plans and emergency arrangements. |

**Table 7.1.5** *Equipment and facilities needed for waste management*

| Purpose | Equipment |
| --- | --- |
| Primary packaging | Yellow plastic bags<br>Black plastic bags<br>Sharps boxes |
| Collection | Bag holders |
| Sealing and labelling | Ties, pull tags or clips<br>Labelling tape (optional) |
| Movement of waste | Trolley (optional) |
| Waste treatment | Document shredder (optional) |
| Storage | Storage room or wheelie-bin |

It is important that this equipment is 'fit for purpose' and designed for waste management uses. In particular, the handling and storing of waste using equipment/facilities which are also used for food/drinks, medical preparations or accessible to patients should be avoided.

## Waste disposal

The only disposal method which is currently proven for the destruction of all types of clinical waste is incineration, although alternative technologies, such as microwaving, are now beginning to enter the UK marketplace following their application in the USA and Europe. Typically, incineration of clinical waste costs £250–350 per tonne.

Domestic and similar wastes may be disposed of by a range of methods, the most common being landfilling. Alternatives are incineration and, for certain elements of the waste stream, recycling, composting or anaerobic digestion may be applicable. The typical cost of landfilling domestic type waste is currently £8–12 per tonne, plus £7 per tonne landfill tax. Thus, the differential between disposal of clinical waste and domestic type waste may be a factor of 10–20 (i.e. it is twenty times more expensive to dispose of clinical waste than domestic waste). This is a major incentive to ensure that segregation practices minimise the quantities of clinical waste being produced.

The duty of care on general practices is especially relevant to the transfer of waste to a contractor for its disposal. The objective of the duty is explicitly to ensure that waste producers cannot 'wash their hands' of their waste once they have handed it over for disposal. It is an obligation on the general practice to ensure that the waste is disposed of in an appropriate manner at a suitably licensed facility. As a minimum, a general practice should check the following to discharge its duty of care:

- registration of the transporter as a waste carrier;
- waste management licence and any other authorisations of the final disposal facility;
- records of disposal.

A general practice is also obliged to ensure that an accurate description of its waste is given to the waste disposal contractor, so that there can be no ambiguity as to the nature of the waste which might lead to its inappropriate disposal.

## Enlisting staff support

Waste management is possibly unique in demanding the co-operation, understanding and participation of all staff in order to achieve a safe and effective system. This includes doctors and nurses, who as the main producers of clinical waste play a significant role in segregation, assistants and domestic staff, who typically will be responsible for handling waste, and the practice administration and managers, who will need to ensure that the waste management system operates efficiently, cost effectively and meets health and safety requirements. Therefore, enlisting long-term staff support is essential to a successful waste management plan.

The greatest barrier to staff support is a combination of inertia, lack of understanding and beliefs that new procedures are onerous and waste management costs are an unnecessary overhead. However, through careful designing of a waste management plan and training these barriers can be overcome and, in addition, there is a number of clear incentives to establish good waste management practices, which are both 'carrot and stick' in nature.

The positive incentives are that when waste is properly managed, the health and safety and pleasantness of the working environment of the general practice are improved. All staff will see the benefits in terms of hygiene when waste is properly contained and regularly removed for disposal, particularly those whose jobs include handling waste. Implementation of segregation practices also minimises the costs of waste management, since disposal of non-clinical waste costs 5–10 per cent of the cost of clinical waste disposal.

The 'sticks' are that the health risks associated with waste, especially clinical waste, can be high and, as a result, the financial liabilities of mismanagement are also punitive. Failure to invest relatively small amounts of money in equipment or time in training, or ignoring potential problems, can result in significant health risks to staff and others.

Coupled with the enlistment of staff support is training, which is fundamental to implementing a waste management plan. Formal training is a prerequisite if the hazards associated with waste, the proper use of equipment, optimisation of segregation and maintenance of health and safety standards are to be understood and the objectives of a waste management plan achieved.

## Acknowledgements

Thanks to Lynne Nicholas, practice manager at Berinsfield Health Centre, Oxfordshire.

## References

Department of the Environment, *Waste Management Paper No 25* (in preparation).

Health Services Advisory Committee, *Safe Disposal of Clinical Waste* (1992) Health and Safety Commission, London.

London Waste Regulation Authority (1994) *Guidelines for the Segregation, Handling, Transport and Disposal of Clinical Waste,* London Waste Regulation Authority.

*Controlled Waste Regulations 1992.*

## 7.2

# Practice Premises

*John Hearle*
*Aitchisons Raffety Buckland*

## Introduction

One of the key elements to any good practice is quality premises. This relates not only to the benefits of working in accommodation of good architectural design and a full range of fixtures and fittings but also to the value that is linked to the property.

Quality and value are intrinsically linked to the extent that the valuation and appraisal manual produced by the Royal Institution of Chartered Surveyors specifically includes guidance for valuers looking at surgery premises, and emphasises this element and advises the valuer to consider how the design and layout of the premises provide for the relevant factors which portray quality. The guidance notes even set out various elements which should be considered by the valuer:

- adequate division of accommodation for medical/patient/staff purposes;
- security;
- confidentiality;
- circulation;
- provision for the disabled;
- level of medical fixtures and fittings;
- pram parking;
- car parking;
- clinical waste storage, etc.

The value should reflect the often substantial investment the practitioners have made in the building.

For property occupied freehold, good premises should provide a realistic return in the form of rent reimbursement, and an eventual capital return to retiring partners. If the property is occupied leasehold, rent reimbursement should cover the cost of the lease rent and, if not integral, contribute towards the cost of insurance and external decoration and repair.

Over the last few years the recession, together with a lack of understanding in respect of surgery premises, has resulted in too many cases where the above did not materialise. In order to make the equation work it is not simply adequate to ensure that practice premises are of a good quality. It is also absolutely essential to employ the services of a specialist valuer who should both check and verify any rental assessment placed on the premises by the District Valuer (DV) and also act on behalf of the partnership in relation to the premises and aspects of partnership changes. The valuation of surgery premises is a specialist subject recognised by the Royal Institution of Chartered Surveyors, made clear in the guidance notes mentioned above. In the past the failure to use specialist valuers has resulted in incorrect levels of rent reimbursement and partnership valuations being assessed on a simplistic alternate use value.

In order to identify a valuer with adequate expertise in doctors' surgeries there are various approaches the practice could take. The Royal Institution of Chartered Surveyors keeps records of experts. The GPFC publish a panel of specialist surveyors and valuers and finally many of the health authorities keep their own lists (in respect of the two former contacts reference points are noted at the end of this chapter).

## Rent reimbursement

The rules and regulation of rent reimbursement are dealt with in the NHS General Medical Services Statement of Fees and Allowances (SFA). In basic terms the majority of freehold properties are reimbursed the Current Market Rent (CMR) often referred to as 'notional rent'. These figures are assessed by the DV every three years and the Statement of Fees and Allowances (paragraph 51, schedule 4) contains the definition of CMR together with the various assumptions as to the terms and conditions of the lease that should be adopted by the valuer. For leasehold premises the CMR is also reimbursed, although in such instances the DV will have regard to the actual lease and adopt certain adjustments to the terms contained so as to make it compatible with the 'notional rent'. There is however a marked difference in the CMR for leasehold and freehold property. In the 'notional rent' on a freehold property we are dealing with assumed terms and thus the figure can rise or fall at review. However, for a CMR on a leasehold property one deals with actual lease terms and with actual rent reviews. Thus, if a review clause is not implemented there is no change and no requirement for the DV to become involved. On a leasehold surgery this procedure can be adopted in times when rents are falling which, in turn, will prevent a fall in reimbursement. Freehold surgeries, despite any mortgage commitments, have no such protection.

While the reimbursement of CMR is the more normal course of action, it is also possible to be reimbursed under the Cost Rent Scheme. This is primarily used for new projects (new building or refurbishment) where the reimbursement is calculated by reference to the actual rebuilding costs and land purchase costs with ceilings set by a specific formula incorporated within the Statement of Fees and Allowances. Cost Rents are intended to cover the practice's interest payments on the capital necessary to buy land or property and build or convert the premises into a suitable doctors' surgery. They do not have regard to any form of open market rent and, furthermore, are guaranteed to the practitioners until they decide to change back to the Current Market Rent scheme or until there is a major structural or legal change within the premises/practice. The prime disadvantage is that Cost Rents require detailed health authority approval, are cash limited and thus few in number.

While Cost Rents are, in essence, fixed by a formula the CMR is an opinion expressed by the DV. All practices have full right to question whether or not such a figure is correct. When a new assessment is received, if the practices are not happy they should go back and express this feeling to the health authority. The health authority will ask for their evidence as to why they feel aggrieved and this is usually put forward by a brief valuation report prepared by a specialist valuer. The health authority will then ask the DV to discuss the situation with the doctors or their representative. This is not a contentious point and should not be regarded as something which may upset either the health authority or the DV. It is normal practice within valuations and should result in a fair and reasonable figure being agreed. Full procedural matters are set out in the Statement of Fees and Allowances (paragraph 51:35).

Should there be any further dispute and the parties are unable to agree a figure there is the right to further appeal to the Secretary of State. However, this is not utilised to any great extent and can be a time-consuming and costly process. Furthermore, the Secretary of State is represented by the Appeals Authority which normally pass any valuation matters back to the Chief Executive of the Valuation Office Agency, the employer and controller of all DVs.

The unfairness of the appeal system does not help here as while you will have the ability to employ a specialist valuer to put forward full and detailed evidence of your case, such evidence has to be submitted to the Appeals Authority and in turn the Chief Executive Officer and DV so that they may both prepare their own report and also put forward contrary arguments to your own evidence. Unfortunately, neither the practice nor the specialist valuer will have any opportunity to see the report of the DV or make any counter-representation.

## Valuations for partnership purposes

At the time of writing this chapter the valuation of doctor surgery premises for partnership purposes is the subject of great debate. It is not a matter of a simple valuation but will be very much guided by the instructions and assumptions contained in a Partnership Agreement and the statutory requirements of the NHS Act 1977. It should be noted that partnership agreements should be thoroughly considered and discussed with both valuer and solicitor prior to completion.

In addition to the above, the valuer will be guided by the Royal Institution of Chartered Surveyors Appraisal and Valuation Manual, which contains specific advice on the valuation of doctors' surgeries for partnership purposes. This covers both the general advice of an assessment based on the open market value and also the possible ability for some practices to reflect cost (by adopting a depreciated replacement cost basis of assessment). It furthermore highlights the problems of valuation and goodwill.

One of the most important elements which will control partnership valuations is the NHS Act 1977 where Section 54 makes it illegal for GPs to sell goodwill. This in itself is not a problem but unfortunately the Medical Practices Committee has defined goodwill as anything substantially in excess of market value. In turn, the Royal Institution of Chartered Surveyors defines market value and open market value in the terms of strict assumptions, an important element of which is that the property should be assumed to have vacant possession and any bid from specialist purchasers must be excluded. This means that any element of Cost Rent must be disregarded from such an assessment as it is a specialist element relating to specific practitioners only (indeed this point is confirmed by the Royal Institution of Chartered Surveyors in their Valuation and Appraisal Manual).

Contrary to the above, there is now a belief that for large purpose-built or substantially converted surgery premises where the projects were implemented under the Cost Rent scheme and where the practice still continues to receive a Cost Rent, that the valuation for partnership purposes should in essence be 'the value to the practice' and not the market value. The value to the practice could have regard to the Cost Rent and/or a depreciated replacement cost of the property. While such belief is based on a certain element of fair play and reasonableness it technically still falls foul of the Medical Practice

Committee's definition of goodwill in that if the assessment of value to the practice exceeded market value, the difference could be deemed as goodwill by the MPC and thus, in their eyes, be illegal.

The debate in respect of partnership valuations and what they can and cannot include continues, although the GMSC has resolved to find a solution to the 'valuation problem' and has set up a working party to look into the matter. It is hoped that discussions with MPC will eventually solve the problem although in the meantime it is absolutely essential for practices involved with partnership changes to obtain good and professional advice from both a specialist valuer and solicitor.

# Procurement of IT Equipment

*Robin Hopkins*
*Institute of General Practice,*
*University of Exeter*

A computerised information management system is likely to be one of the single largest capital investments within any form of business and in order to be cost effective IT must deliver a real improvement in information management. In order to do this the information system must mirror the information processes that currently take place within the business and enhance various factors within the information flows, enabling new business to be created and costs to be contained within existing business.

In the past information management projects have been driven from two disparate ends – the user who demands some form of 'black box' to perform some specific function and the technical boffin who is an expert in his field and wishes to market his product and the boffin who believes he can see further uses for the information and wishes the user to purchase a system that increases the ability to perform new functions.

In reality the success of any information re-engineering process is dependent upon a number of factors:

- meeting adequately the informational needs;
- interfacing successfully with users;
- providing for further development and user needs in the application in as open-ended a manner as possible.

The major factors for success are the first two items and these can be determined by the definition of an adequate user requirement and ensuring that the applied system meets that specification.

In the early 1990s the Department of Health produced guidelines related to the procurement of any computer system and further documentation aimed in particular at general practice. The majority of this documentation was far in excess of that needed for the purchase of systems aimed for use in general practice. The *Guide to the Preparation of an Operational Requirement* sets out a schedule with just under 100 separate headings. However, the documentation does follow some basic principles.

In the development of any new information system the first step of work is the production of a user requirement which is a document that spells out in simple terms the processes that the information system will perform, what kind of records it will store and process and in what way the user will interface with the system. The success of the eventual product is very closely related to the accuracy and completeness with which the user requirement is produced. Past history has shown that poor user requirements tend to be produced by individuals not actively involved in the current information process. There are many examples of very expensive mistakes (some of them multi-million) both within and without the healthcare sector produced by inadequate user requirement definition.

While most of us are unable to cost justify the production of a bespoke information management system and have to buy in existing equipment, the range of potential competing systems is such that shopping around to find the one best suited to your circumstances can be a daunting task. However, it is most important to find a system that meets your personal user requirements or all that will result is disruption, inefficiency and increased costs.

One of the main benefits in the self-production of an adequate user requirement is in getting all parties to address completely what it is they are expecting from the proposed information system.

The *Guide to the Preparation of an Operational Requirement* is intended to provide in plain language a general description of what the user expects the information system to be able to do, the operations it must be capable of performing and any constraints imposed by the user. Each individual user requirement should be verifiable, realistic and backed by example and reference as well as prioritised.

## The production of a user requirement

How do we go about producing a user requirement? While the process is relatively simple it does need to be exhaustive and involves a number of key steps:

- a detailed analysis of the data elements currently in use within the business;
- a detailed analysis of the information flows within and outwith the business;

- a detailed analysis of the functions needed to be performed within the business;
- a detailed analysis of the sites and user types that need to interact with the information systems.

A standard structure for a user requirement would be as shown in the box.

---

### STANDARD STRUCTURE FOR A USER REQUIREMENT

- **Introduction** describing the purpose of the document, the scope of the information system to be addressed, any definitions or abbreviations used in the document and a general overview.
- **General description of the information system** with an overview of the functional requirements of the system, an overview of system properties, constraints on the system, user characteristics, operational environment and any system dependencies.
- **Specific requirements** state functional requirements of the information system, system properties and priorities and operational constraints.
- **References** to any external documentation.

---

Unfortunately future proofing any information system against a change in the user requirement is one of the areas most likely not to be addressed in the production of the document. This is perhaps one of the most significant reasons for the failure of any resultant information system.

A good user requirement is quite literally worth its weight in gold and will take into account predictable changes produced within the business by the introduction of the information system it is specifying.

### Data protection

There is no doubt that the most valuable asset a practice possesses is the information contained within the medical record. The user requirement should take into account legal and practical issues related to the implementation of the information system and the protection of this extremely valuable asset. For instance, what provision is to be made with respect to the Data Protection Act?

The Data Protection Act applies to all information systems storing personal data and has some interesting clauses related in particular to medicine. All computer systems which process personal data have to be registered with the Data Protection Registrar – a not undaunting process. Thankfully the BMA has for several years been producing an advice package for practices applying for registration and this must be considered essential reading.

One of the prime requirements for the registration to be accepted is the provision of a system to ensure that once data has been collected and stored they cannot accidentally be destroyed. One of the main provisions for this, apart from physical security of the information system, is the taking of back-ups. How are back-ups to be taken and where stored? How often do they need to be produced? Thankfully computer systems do not fail very often. The most likely problem is that the user will do something that is greatly outside the protocol which results in the computer going down, with potential loss of information. Protection against this eventuality is to take back-up files of the database. Most medical systems will produce a back-up on tape. Unfortunately, the longer you use your system the more data you will have to restore and this takes time. For instance, a three-doctor practice with about 6,000 registered patients using the computer for the medical record will over the space of a couple of years easily achieve 2Gbytes of clinical data. This will take of the order of two hours to back up and will require more than one tape, thus negating the possibility of a total back-up being carried out overnight. One solution to this problem is in the form of a separate hard disk on the computer which is used specifically for the purpose of back-ups. This process, known as mirroring, allows the user rapidly to back up the data to a different hard disk which can, in the case of some multi-user/multi-tasking operating systems such as UNIX, XENIX, Windows NT and Windows 95, then be transferred to a tape streamer while the system is in use during the normal working day.

## Hardware provision

The requirement should also take into account the system hardware provision and allowance should be made for the use of appropriate technology. Unfortunately, in the GP market most information system suppliers will not provide software only. This is based on the often erroneous premise that the customer will either have no knowledge of the basics of information technology or that they will be incapable of identifying a hardware fault from a software fault. This inevitably means that the system provider is to some extent able to ransom the customer in terms of hardware prices and performance. In the general marketplace the cost of the technology rapidly falls with time as systems with bigger and better specifications are being produced, often much faster than the practice can write down the costs of its purchase in the practice accounts.

The current trend is for a 'client–server' architecture in which the records are stored on the server which does little data processing and passed to the client which deals with things one record at a time. This sort of architecture has a number of advantages, not the least being placing the system critical data processing adjacent to the user (who can physically only be doing one thing at a time). The end results of this strategy are that the hardware performance characteristics of the server can to some extent be reduced, and thereby capital costs saved. The client on the other hand can no longer be a dumb terminal and has to be a full computer in its own right.

Having stated that the hardware performance of the server can be reduced it never pays to go below the recommended specification of the system provider. Experience has shown that it will pay to improve on that performance if it is at all economically feasible.

## Software performance

Information systems for use in general practice have been around in differing degrees since the mid-1970s and have greatly increased in their functionality. While there is still wide variation in system capabilities most GP software has to be capable of a range of system events. Attempts have been made to produce a common core standard system of performance and towards this end the RFA or requirements for GP computer system accreditation were proposed and implemented by the Department of Health. The RFA sets out a series of core data objects that it is necessary for any GP system to be able to process. It is strongly advised that all new information systems to be purchased for use in general practice should be accredited.

Over the last few years a great deal of attention has been paid to the use of computers to aid a practitioner who already is suffering from information overload. One way to provide help is through the use of guidelines or protocols. Unfortunately, the waters are far from clear in this area. In law, guidelines are there to advise and protocols to be rigidly followed. System developers and researchers have developed and incorporated both guidelines and protocols into information systems with the best of intentions in producing an increased level of care. However, in the USA there have been successful prosecutions both against doctors who have not used a computer-aided protocol in the management of a condition where one is known to exist and against doctors who did use the protocol which some 'expert' witness disagreed with.

There is no doubt that computer-aided disease management in the form of administrative protocols to remind of the need for repeat blood tests, etc. in the management of long-term conditions such as diabetes can be extremely useful, as can user defined prescribing guidelines. However, systems should be designed to reinforce the learning process and not remove the requirement for the healthcare worker to think and take decisions.

Clinical guidelines can be implemented within software in a number of ways. The most useful application is when integrated and interactive with the medical record and if intended for maximum effect should tailor into the existing procedures within the practice. The current trend in software is for reusable data objects that do not need to undergo any form of transformation between different applications. The current range of products supplied by MICROSOFT and intended for use in the general marketplace follows these principles. The ability to be able to analyse data contained within the overall patient database and incorporate the analysis in other documents such as the annual report and business plan can be extremely useful and easily facilitated by systems that follow this standard.

## The procurement process

Having defined the user requirement and gone through the process of identifying the information needs of the practice, the next step is actual procurement. By now the infrastructure should be clear, a document should exist which has been discussed and approved by all parties involved, and the users should be looking forward to the impending change. The next step is the actual selection process.

Despite the production of the user requirement the software acquisition process is often still a minefield. The user should visit software exhibitions and above all other practices with systems in use. The user requirement should be sent to prospective software vendors who should be able to demonstrate how their system best fits within it. Demonstrations by software vendor teams should be sought but treated with caution. The performance of information systems is critically dependent upon the amount of data present in the system and most demonstration systems contain very little. The best demonstration of a system is to visit a busy practice using it on a Monday morning. A short list of vendor systems should be drawn up and users would thereafter be best advised to choose the system that interferes least with existing office processes and has the best user interface. It is no good implementing an extremely attractive looking system that will add two minutes to each consultation by imposing unfamiliar processes on the user.

In terms of hardware acquisition the situation may be forced upon the purchaser by the software provider as previously discussed. However, if not, it certainly pays to shop around. Within certain parameters all computers are the same and software will specify the minimum system requirements for it to run. This can be taken as a base specification when looking around. It does not always pay to go to the cheapest source, which often implies cheapest components and potentially less support. Equally it is not necessary to go to the big names for hardware and a price differential of 2:1 between suppliers is not uncommon.

## Further reading

Benson, T *Medical Informatics*, Longman, Harlow.

Department of Health (1990) *GP Computing: Information for GPs on Practice Computer Systems*, HMSO, London.

European Space Agency (1991) *Software Engineering Standards Issue 2*, ESA Publications Division.

Gilb, T (1988) *Principles of Software Engineering Management*, Addison-Wesley, Wokingham.

Preece, J *The Use of Computers in General Practice*, Churchill Medical Communications, Edinburgh.

Stevens, G (1988) 'Selecting computer software packages – a self help guide', *Journal of the Royal Society Medicine*, 81: 458–60.

Wats, S Humphrey (1995) *A Discipline for Software Engineering*, Addison-Wesley, Wokingham.

## 7.4

# Private Finance in General Practice Premises

*John Walker and Graeme Love*
*D G Love & Partners*

General practitioners have traditionally owned their practice premises or occupied space provided for them in health centres. Owner occupation has its roots in the pre-NHS era and is the foundation for the reimbursement provisions contained within the 'Red Book Rent & Rates Scheme'.[1] Primary healthcare evolution introduced health centres financed by the public sector, but this form of surgery provision is no longer available for new situations and indeed health authorities are being required to divest themselves of property ownership.

Expansion of primary healthcare has continued at a rapid pace in recent years. It is clear from the White Paper *Choice & Opportunity Primary Care: The Future*[2] that the present government intends to accelerate expansion and change with 'local flexibility so that services can be delivered in a way which is better attuned to local needs and circumstances'.

The modern state-of-the-art group practice surgery is complex and costly to provide. The level of capital required to develop new premises today is such that practitioners should ask themselves whether they really want the financial burden of owner occupation and the repercussions associated therewith for the individual and the partnership.

## The alternative to owner occupation

During the past fifteen or so years a number of practices have taken advantage of provisions contained within the Rent & Rates Scheme to lease premises from third-party landlords at reimbursable rentals, being either 'Cost Rent' or 'Current Market Rent'.[3] This has been achieved by either selling their existing premises to an investor who leases them back to the practice or entering into an agreement for the investor to procure the design and construction of a new surgery which the practice leases once it is complete.

The more successful new surgery developments have been undertaken by investors who intend to retain the building for the long term, gaining their investment return gradually over a number of years. This investor is able to spend more on the building's specification, including built-in fixtures and fittings, than the property developer who carries out the scheme and sells (with a lease to the practice in place) to the long-term investor. This latter form of developer gains the return from a margin between the cost of the development to them and the market value sale price to the investor.

As with most alternatives there are advantages and disadvantages associated with each option. From the practitioner's viewpoint, perhaps the greatest single advantage of owner occupation lies in the capital asset and additional income that can be obtained from a system which pays the practice to provide the premises from which they operate. A 'Cost Rent' pays for mortgage interest at least. Once 'Notional Rent' exceeds mortgage repayments, the practice's income increases. On retirement a practitioner sells to an incoming partner and secures a substantial capital gain which has cost the individual virtually nothing.

However, this scenario masks a number of realities which may be encountered in practice. Negative equity is not confined to those who purchased houses at inflated market prices; a number of general practitioners are also experiencing such difficulties. Partnership change becomes stifled, additional partners are reluctant to buy into a negative asset, retiring partners may find they have to accept a capital loss or finance repayments from their pensions.

The surgery which benefits from equity in its value may also prove to be a hinderance to partnership change. Incoming partners are often at a state in their personal lives where they are committed to a substantial domestic mortgage and have young families to provide for. The additional burden of mortgage repayments on the practice premises may be more than they are prepared or feel able to meet. The practice could then find itself taking on a new partner who can afford to join them rather than a new partner they would have preferred.

New partners joining long-established owner occupier practices could find themselves with a 20 per cent interest in the premises and a liability for 40 per cent of the mortgage repayment – perhaps not the best basis for harmonious working. These various difficulties associated with owner occupation can be successfully overcome by leasing practice premises.

## Private Finance Initiative

The Private Finance Initiative (PFI) was introduced by the government in October 1992. It is aimed at procurement, via the private sector, of major capital projects in the public sector with the objective of reducing public expenditure. Project risks are transferred to the private sector. These include ownership, building provision and service delivery. In return the public sector utilises the assets and services, paying an agreed schedule of rate. PFI envisages long-term relationships focused upon service provision over 25 to 60 years.

Bringing a scheme forward under PFI requires the European Community regulations for the procurement of public sector projects to be followed. Proposals from the private sector are then tested against the Treasury Investment Appraisal Guidelines to demonstrate value for money. The process is lengthy and there is growing frustration among private sector bidders at the slow rate of progress and the costs involved in formulating and progressing a PFI bid.

Private sector surgery landlords do not generally operate within the formal PFI sphere. This is mainly due to the costly bureaucratic system of formulating bid proposals and the time that is required to bring matters to fruition. However, since the contract for development by third parties and occupation by a practice partnership is a transaction outside of the public sector, there is no requirement for practitioners to consider the PFI option for premises procurement.

The White Paper *Choice & Opportunity* suggests novel ways in which general practice and other frontline services may be organised in the future. The issue of a practice rather than individual doctors holding the contract and a salaried option for GPs could open the way for PFI to be applied to primary care.

Private sector investors range from small concerns with perhaps one or two surgeries, purchased with mortgage finance, to substantial commercial organisations utilising inhouse finance. There is even an element of pension fund/insurance company institutional investment within this sector. The latter, due to their constitutions, may not always be able to take on the role of developer and longer term investor, causing them to utilise the services of a development company from whom the institution will purchase the completed scheme.

For those practices that prefer to retain control during the development of their surgery premises but do not intend to retain long-term ownership, short-term bank finance is available for site purchase, building construction and professional fees. The terms for this form of finance will vary but they are inevitably improved when long-term funding is already secured, for example, by a forward sale of the completed scheme to institutional or other investors.

This will permit the practice to ensure that the whole of the sale price advantages them either in the form of an improved specification or retention of any cost/market value sale price margin. However, the practitioner must recognise that property development is a risk business and, while rewards can be great, many schemes result in losses to professional property developers. The question must therefore be asked: 'Should the practitioner inexperienced in property development be venturing into a project with hundreds of thousands of pounds of potential liability at stake?' This question is equally applicable to those considering owner occupation. It is perhaps more appropriate for such risks to be undertaken by those who deal with them as an everyday occupation and on various projects which permit the risk factor to be spread and hence discounted.

Finance for surgery development is generally available in the marketplace. Practitioners are able to raise mortgage loans for owner occupation from traditional sources such as banks and building societies as well as the General Practice Finance Corporation Limited (GPFC)[4] that are specialists in provision of surgery mortgages. At the time of writing, the mortgage market is competitive and practitioners, who are generally regarded as a sound financial risk, are able to select from a range of products, including long-term fixed rate finance.

### Rent reimbursement

Reimbursement for the cost of premises to a practice comes in the form of rent and generally falls under one of three headings.

1. **Cost Rent.** This was based upon the broad premise that mortgage interest payments on a property will exceed the rental value of that property for a number of years until ultimately, due to value changes, the rental catches up. The Cost Rent scheme was never available as of right but was provided as an alternative discretionary form of reimbursement designed to permit development of new surgery premises to take place, which would otherwise have been stifled for financial reasons.

   Cost Rents can be reimbursed to both owner—occupier practitioners and tenants of third parties, (i.e. the landlord may receive the Cost Rent). Existing Cost Rent contracts will remain, however, new Cost Rent finance is no longer generally available.

2. **Notional Rent.** This is the reimbursement available as of right to owner–occupier practitioners with 100 or more patients on their list. The figure is determined at three-yearly intervals by reference to the actual property and a stated basis of assumptions specified in the 'Rent & Rates Scheme'. At the time of writing there is much controversy surrounding downward movement in reimbursement, following tri-annual reviews in certain instances. This arises from property value reductions generally and as a result of the 'Rent & Rates Scheme' requiring that the review be undertaken.

3. **Current Market Rent.** This is the reimbursement available as of right to practitioners with 100 or more patients on their list and who rent from third party landlords. The figure is determined by the property itself and the lease terms. It is capable of variation at three-yearly intervals but this will be longer if the lease terms dictate as such. However, it will only be varied if the landlord implements the lease rent review process. Accordingly, if rental values drop, the landlord should not initiate the review and can thus protect the practice from a reduction in reimbursement.

## Commercial leases

It is important for both parties involved in a landlord and tenant situation to recognise the needs and limitations of the other party. Ideally the relationship should be that of co-operation. A partnership permitting the landlord to obtain the maximum income available from the property without financial penalty to the tenant practitioners is the objective. This form of arrangement should permit the practice to get on with its business of delivering primary healthcare to patients within a conducive environment. Happy landlords and happy tenants can work together to help achieve the objectives of both parties. This may include alteration and extension to the premises at the landlord's expense, to meet expanding needs of the practice.

Landlords' objectives are quite naturally of a financial nature. Time is needed to recover original investment costs and obtain a commercial return on these monies. This precludes entering into short-term leases or leases with tenants' break options on property of a specialist nature, where an alternative tenant may well be non-existent. The modern group practice doctors' surgery, by the nature of its layout, construction and often geographical location, renders it of a specialist nature with a limited alternative use market.

Aspects which the parties to the lease should address in a co-operative fashion will in addition to the length of a lease include among others:

1. A mechanism to protect the tenant practitioners from having to pay a rent which exceeds the rental proportion of their

reimbursement entitlement from time to time but tenants must realise that this protection can only remain while the whole of the premises qualifies for reimbursement.

2. Commercial property leases, particularly those of an institutional landlord, usually provide for the tenant to undertake external maintenance and repair of the building and to be responsible for the premium cost in respect of insuring the structure against damage by fire and other perils. The 'Current Market Rent' reimbursement makes provision for payment of an allowance to meet the cost of these lease liabilities. Any mechanism of the nature outlined at (1) above must ensure that the tenants' allowance does not pass by default to the landlord.

3. Modern group practices are subject to regular and relatively frequent partnership changes due to retirements and resignations. Partners who are parties to a lease are contractually liable, both jointly and severally, for the performance of the lease terms and conditions including financial issues. Outgoing partners will want to ensure that their personal liability ceases on, or as soon as possible after, their departure from the practice. Landlords should recognise the needs of the individual and provide an outgoing partner with a release from all future liability under the lease. However, tenant practitioners must appreciate the landlord's need for security of investment which is derived from having a number of individuals liable for the lease conditions. Generally a pre-agreed minimum number of partners who are liable for the lease conditions will be required by the landlord. This need not be the full number of partners entering into the lease but will be influenced by the size of the practice, but cannot equal four persons due to the law of property provisions.

## Site selection

Site selection and acquisition is perhaps the most difficult aspect to resolve in the entire process of premises procurement. It is the key to realising the partners' objectives of providing surgery accommodation appropriate to the needs of their practice. Without a suitable site, all plans for owner occupation or leasing new purpose-built premises cannot come to fruition.

A structured approach to the site search will help to focus efforts and identify opportunities which may be available either on or off the general property market. It is an area where professional help with appropriate local knowledge and experience of primary healthcare property requirements will prove invaluable. The aid of a suitably qualified valuation surveyor and an architect to assist the practice in identifying available opportunities will be of great benefit and can assist in identification of the search area. This may be achieved by examination of the patient catchment to determine the density of patient distribution within the area covered by the practice. Where a practice does not intend to increase its list size the objective will be to retain existing patients by locating as conveniently as possible to serve their needs. For those practices that wish to develop their lists, it may be appropriate to try to achieve a balance between convenience for existing patients and ready accessibility from neighbourhoods under-represented in the patient density distribution. When considering accessibility principal road networks and public transport availability will influence the preferred location.

The health authority will need to approve the finally selected site and be satisfied that the practice's proposals are appropriate within the context of the local strategy for primary healthcare provision. It is appropriate to consult with the authority at an early stage to ensure that the practice has support for the principle of being located within the identified site search area.

The size of a site can be established in general terms in consultation with the architect. It is important for this to be optimised to avoid unnecessary costs but both immediate accommodation needs and provision for realistic future expansion should be considered. Site availability will, in practice, often be limited to very few options, none of which may prove to be ideal. Comparison of alternatives can be aided by the architect's input with sketch feasability studies for each. The practice can then consider and weigh the alternatives against a check list menu of:

- location;
- size;
- costs;
- building arrangement;
- building cost due to arrangement;
- accessibility to patients;
- likelihood of planning consent;
- future expansion possibilities;
- public utilities;
- car parking;
- public transport;
- road network.

Once the preferred site has been identifed it has to be secured, possibly in the face of competition from others for alternative uses. The practice will need to ensure that they have the finance available to enable them to perform and conclude the transaction. This may need to be earlier than the practice would ideally prefer, the cost of interest charges being weighed against the certainty of site availability.

How much to pay for the site, how to set about the negotiations to purchase at the best possible price, how to formulate a bid and any conditions to be attached to a public sector land disposal 'tender' are all matters for the valuation surveyor to advise upon. A valuation surveyor, if appointed at an early stage, will have a sound knowledge of the practice objectives and the constraints which they face.

## Design

In consultation with the architect, the practice will be able to establish the range of accommodation necessary to satisfy its current needs. These will reflect the number of partners, approved ancillary staff and attached healthcare providers.

Future expansion provision should also be carefully considered. For example, an expanding neighbourhood population could indicate an additional partner within three to five years. Clearly it would be economic to provide accommodation at the outset for predictable expansion in the short term. This will avoid costly (in pro rata floorspace terms) capital outlay and disruption to the operation of the practice at a later date. Less predictable future expansion needs may be catered for by designing the building readily to accept an extension or further first-floor accommodation once the need can be justified.

If the pilots proposed in *Choice & Opportunity* prove successful, the need for a wider range of ancillary and complementary facilities will become established within group practice surgeries. Future design of premises may well need to cater for such developments and practices may wish to consider making provision within their proposed building to accommodate likely changes in primary care delivery.

Car parking is always a contentious issue. Local planning authorities set levels for car parking to be provided in association with new development. As with all such policies they are subject to change and can range from one of positive restraint, where use of private cars as a means of transport is being discouraged, to a minimum standard approaching one space for every staff member and four or five spaces per practitioner for patient parking. The former may cause operational difficulties for the practice and the latter may prove to be a costly over provision where practices operate an efficient appointment system. Car parking absorbs substantial areas of land, which is costly to purchase, lay out and maintain. A perceived deficiency of car parking by the local planning authority may frustrate plans for future expansion. Early consideration of car parking implications is essential to a successful scheme and must form part of the feasibility study to determine site size requirements.

Essential to the design input is continuous consultation with the health authority which must ultimately approve the scheme for reimbursement under the 'Rent & Rates Scheme'. While this scheme contains schedules of floorspace which may be provided for various sized practices, it should be noted that these specifically relate to 'Cost Rent' reimbursement. The schedules may be used as a guide to the amount of floorspace which will be reimburseable under 'Notional' or 'Current Market' rent. They are not set in tablets of stone and these areas may legitimately be exceeded in order to create the most beneficial scheme for the practice.

During the consultation process, the extent of the floorspace which the health authority is prepared to approve for reimbursement will become clear. The practice will need to ensure that the scheme proposed will be wholly reimbursable as any shortfall will result in the partners having personally to make good the deficiency. This is applicable to both owner occupied and leased practice premises.

## Consultants procurement team

The procurement of health practice premises is a specialised field. The best value in terms of quality and cost will only be obtained by the appointment of those who have substantial experience in design and construction of similar projects. Before appointing any professional to the team or entering into arrangements with developers and investors, practitioners should satisfy themselves that they have the necessary experience to produce the best possible end product for the practice. Ask for references or preferably visit other practices for whom the developer or consultant has previously worked. This is a vital process and the right selection of professional consultants, developer, contractor and investor (where appropriate) will avoid costly disappointments which can occur due to inexperience.

The make-up of the team will comprise multi-disciplinary professionals and commercial concerns including:

1. **Architect.** A registered or chartered architect is essential. They will be responsible for the design which dictates the practice's working environment for many years. Seek out specialists in surgery development for their experience will be invaluable in interpreting the health authority's requirements and criteria. If appointed by the practice, the architect will be directly liable for any professional negligence against which they are required to carry professional indemnity insurance. If appointed by a developer, the architect will provide a collateral warranty to the practice to protect against negligent design. Once again this will be backed by insurance.
2. **Valuation surveyor.** A member of the Royal Institution of Chartered Surveyors or Incorporated Society of Valuers & Auctioneers is recommended. The valuer can assist with financial

appraisals, provision of advice on site purchase, lease terms and reimbursement rentals. They should be appointed at an early stage to ensure that the practice is fully briefed on the financial implications associated with the property proposals. Ensure that the valuer is well versed in the nuances of the 'Rent & Rates Scheme' and is experienced in the valuation of surgery premises. Not all valuers possess the experience necessary to provide the practice with full advice; a specialist should be appointed. Once again professional indemnity insurance cover will protect against negligence. In circumstances where the practice envisages entering into an agreement with a developer they should still appoint their own valuer and not rely upon the developer's representative whose duty is to act in the best interests of their client.

3. **Solicitor.** The solicitors should be appropriately qualified and possess a Law Society Practice Certificate. They will deal with the legal work on site purchase and, if premises are to be leased, the agreement to be entered into for the development of the surgery and the actual lease document. Dependent upon existing arrangements, it may also be appropriate to amend the partnership agreement to reflect new circumstances. Negligence is covered by the Law Society's mutual insurance arrangements. The appointment of a solicitor who has experience of medical practices and premises is considered to be essential. Solicitors tend to charge for their work on a time basis, including their research time, and practitioners will wish to ensure that they are not paying for the solicitor's learning curve in this specialist field.

4. **Contractor.** One who has a proven track record in constructing group practice surgeries is essential. The architect will advise upon a selection of appropriate contractors who should be asked to tender for the construction. If an agreement is to be entered into with a developer, the practice should insist upon approving the contractors' tender list. A developer experienced in the provision of surgery premises should have no objection to this as they will only be inviting tenders from suitably experienced contractors. The practice will wish to know what warranties will be provided to them by the contractor and will also wish to see evidence of adequate insurance to back the warranties.

5. **Developer.** A specialist in the field of primary healthcare provision is essential. They will understand the needs of the practice and the necessity of the health authority approval system. They will also appreciate the safeguards regarding rent and reimbursement which the practice will need. The practice should remember that they are essential to the developer but that the developer is the risk carrier in the partnership and there must be sufficient return within the project for it to be viable. An

appreciation of the developer's future intentions once the buildings are complete, e.g. hold the investment or sell it on, will help the practice in selecting a suitable developer with whom to form a partnership.

The developer approach to surgery procurement can be compared to the one-stop shopping principle. The developer will take responsibility for all aspects of the project, including the management of all professional consultants and the building contractor. This approach is more widely known as a Turnkey project with the practice partners having the role of client but without the capital expenditure commitment. This hassle-free approach has proven to be very attractive to medical practitioners who generally obtain a better quality result than they would have by the DIY method.

6. **Investor.** The practice may have little control over who purchases the building with the lease to the practice unless they undertake the development themselves and sell it directly. Even then they will have no control over onward sale by the original purchaser. However, the lease terms may well influence the type of investor to whom the property will be of interest. A document containing reimbursement/rent protection and mechanisms for retention of external repair and insurance allowance will not be attractive to those investors who are not familiar with primary healthcare surgery provision and the terms of the 'Rent & Rates Scheme'.

## Summary

The rapid expansion of primary healthcare has dictated that practitioners operate from ever more complex and costly premises. The process of premises procurement and the liabilities associated with ownership are now such that GPs may feel more comfortable with passing the risk to specialists and renting from them rather than undertaking development projects themselves and owning their surgeries. There are a few specialist companies who can project manage a surgery development for practices. They can take on the full project including financing from start to finish, handing over the purpose-built surgery, fully fitted, requiring just the medical records to be put into place before it is opened. The latter is achieved at no cost or risk to the practice and the developer assumes responsibility for over-budget expenditure or shortfall in reimbursement upon completion.

## Notes and references

1  General Medical Services Statement of Fees & Allowances.
2  *Primary Care: The Future* (1996) The Stationery Office Limited, London, October. *Primary Care: The Way Forward in Wales. Primary Care – The Way Ahead*, Scotland.
3  See General Medical Services Statement of Fees & Allowances – 'The Red Book'.
4  Norwich Union Insurance subsidiary.

PART EIGHT

# PROCEEDINGS FROM THE AMGP 21ST ANNUAL COURSE, NOVEMBER 1996

# Introduction: Facing the Future

## Choices, choices, yet more choices

The Association of Managers in General Practice (AMGP) is the only national professional body that provides support and development solely for those managing in primary care. It is the specialist association for those working in the generalist sector.

AMGP has held an Annual Course since 1975 – for 21 years. Each year has a theme which builds on those of previous courses. The intention is to stimulate and prepare those managing in primary care to think widely and to face challenges that confront them. This event provides the opportunity to network, gain new knowledge and skills and a greater understanding of current topics.

In 1996 the Annual Course was held in Scotland for the first time – in Glasgow. The theme was 'Choices, choices, yet more choices!'. This addressed the issues of rationing and prioritisation of healthcare and enabled delegates to extend their knowledge and practise their skills in decision-making. This was accomplished through:

- keynote address by Gerry Malone, Minister of Health (Chapter 8.1);
- skills workshops;
- the Oregon experience workshops (Chapter 8.2);
- the Sally Irvine Lecture given by Dr Colin M. Hunter (Chapter 8.3);
- a debate: 'People with self-inflicted illness should receive different priority for treatment' (Chapter 8.4).

The evaluation of the course by delegates was excellent and we share some of its content with you in the following sections. It should be pointed out that the speeches here have been reproduced verbatim and are not presented as reworked official conference papers. We hope this will stimulate discussion and thinking within your teams on how you will face the challenges of the future.

# 8.1

# Extract from Keynote Address to AMGP 1996 Annual Course

*Right Honourable Gerry Malone*
*Minister for Health*

---

I understand the power of the case you put. [The rights of staff employed by general practitioners to have similar pension rights to their colleague NHS staff]. As you have quite rightly said, this is an issue that has been around for sometime. It is an issue about which I was speaking at about this time last year in a number of contexts. Some of the points that need to be resolved within government are around the important detail – it isn't a minor detail – about terms and conditions and transfers and contributions, and all these things that frankly to anyone who is a layman in the world of pensions or superannuation are extremely complex. That agenda has proceeded along the road to resolution, but what I cannot do today, and I wish that I could, is to tell you that there is a certain outcome. All that I can say is that I understand the force of the argument. I can say that, of course, what a benefit it would be if there were an easier ability to transfer around the system, which is increasingly becoming a primary care led NHS. The way in which these arguments have been forcefully put, not only by your organisation but by those who have run campaigns on this issue, has been helpful and I must say that the constructive way in which they have all been put has, I think, informed us of the way that we should move forward. I am afraid I can say absolutely no more than that.

You will understand at this particular time of the year that this is not unusual across a range of policies. But I do assure you that the seriousness of the issue, the importance of reaching a resolution and a determined view one way or the other, is something that has borne on me thoroughly. One of the reasons for that is because as managers in primary care you are in the front line of NHS service delivery. It is a challenging role and much is expected from you. I welcome the steps you are taking to reinforce your professional status and to equip yourselves for the challenges of modern primary care. That is happening collectively, it is also happening individually.

We have here today someone who has won for her practice the first Investors in People award. That is Val Hempsey from Newcastle. Never slow to put her case forward, I was going round the exhibition and she said to me: 'Do you know I am the first person to have won an Investors in People award for my single-handed practice? Maybe you will use that in a speech some day.' How little did you know how quickly that would be put to excellent use. The reason that I use it is to point to the fact that not only is collective innovation important, important though it is especially in building a professional association like your own and setting objectives, but so is individual initiative and that is the strength of the primary care sector and nowhere is it a greater strength than in those who manage practices.

Let us just remind ourselves of the importance of primary care. Some 90 per cent of patients receive all the treatment or advice they need without recourse to secondary services. As I think the context of primary care changes, we may not see that percentage figure move but what we will undoubtedly see is the content of what happens in a primary care setting changing very dramatically indeed. So there are two things that I would like to do in my address today. One of them is to set in context the importance of primary care and the primary care led NHS, and share some thoughts with you about the White Paper and legislation that is to follow and then dwell, if I may, on the important challenges that the very stimulating theme of this weekend raises.

Now I think you quite rightly said that there is a lot of talk and jargon around the primary care led NHS. I often think that it is a phrase that slips lightly off the tongue, but the implications run very deep. When we looked at this initiative, in which I am frankly delighted to have been involved in such depth, there were a number of things that we wanted to improve: the range in quality of services, responsiveness of services to patients, co-ordination between the primary and secondary care sectors and also getting value for money, both for the patient and for the tax payers. The policy of a primary care led NHS isn't simply a matter of organisation, process and policy, it is more a set of ideas. I think if we look at that set of ideas there are perhaps three main elements.

First, **decision-making**. Those making decisions need to consider questions across a whole range of subjects: access, quality, effectiveness and cost as well as the needs of individual patients and also public health priorities, and it is to that latter area that you are addressing your theme this weekend. These decisions should be made as close to patients as possible by those most familiar with all the competing factors.

Second, **the process of delivery care.** Healthcare or advice should be acceptable and provided by an individual with the necessary skills. Making services available in primary care often meets both these requirements and it often requires us to break down traditional boundaries. One of the ways in which those boundaries can be broken down is by group and innovative management.

Then, third, there is that question of **the relationship between the professionals** which can often be awkward, and I look to you as managers to be the oil in the machinery. We need continually to seek ways to strengthen co-ordination and co-operation between GPs and health authorities, between secondary and primary care, between health and social care, and between and within the primary healthcare team itself. As managers in primary care you have that crucial role as leaders and facilitators in guiding forward progress.

And so in October last year the Secretary of State set out a programme and we published this year the primary care White Paper *Choice and Opportunity*. I think that this is likely to have perhaps the most significant impact on the management of GP practices and open up more exciting possibilities for the future of general practice than anybody could have thought of. The 'listening programme' was the foundation stone upon which all this was built. I think we identified during that programme the essence of the proposals for primary care that we would put into the document. And they were these:

- choice, opportunity and flexibility for those providing services;
- high standards for patients;
- consistent quality across the country;
- good value for money within available resources.

The debate was launched last October, the widest possible range of people took part: healthcare professionals that support primary care; those involved in management; educationalists and others. As a result of that, *Primary Care the Future* was published in June which summarised the debate. And as you have been setting for your professional organisation your codes and your principles, so in *Primary Care the Future* we set out a number of principles as well. They might sound very straightforward, but I think when you are ever thinking of taking a service on, as we are with primary care, it is important to focus on them — and they were:

- quality;
- fairness;
- accessibility;
- responsiveness;
- efficiency.

To support all these principles, *Primary Care the Future* identified some issues that needed to be addressed as an agenda with seven themes:

- resources;
- partnerships in care;
- developing professional knowledge;
- patients and carer information and involvement;
- securing the work force and premises;
- better organisation;
- local flexibility.

There has been a number of proposals made: the changes to the GP contract, extending the role of pharmacists, opticians, nurses and other professionals. These were widely endorsed by those working in primary care and their representatives. And so there followed an agenda-setting round. The purpose of that was to ensure that we had actually heard the right messages from everyone involved in primary care and that we were stepping on the right road forward.

Looking at the general practice aspects of the proposed legislation, one of the main aims was to enable new approaches to contracting or general practice to be developed locally, piloted and evaluated. And, as we now move on to the point where the Bill will be published in the near future, I simply want to set out some of the principles that I set out on the public platform before, but I want to reiterate them because they are important.

Participants in pilots will be voluntary. It will be up to individual practices to decide whether they want to take part, and if it is the case that they feel it is not a future that suits them then they will not be obliged to persist but can go back to a conventional way of delivering services. There will be no disadvantages either for GPs who remain in the current contractual arrangements. I do not see this as being something that is going to be a template imposed from the centre. People may well choose to deliver service in a different way, but that does not mean to say that they are delivering a better or a worse service. Incremental change in the way we deliver service is something that has always happened in the NHS. Quite often it has happened by stealth. Here is it happening on purpose. I fully expect for developments that are successful, others will want to follow in that path, but there is going to be no obligation to do so. What is intended is to encourage local people to develop and put forward their own ideas on different contractual arrangements, which could better suit their circumstances and the needs of the service locally. And although, of course, we do not have any firm agenda, because this will be discussed with all the professions involved once we have published the Bill, there are clearly a few things that are in my mind, springing from such a comprehensive tour of the primary care sector. Let me just share some of these with you.

For example, a salaried option for GPs, either within partnership or with other bodies such as NHS trusts. This might provide a wider range of employment opportunities, more scope to tailor services to local needs, more of an ability to get into these difficult areas where recruitment is a problem, particularly in the inner cities. That was a message we heard quite frequently around the country. Practice-based contracts; these might reflect the nature of the practice to be embracing non-medical professionals as well, and open new possibilities for the development of skill mix and careers. Perhaps an opportunity for practices to hold a single budget for both GMS and HS services – if we are going to hope that we will secure more integrated services for patients in the future, that was one option that we heard frequently during this process that I thought sounded very attractive in principle. And what all of this does is that it opens up new opportunities for improving services, dealing with some of the long-standing and irritating problems that people experience, and introducing more flexible careers structures to meet the needs of a changing workforce. The legislation also puts forward changes to the system for appointing single-handed GPs, reflecting the widely endorsed recommendations made in maintaining medical excellence to ensure that those appointed to vacancies fully meet the standards required. Legislation will also reduce bureaucracy in the appointment process.

Now a clear message from all the consultations has been the need for action to encourage local flexibility so that services can be delivered in a way which is better attuned to local needs and circumstances. The more flexible arrangements should promote high-quality services, provide the opportunity and incentive for primary care professionals, with special emphasis on the role of practice managers in making this happen, to use their skills to the full and provide more flexible employment opportunities in primary care. And another consistent message has been that changes should be by consent and consultation involving volunteers and should be taken forward through pilots with proper evaluations. And, as I said at the outset, there is a principle that informs us as we move forward.

The legislation will be framed to address all of these points. I believe, as managers, you have a pivotal role in seeing that our proposals are converted into action and that benefits for patients begin to flow. So I expect you all, either as individuals or collectively, to be involved in this process from the publication of the Bill, until it sees its way through to legislation.

We expect to have the Bill in Parliament before Christmas. And I think it is significant that something that was not intended originally to be in the Queen's Speech has now taken such prominence and importance that it is a programme Bill in the Speech and will be set in legislation during the course of the next few months. I think we are all aware, and in Westminster particularly the government ministers, that for one reason or another this is likely to be a shorter parliamentary session than those that normally face us at this time of year. And so it was important that we got the Bill as a programme Bill, so that we could get it through.

*Choice and Opportunity*, which I am sure you have all had a good chance of having a look at, is of course the first of two primary care White Papers that the Secretary of State will publish this year to establish both the practical and legislative steps that are needed to improve primary healthcare services. The second White Paper, due to be published before Christmas will be a more practical document setting out measures across the full range of primary healthcare professions needed to achieve high-quality care for all patients by giving proper support to nurses, doctors, dentists, pharmacists, and optometrists. And that White Paper too was based on the listening exercise and the agenda-setting round, and I look forward to its publication later on this year.

Madam Chairman, you have tackled a very difficult subject. Priority setting is something to which we apply our minds consistently, I believe, in the NHS. Sometimes we have done it unconsciously. Now we have an opportunity to do it in a more considered way. And I think that it is not an area that anybody within the NHS conducts, be they ministers, be they clinicians, be they managers of general practice, so I welcome this challenging agenda that you have set yourself. And of course you go right in at the deep end, don't you, with Oregon, that very uncontroversial list of priorities that didn't attract any publicity at all, when it was first set out! It did, because it was indeed challenging. Indeed I had the Governor of Oregon in my office not that long ago, and he told me just how challenging it had been. But he was also able to tell me of its successes.

But there is one thing that I hope you will bear in mind about the Oregon experience. Because, informative though it is to the way we think about these matters, we do have to understand that the Oregon experience was rooted from exactly the opposite direction in priority setting which is our challenge here in our NHS. Because in Oregon the question wasn't about restricting what was available so that it becomes available to fewer people; it was about restricting what was available to very few, so that it could become available to many more people in the population who weren't actually getting treatment at all. And it is important, I think, to understand what happened in Oregon in that context. Because that is why the public participation was probably more successful than it would be likely to be if one were setting out from a similar basis in this country. Because those who were involved in the process had been excluded from the healthcare system (many cases almost totally) and for them participating in this process of priority setting meant their first ability to reach into a healthcare system that had been shared only by a minority. So when it comes to the question of conducting public debate and acceptability of these difficult issues, I am sure you will bear in mind that this is the end of the spectrum they were coming from in Oregon, whereas we have, I think, a more difficult task in explaining, often to people who may have been used to certain services being available, that they wouldn't be for a wide range of reasons.

Why should primary care be involved in this at all? Well, I think primary care has a crucial role, especially as they move towards the primary care led NHS. For three reasons. First of all, primary carers are becoming far more involved in the purchasing of care than they ever were before in the Health Service up until the early 1990s. So in the role of direct purchaser, primary care is involved and has to address these issues. If not involved in direct purchasing, the second reason is that we have seen such a change in the way in which services are commissioned with the involvement of primary care. Then of course there is the third reason, that primary care, being the deliverer of 90 per cent of what actually happens to patients in this country, has a direct interest as a provider of services in this issue. And I think we all have to remember within the NHS, from ministers upwards, that priority setting is a matter for each and every one of us. That nobody can opt out of the very difficult issues that priority setting raises, that it is for you in general practitioners' surgeries as much an issue as it is for me sitting in Richmond House.

There is a foundation stone that I would like you to remember in your deliberations this weekend, and it is one which I also try to remember when addressing the issue. And that is that whatever we do, and whatever we think about priority setting, as it relates to specific services or cohorts of the population, the clinical freedom to deliver a treatment which is essential to an individual, in the eyes of a clinician, is something we must never disregard as a backstop within the NHS. And as we move forward, with some health authorities addressing this issue in a way which attracts a high public profile, I think that there is one thing that we should all remember as a simple principle when addressing the public. And it is this. This must be a service which never says never in respect of any particular treatment. Because what I have always discovered is that if we have protocols, the first thing that happens is you find some patient that breaches them. With the sort of population that we have, with the range of medical treatments that are available, it is I think impossible to set any absolutes in priority setting. This doesn't mean to say that you avoid the issue, but if one does it in an absolute way, then I think the public sees it as a threat and that is not a sensible way forward. Because the public has to be engaged in this debate and the public has to be taken along with it.

I was just looking through your Code of Principles before I started my speech and I was caught by Principle 2.12, saying that you have to be accountable for using and influencing the use of all resources as effectively, efficiently and economically as possible for the consistent delivery of service quality through the setting and obtainment of performance standards and targets. I wondered whether at the end of this weekend you wouldn't perhaps be amending that principle to widen it a little, to have a greater public view of priority setting, because imbedded in that is the implication that you do have a responsibility as an organisation for looking at broader issues of the public interest of this sort.

As you carry on your discussions I think perhaps you should have two sorts of priority setting in mind. First is a comprehensive understanding about what is most effective and therefore what is worthwhile and should be delivered more than something that is less effective. And let's get exactly to the core of that principle of your organisation that I spoke of. This is something that is supported by an increasing use of effectiveness criteria and data across the NHS. I give you one example for that, the Cochran Initiative collaboration, where now we are able to share across our system effectiveness data which inform us about whether or not a practice is worth continuing, whether or not a therapy is right for a set condition. And using that increasing body of data across the service involves very difficult choices, but direct choices. It involves you if you are exercising your role as purchasers, in discussions, often with clinicians who cherish a way of doing something in clinical practice which the evidence before your eyes shows you is not as effective as it was thought to be. And I think that if we dodge the challenges that brings, and we don't change our purchasing criteria and the way in which we buy and invest in service for our patients, in the light of best knowledge of effectiveness, then priority setting in a broader sense is not an issue that we can even begin to address. Because before we get into that second set of difficult priorities, which is using our judgement to decide often who should be treated first in our NHS, it is important that we have looked at that first criterion to drive as much value out of the service as possible and, in terms of addressing the issues, I think it is important that we address them in that way.

But we do have a limited budget within our National Health Service. It is a growing budget and there is a pledge on the table that it will continue to grow throughout the lifetime of the next parliament. But we all understand that even within that growth it is indeed a limited budget, and before we decide who perhaps will be excluded from treatment, it is vital that all of us have in place a process of deciding how effectively we are using that resource so that the maximum number of people may be treated. We also, I think, have to look more broadly perhaps than our practices to the population that is being served.

I was in Ealing last Monday, at the local hospital, where the cardiac services there, in conjunction with GPs in the area, had developed some rapid diagnosis techniques for cardiac problems. Instead of waiting for outpatient services, for there the waiting time was about seven or eight weeks, they were being seen within seven or ten days. The reason for that was that GPs, along with their colleagues in the acute sector, had identified the fact that there was a population they were serving where the risk to the cardiac problem was 30 per cent higher for a certain cohort than in many other areas. There is a practical example of how to use the second principle from the basis of primary care. Ensure that these issues that go beyond perhaps your own practice are being addressed.

I don't think anybody can fail to understand that decisions taken about priorities are always tough. You are often upsetting traditional ways of delivering treatment. You are often asking people to think in a different way. We also have to stop and think about what may well be the toughest message of all. Sometimes the toughest message of all is to point out to some cohorts of the population that perhaps they don't need treatment at all. It is not a message that many people like to hear and I think we have to be upfront in this, and understand that those who don't need to consume resource of service are told that at the earliest possible stage.

My reason for saying that stems from a recent visit which I made to Indonesia, leading a healthcare delegation. That was a country that faced priorities issues that make ours pale in comparison. After a function where I had been talking with the Indonesian Health Minister about what we were doing about tertiary care in this country, our specialist centres, our research, and our innovative practice, he rather subtly and lightly reminded me that he had a population of 190,000,000. He had just managed to carry out for the first time an immunisation campaign for polio with children where they had immunised, within the course of a three-day period 23,000,000 across a country that comprised of 13,000 separate populated islands, and I began to think, my goodness, there is the context for priority settings, isn't it?

Although we don't face those stark choices, I think we do have to understand that first business in the National Health Service must always come first, and we have to decide who is going to best benefit from treatment, sometimes in a very difficult way. So I am glad that you are leading the debate on this very important issue. It is one that absorbs us in government and I am delighted that you will be making your contribution. And I think what you have on the first page of your conference brochure says it all, 'Start preparing your team now to make better choices tomorrow'. You will be as involved in the fundamental choices of the way in which our health services look forward as you are in the practical detailed day-to-day way in which practice is improving in primary care. I am delighted you have chosen this challenging subject. It has been a pleasure to address you and to share my thoughts with you this afternoon. Thank you.

# The Oregon Experience

*Geoff Meads*
*Health Management Group*
*City University, London*

In the 1980s the State Department in Oregon, USA, involved many sections of the community in prioritising its healthcare. As rationing and prioritising of healthcare is now facing us in the UK, it was decided to involve the conference in this process. During the morning workshops there was the opportunity to gain skills in decision-making in a variety of scenarios: selecting staff, negotiating, forming high performance teams, becoming aware of one's own blocks, deciding if the organisation is 'fit', presentation skills, ensuring the legality of situations.

Geoff Meads made the following introduction to the afternoon workshop sessions.

## Introduction

Why am I here? Ostensibly as an NHS manager turned applied academic with strong interest in primary care and its performance – ex Cambridgeshire FHSA general manager; Wessex director of primary care; S&W performance management chief; NHSE policy architect, etc.

But more pertinently for today as:

- a very recent emergency hospital inpatient discharged, after tests, to wait for the appointment to go on an elective waiting list (gall bladder);
- a former social worker who never knew what it was like not to have local rationing formulae – and very different in Hampshire, Corby and Cambridgeshire. For example:

- in Hampshire, 1 in 100 referrals become 'Cases'/Men. Health equalled 'Sections';
- in Corby, 3 x level staffing, all referrals become 'Clients' and SI monies paid for lift insulation, +100 MI people per day attending SSD day centre.

NHS as it becomes community focused will increasingly have to do its priority setting at the frontline. Putting the two items together this week I am much more aware (as you will have to be in future practice) of the paradox of the contemporary NHS. We wait less than 48 hours for highly qualified contact on minor conditions requiring often no medical treatment, and more than 48 weeks for less qualified interventions requiring sometimes major surgery. This paradox becomes more and more visible and less defensible now that HAs are responsible for performance managing the combined HCHS/GMs resource.

## Purpose (this afternoon)

The aims are twofold:

- to provide an opportunity for you to rehearse the kinds of situation you are and will increasingly be facing in terms of controlling demand, both for secondary and, increasingly as well, for general practice/PC services (with others in the same boat);
- to help you ensure that the kinds of approaches and principles you use in this 'rationing task' are ones which you feel have integrity — in which you can feel secure and confident, as an individual and as a professional manager.

Our aim then is not for you to come away with a firm list of treatments and patients to include/exclude. That is the impossible task. What is feasible is to recognise that viable processes for priority setting can be developed and managed effectively so long as they are based on the ever-changing balance/tension between values/evidence/local circumstances/resources.

## Our context

- Decisions that used to be taken nationally are now taken at local levels — over how money is distributed, services planned, drugs approved, etc.
- Decisions that used to be taken locally by elected or professional representatives or by appointed board members on HAs, etc. are now being taken at practice level (DHAs reduced by 50 per cent, 104 FHSAs and RHAs abolished and old committees usurped by a 1,001 new associations and alliances).

This means new pressures of public accountability on practices with consumer/user a more important relationship than the patient or elector here. Practices must be able to demonstrate their popular support and credibility, e.g. via the 4 Ps:

- Practice accreditation;
- Patient enrolment;
- Probity (audit);
- PPG compliance.

There is a new primary care paradigm of public accountability in an NHS where decision-making for the use of public funds has been increasingly delegated to small independent sector organisations for whom good health must equal good business.

## Methods for this weekend

My approach is to bring together two sources of material from the UK and the USA (still a major source of the reforms) as a toolkit for your use.

On the one hand, from the UK, we are inviting you to use in groups tomorrow:

1. A checklist of 10 different possible methods of controlling public demand at practice level.
2. A definition of contemporary NHS values as a basis for you being able to put these into terms that fit your own local practice situations.
3. A briefing on the kinds of patients and their conditions for which practices may increasingly have to exercise choice.
4. And most important in this month of the Primary Care Bill and the ending of the general practice monopoly – five different types of new primary care organisations for you to work in – each designed for your local circumstances.

And on the other hand, from the USA, we have the lessons of the past six years in Oregon – the most publicised experiment anywhere in priority setting – where of 709 identified healthcare procedures, there is now no longer any public funding agreed for over 120.

Why select Oregon for us today? First, because many feel that we in 1996 are reaching the same position as Oregon in 1990, i.e. having a healthcare system that was becoming both unaffordable and directing its expenditure at the wrong things. At least, however, we never get things quite as wrong as our American friends. By 1990 Oregon (like the rest of the USA) was:

- spending 14 per cent of GDP on healthcare (against 7 per cent in the UK);

- had no fewer than 33 hospitals for 450,000 people;
- still had 100,000 people without health cover and a quarter of a million under-insured;
- like other states it was using its Medicaid budget to pay for only certain groups of disabled and disadvantaged, largely for hospital procedures. In Illinois, for example, 60 per cent of black pre-school children had no immunisation but $200,000 payments for organ transplants were guaranteed and expenditure was predicted to rise by 50 per cent in the 1990s alone as high-tech innovations advanced.

Secondly, because Oregon is working and it has a lot of lessons for us here:

- As we look to regain a consensus of support for the contemporary NHS, Oregon's reforms became law in 1993 with all-party backing. The Commission that drafted the priorities held 47 local meetings, 12 hearings to take evidence in public, and did a telephone survey of 1,001 people. The 11-person Commission consisted of a health visitor, a social worker, and four consumer representatives alongside five doctors – a real professional public alliance.
- We are seeking to achieve a better balance between primary and secondary care and reshape services away from hospitals. Oregon had 17 categories of healthcare split into 'Essential', 'Very Important', and 'Valuable to Certain Individuals' groupings. The first 'Essential' category is always guaranteed funding and in it went maternity care, universal vaccinations, and other health promotion packages.

  Into the bottom category went some major organ transplants, under-40 diabetes screening and aggressive end-stage AIDS and cancer treatments. These are no longer state funded in Oregon. And it reached these priorities using a combination of physicians' panels on clinical effectiveness, Coopers & Lybrands actuaries on cost effectiveness, alongside its public consultation (i.e. recreated what we used to call the NHS family of our society).

## Conclusion

So we have a lot to learn from Oregon – both in methodology, but more importantly, in local style and approach. Theirs is an experiment that goes on – today they still have a budget deficit (but less than most states), some new waiting lists and disputes over effectiveness in relation to some excluded procedures. The search for viable methods of priority setting in healthcare is never ending.

But Oregon has shifted the debate from who deserved treatment to what should be treated and why? In doing so there are real lessons for us and warnings. Some of the conditions no longer paid for in Oregon are those most common in UK general practice: from viral sore throats to nappy rash.

So we invite you tomorrow afternoon to join your Total Purchasing Pilot/Rural Practice/Seaside Community Care Centre/Suburban Surgery or City Multi-Fund; and go with us on the Oregon trail.

> The word (rationing) is invoked in order to make the flesh creep, not to prompt arguments about how best to deal with the inescapable.
>
> (Klein, 1992)

> This is an argument that will never be finally settled, but in which we can try at least to ensure that it is conducted with due concern about openness, the appropriate use of evidence, and attention to what counts as good currency in the debate.
>
> (Klein, 1993)

## Practice priorities - Oregon style

### Six steps

1. Select organisation.
2. Define national values and local standards.
3. Test methodology.
4. Build up a 'winning constituency'.
5. Apply and defend priorities.
6. Reduce and redeploy resources.

The delegates were allocated to take the role of specific practices (Table 8.2.1) and worked their way through the following three exercises as if they were representing that practice:

- selecting the four contemporary NHS principles that most suited the practice allocated to their group (Table 8.2.2);
- prioritising the list of practice techniques for priority setting, again relating to their particular practice (Table 8.2.3);
- selecting the three patients they would exclude from treatment if their budget was limited to only nine treatments, irrespective of cost of each of the treatments (Table 8.2.4).

**Table 8.2.1** *Oregon case example*

---

## A. THE SUBURBAN MANAGED PRACTICE

Practice A is located in a lower middle class Midlands suburb of 60,000 population. With only the parts and accessories element of a once major car manufacturer remaining, many local people now either commute to the city for work or run their own small businesses. Unemployment remains, however, 5 per cent above the national average and private healthcare is marginal. There are three large housing estates of which two are now predominantly managed by local housing associations. Police are increasingly concerned about drugs and alcohol abuse among teenagers both here and in the more leafy neighbour-hoods. The age profile of the community is family oriented and relatively young. There is a small general hospital of 350 beds, the future of which is subject to informal consultation given the proximity of two 600-bed trusts within 20 miles.

Practice A consists of six male principals and two part-time female assistants. It has a registered list of 14,000 patients. Led by the senior partner, who is also the fundholding lead, it wants to negotiate a more financially advantageous care contract with the health authority to provide as a 'block' traditional GMS with additional payments for out-of-hours, residential home services, health promotion clinics and some extended surgical procedures. Community health services are also located at the health centre occupied by the practice, with two other smaller practices. The local community trust owns the centre and manages its staff directly.

---

## B. THE SEASIDE COMMUNITY CARE CENTRE

Practice B is the larger of two in a small east coast town of 12,000 people. Fifty per cent of these are retired, many from out of the area and there are also significant numerical changes as a result of largely summer tourism. The town is a regular stopover for homeless and New Age travellers. The large number of residential and nursing homes is predominately private and most employment is in the service sector. The nearest general hospital is 17 miles away and, because of the local terrain, this is 30 minutes driving time. The district council has an Independent majority.

There are 3 partners in Practice B with one trainee and an even gender balance. The senior partner is a local councillor and all the partners are also on the board of a local charitable trust which is sited alongside the practice. This attracts widespread financial contributions locally, which helps pay for local respite care, occupational therapy AIDS volunteer, and there are night-sitting schemes. The junior partner has negotiated a number of practice-based contracts including hospital-at-home, community nursing, dermatology clinics, chiropody and physiotherapy services with the health authority. The Social Services Department has also located a care manager with a complement of part-time homecare assistants at the centre. The middle partner is co-proprietor of one of the homes, each of which has a designated GP.

## C. THE CITY MULTIFUND

The 12 C practices and 40 GPs in the multifund are the majority of those located within five miles of the centre of a major northern city on its east side where Jarman deprivation areas are liberally scattered. Together they cover 70,000 people, but with an annual registration turnover of 45 per cent. Tower blocks predominate although there are some 'yuppie' style conversions and EU funded development of new technology industries. The area is a traditional Labour stronghold and has been successively capped on its rate support grant. The large local authority welfare rights community centre was recently forced to close.

The largest practice in the fund consists of five partners and most are in relatively modest older premises, although the fund's new contracts manager has begun negotiations with the NHSE regional office for London-style special funding towards a local resource centre. Morbidity levels are high in national terms and traditionally people have travelled across the river, that divides the city, to the university teaching hospital. The withdrawal of outlying health authority contracts has left this in financial crisis and the multifund is also looking to move more services to its own locality. It has entered into a contract with Health Call for out-of-hours services and is campaigning for extra funding in its GPFH allocation on the basis of local need. The health authority is sympathetic but keen to see rationalisation of service outlets.

## D. THE RURAL PRACTICE

Practice D is situated in a rural river valley between a market town and a main city in Devon. The practice covers approximately 18 sq. miles. The practice area is oval in shape and runs on both sides of a large river – this river can only be crossed in two locations within the practice area – therefore leading to extra mileage during visiting and the problems of possible flooding during the winter months. When visiting within the practice area, steep hills and narrow lanes also make for interesting times during the winter months for the doctors, health visitor and district nurses. The practice population is 3,500.

There are three partners in the practice, one full-time senior partner, one female partner working three-quarters time and the third partner working a quarter time, with the rest of his work being based within the new health authority dealing with clinical effectiveness. There are eight members of the directly employed practice team, all working part-time:

- practice manager;
- practice nurses (2);
- dispensary manager;
- computer manager;
- senior receptionist;
- practice secretary;
- dispenser receptionist.

A university student helps during the holidays with general projects within the practice team. Attached staff include: three part-time district nurses/part-time health visitor/community psychiatric nurses for the elderly and podiatrist and physiotherapist.

The practice is 100 per cent dispensing to all its patients and there are special collection services for outlying villages for repeat drug medications. It is also a training practice. It is not fundholding but was a founder member of the local doctors commissioning group. One partner sits on the executive committee of this group.

The practice is fully computerised, all partners and staff using the computer. Medical records are not pulled for surgeries any longer. Almost a paperless practice. They are linked to the health authority, a drug wholesaler for daily ordering and are about to come on line with CompuServe.

## E.   THE TOTAL PURCHASING PILOT

The Total Purchasing Pilot E comprises three practices situated in and around a market town in the south of England. It covers an area of approximately 15 sq. miles and serves an urban and rural population. The total practices' list size is 36,000 with a large proportion of elderly. However, in the town itself there is a fair number of disenchanted youth and, with high unemployment, there is little for them to do. In the surrounding countryside there is a mixture of farming families, some having enormous problems as a result of BSE, with the young having moved away from home as soon as they could to seek work elsewhere, and newcomers who have bought up property for weekend accommodation or to renovate as their main dwellings.

The three practices have: 5 full-time partners; 3 full-time; 1 three-quarters time and 2 job-sharing partners; 4 full-time and two three-quarters time partners. All have practice managers, two having separate fund managers and one where the practice manager also absorbs the role of fund manager. They have full complement of ancillary staff, practice nurses and attached staff.

Total Purchasing has led the group to concentrate their energies on developing the local community hospital which is GP managed and staffed. They are working with the health authority and trusts towards earlier discharges from the acute units, bringing patients for recuperation and rehabilitation back into the community hospital or, where more appropriate, into their own homes. They are endeavouring to make the best use of the local resources. This includes operating an accident and emergency service staffed by the GPs and practice nurses. They are having problems with bringing maternity back into the community because not all of the GPs are agreeable to undertaking the full obstetrics cover.

**Table 8.2.2** *Contemporary NHS principles*

The following seek to move beyond conventional value statements about a comprehensive, free and universal NHS to a list of six principles that now provide a litmus test for the translation of contemporary policies into practice:

1. **Subsidiarity.** Decisions about healthcare increasingly taken by individuals and families (or their own representatives).

2. **Devolution.** Local control over the differential use of resources.

3. **Health gain.** Targeting investment, particularly at areas of high need to achieve set targets.

4. **Care in the Community.** Maximising informal/independent sector support, reduce public institutional usage.

5. **Efficiency.** Continuous improvement in activity levels allied to more effective clinical impacts.

6. **Choice.** Right of those 'purchasing' care to make informed selection between alternative (competing) providers.

**Table 8.2.3** *Practice techniques for priority setting*

### HOW DO WE CONTROL DEMAND ON OUR PRACTICE?

Within the context of contemporary NHS policy and values the following is suggested as a range of methods local practices might apply to cope with increasing workload pressures, either by containing and redirecting demand or increasing the supply of services. The basic assumption, of course, is finite resources which are perceived as insufficient.

Using a 1 to 10 scale with 10 signifying the most preferred option, please score the following 10 techniques in terms of their potential use in legitimising the 'rationing process'.

1. **Patients can enrol** (e.g. via annual subscriptions, personal registration fee, etc.)
2. **Patients can learn** (e.g. respond to self-help information, alternative services, etc.)
3. **Patients can be diverted** (e.g. fewer surgeries, rationalised number of service outlets, etc.)
4. **Patients can see somebody else** (e.g. a counsellor, nurse practitioner, physio, etc.)
5. **Patients can be triaged** (i.e. via frontline nurses, telephone helplines, etc.)
6. **Practice can set priorities** (e.g. with patient or local counsellor representatives)
7. **Practice can expand** (e.g. with private funds, joint ventures, assuming charitable trust or limited company status; combining with retail pharmacies or insurance companies, etc. to extend income and capital base for more services)
8. **Practice can charge** (e.g. more fees for non-essential services, self-inflicted conditions, etc.)
9. **Practice can go (part) private** (e.g. become a preferred provider for an insurance company)
10. **Practice can go fully private** (and contract back on local basis with health authority)

**Table 8.2.4** Spreadsheet on patient treatments

LIST

| No.Treatment | Sex | Age | Condition | Social | Likely outcome | Other considerations |
|---|---|---|---|---|---|---|
| 1 Grommets | F | 4 yrs | 75% deaf;V. poor speech just started school | 2nd child, behaviour problems due to deafness – not hearing teacher in class. Her friends don't understand her. | Hearing, speech and behaviour likely to improve | Self limiting condition – likely to clear in a year or two |
| 2 Vasectomy | M | 33 yrs | Healthy | Wife had postnatal depression following previous births & attempted suicide. Other birth control not suitable | Birth control and, therefore, no more post-natal depression for his wife | |
| 3 Hip replacement | F | 50 yrs | Pain ++; unable to walk unaided | Employed as secretary; Single parent of two teenagers; not coping | Full mobility; able to cope | |
| 4 Knee replacement | M | 32 yrs | Pain, restricted movement | Self-employed plumber; 2 children; unable to work; on benefits | Full mobility; ability to resume work and come off benefits | |
| 5 Coronary Artery By-pass | M | 45 yrs | Had procedure done 3 years previously; poor condition | Still smoking; Housefather caring for 2 children; Wife mentally ill | If he continues to smoke there will be limited success and only a moderate improvement in quality of life | |
| 6 Hip replacement | M | 70 | Both hips v. bad. Cannot walk at all. Has heart disease | Lives alone. Will have to go into sheltered accommodation if not treated. Wife just died | Should get reasonable mobility but HD may limit his quality of life | Hips will have to be done separately so two operations necessary |

**Table 8.2.4** Spreadsheet on patient treatments contd

LIST

| No. Treatment | Sex | Age | Condition | Social | Likely outcome | Other considerations |
|---|---|---|---|---|---|---|
| 7 Arthroscopy | F | 20 | Fit and healthy apart from this problem with knee | On trial for Olympic diving team as Britain's main hope. Will be too old by next Olympics | After period of recuperation will be ready for diving trials | Continuation of diving career could damage knees further |
| 8 Angioplasty | M | 65 | Pain, limited mobility | Just retired and looking forward to gardening | Complete recovery | |
| 9 Angioplasty | M | 77 | V. ill, pain and weakness | Wife diabetic and difficulty in caring for him; married 53 yrs | Improvement in quality of life | Danger in the procedure itself |
| 10 Dermabraision | F | 24 | Severe acne scarring. V. depressed as result | Becoming a recluse – no confidence, no social life, job is at risk because she takes so much time off because of depression. Under the psychiatrist. | Improvement in appearance, self-confidence, lifting of depression. | |
| 11 Haemorrhoid-ectomy | F | 50 | Bleeding, very painful, not sleeping | Is a practice nurse and has had to take time off work from busy surgery. Otherwise fit, healthy and happy | Satisfactory | |
| 12 Reconstruction of hand | F | 4 yrs | Congenital abnormality to hand. Unable to hold anything in that hand | Starts school in a year. Wants to be like her friends | Give increased ability to handle objects and enable more normal development of hand | |

## The results of the Oregon experience

### Contemporary NHS principles

In our circumstances contemporary NHS principles mean locally we should ensure that:

*Suburban practice 1*
1. Patient involvement should develop and maintain local services utilising existing resources.
2. Appropriate family-centred health and social education is provided.
3. There is improved access to female GPs.
4. Drug and alcohol services are targeted to areas of need.

*Suburban practice 2*
1. No contracts for any services will be negotiated until full consultation with local interest groups, i.e.:
   - patients;
   - social services;
   - education;
   - police;
   - mental health, etc.
2. Any decisions made following the consultation process must be based on health needs analysis.

*Seaside community care centre - 1*
1. By forming purchasing partnerships with neighbouring practice we maximise use of resources for our patients.
2. Resources are targeted to care in the community, including independent nursing home and local charitable trust.
3. Maximise social support to travellers and prioritise the health of the homeless.
4. The practice offers comprehensive medical care to tourists.

*Seaside community care centre - 2*
1. Patients have access to transport to ensure getting to hospital.
2. Basic level of medical and screening programmes should be available to the homeless.
3. Services to the under 60s are in place, with a strategic shift to primary care, incorporating drop-in services for temporary residents.

*City multifund - 1*
1. We ensure that health and social needs are targeted.
2. Primary care developed through resources released through rationalisation.
3. Community/emergency hospital is established.
4. Local resource centres combining health visiting, social services, counselling out of hours.

*City multifund - 2*
1. Rights to equality of resources based on clinical need.
2. Interventions based on evidence of efficiency.
3. Targeting vulnerable people.
4. Establishing a community identity and meeting the needs by community provision.

*Rural practice - 1*
1. There is an efficient patient transport service.
2. We will provide peripatetic services to the practice area.
3. There is efficient use and development of community expertise.
4. We enhance the delivery of patient care through IT development.

*Rural practice - 2*
1. Branch surgery facility on the other side of the river.
2 Expansion of ancillary services (part-time) e.g. community psychiatric nurses.
3. Training and education – staff and patients.

*Market town Total Purchasing Pilot - 1*
1. We focus resource initiatives to develop care in the community.
2. That healthcare is focused on preventative case/patient education and awareness.
3. Overall development of community hospital, i.e. day cases, outpatients, X-ray and early discharge.
4. Adequate access is provided for general medical services.

*Market town Total Purchasing Pilot - 2*
1. Full provision of mental health services including counselling services.
2. We work towards early discharge from acute to community hospital.
3. Work with public transport to provide adequate services in the area.
4. Full provision of healthcare for the elderly is established and regularly reviewed.

## Practice techniques for priority setting

The delegates ranked the techniques in the following order:

**Ranked**
1 Patients can be triaged.
2 Patients can see somebody else.
3 Practice can set priorities.
4 Patients can learn.
5 Practice can expand.
6 Patients can be diverted.
7 Practice can charge.
8 Practice can go (part) private.
9 Patients can enrol.
10 Practice can go fully private.

Only the two inner city groups had over a 50 per cent similarity in ranking in the techniques and those joint rankings were as follows:

**Ranking**
1 Practice can set priorities.
2 Patients can be triaged.
7 Practice can charge.
8 Practice can go (part) private.
9 Practice can go fully private.
10 Patients can enrol.

## Prioritising patient treatments

The following cases were ranked at the bottom of the list for priority for treatment:

| | |
|---|---|
| Patient 7 Arthroscopy | Potential Olympic diver. |
| Patient 2 Vasectomy | Patient with suicidal wife. |
| Patient 9 Angioplasty | Patient 77 years old. |
| Patient 5 Coronary artery bypass | Same operation done three years previously. Patient continued to smoke. |

The two conditions that came top of the list were:

| | |
|---|---|
| Patient 3 Hip replacement | 50-year-old single parent. |
| Patient 14 Knee replacement | Self-employed plumber unable to work because of condition. |

## Main conclusions

The exercise raises important concerns about what happens to priorities for secondary care once responsibility for this is devolved to individual practices and more people from a range of professional backgrounds are involved. The overall impact was captured in the slogan 'The More you Localise the More you Personalise', with social/ personal conditions, access to alternative funding and degree of self-inflicted harm, all counting as more influential criteria in the group exercise than clinical efficiency.

The exercise, however, was highly encouraging in terms of the impact of devolution and wider participation in priority setting for primary care itself. There was a general consensus that wider direct access to a limited number of professionals would constrain demand so long as this was in the context of an individual practice-based workload policy and agreement with its patients. As primary care remains the gateway to most secondary and continuing care, this confidence in being able to make better use of resources at the front-line access point has significant positive implications for the viability of the future NHS.

For practice managers specifically there were a number of sharp lessons. The territory of clinical decision-making needs to be avoided, and financial and clinical decision-making need to retain their separate integrity. But, on the other hand, the exercises clearly demonstrated the capacity of practice managers to design and implement the working processes and procedures whereby these decisions can be made, and priorities for patient care set. In particular, all the groups were able effectively to convert contemporary NHS policy objectives into specific frameworks of local values for application at their own practice levels. From this it was clear that the practice manager has moved effectively into the local general management role in primary care today.

# Challenges into the Next Millennium
# The 1996 Sally Irvine Lecture

*Colin M Hunter*
*Scottish Council of the Royal*
*College of General Practitioners*

I am deeply honoured to be asked to deliver the third Sally Irvine Lecture and would wish to record my gratitude to the Association of Managers in General Practice and Sally Irvine for giving me the opportunity of delivering this prestigious lecture. In my capacity as Chairman of Scottish Council of the Royal College of General Practitioners it gives me great pleasure to welcome members and guests of the Association to Scotland for the AMGP Annual Course.

## Lecture structure

I plan to spend the principal part of the lecture gazing into my crystal ball and developing some of the issues I think we might face over the next ten years — as managers, as general practitioners, and as individuals, in the contexts of general practice, the expanding world of primary care and the NHS as a whole. In particular, I will consider a few of the challenges which the Association itself might face. I do not claim that the list is exhaustive or indeed promise that any of what I say will come to fruition. Who could have predicted in 1986 that primary care would have a leading role to play in the design and delivery of the Health Service into the next millennium?

I draw my experience from Scotland and the Scottish Health Service. I believe from discussions with colleagues south of the border that the issues are largely the same and that although the pace of development in particular areas is different, the general thrust of change is in the same direction. During the lecture I will refer to the practice manager as female, although I acknowledge that an increasing proportion of managers within the profession are male.

Before I move to consider the future, I would briefly like to visit the past and in particular to consider the enormous change in practice management which, to a degree, reflects the enormous change in general practice itself. To do this I will visit my practice at three stages in time – 25 years ago, 11 years ago when I joined the practice, and now.

### Practice management pre-1970

Twenty-five years ago the practice was single handed. The entire staff consisted of one person. Chrissie had been with the practice since 1949 and had acted simultaneously as practice manager, receptionist, nurse, counsellor, dispenser and housekeeper for the doctor. She was the records system and in many ways was ahead of current developments as she often acted as nurse practitioner – dealing with complaints which she felt were too trivial to bother the doctor with. She deliberately limited access and today recounts how, when patients arrived outwith normal consulting times, she turned them away, telling them that the doctor worked very hard and was entitled to his mid-afternoon nap. Records were minimal – she kept a book noting who had attended, their diagnosis and a note of any medicine she had dispensed. No other notes were needed because Chrissie knew everything about everybody, and indeed her knowledge of family history would put even the best of modern record keeping to shame. She works with us still on a Thursday afternoon and Saturday morning and believes with conviction that 'all these staff and all these doctors offer no better a service than in "the doctor's day"!'

### Practice management in 1986

When I joined the practice in 1986, I replaced the retiring senior partner. Colin Harris had, at the ripe old age of 36, taken on the mantle of senior partner and all that this entailed in these times. The practice was progressive and, as with many forward thinking practices, had appointed a practice manager, Maureen Campbell, promoting her from the role of receptionist. Her main duties were to arrange rotas for the staff and ensure that claims were expeditiously processed and sent to the health board. She was, by today's definition, an administrator.

### Sally Irvine

Nineteen eighty six was a momentous year for me as not only did I become a principal in general practice, but I also had my first indirect contact with Sally Irvine. Daunted by the prospect of 'this senior partner mantle', Colin Harris had seen advertised the first management appreciation course to be held at the Royal College of General Practitioners in London. Course tutors were Sally Irvine and June Huntington. The day I started in the practice, he and Maureen Campbell set off to attend that very course. Colin still describes the course as 'totally inspirational'. Within a week of his return to the practice, and with Maureen's support, he completely changed the way the practice was organised and managed. For a short period my partners and I could have seen this Sally Irvine individual far enough away, as Colin produced paper after paper and sometimes arrived on a partner's doorstep after midnight to discuss the next stage. Within a very short period, we were all able to see the light and many of the changes which were instituted at that time still stand us in good stead today. For example, partner meetings were held at fortnightly intervals, were during the working day and had a timed agenda and minutes. Most importantly, the practice manager attended and was able to participate in the meetings. This was a far cry from meetings held infrequently, in times of crisis, often spilling into the 'sma' hours', with few decisions made and only on occasion the manager hearing of the outcomes.

We have therefore, as a practice, a great deal for which to thank Sally and June. I have had many contacts with Sally over the past ten years, two of which are worthy of mention. The first was when I invited her and June Huntington to run a management appreciation course in Stirling immediately before the first Scottish practice managers' conference. Funds being limited, they found themselves undertaking a session on motivation on the last day of the conference itself. This was quite a tall order as we had over 200 delegates and ran 20 groups. The second main contact was during her last year as Administrator of the College when she chaired a small think tank group taking stock of the College internal management practice. I was able to appreciate her skills of chairmanship, analysis, and people management at close quarters and to learn the importance of facing difficult situations in an open and positive manner. I gained a great deal from watching her, as I am sure we have all gained, either from personal contacts with her or through her writing in relation to practice management.

## Practice management 1996

The continuing changes in the job description of the practice manager over the last ten years have, in line with other innovative practices in the country, reflected some of the most significant changes in general practice during that time. The manager actively manages and carries a huge burden of responsibility. She not only attends partners' meetings, but chairs them. She is responsible together with the partners for developing strategy within the practice and supervises the implementation of that strategy. She supervises the management of our multi-million pound fund, the management of the total fundholding project, and provides support to the assistant practice manager who deals with the day-to-day running of the practice and supervision of the clerical staff. She is becoming more involved with the non-clinical management of the medical and nursing staff. She is continually involved in educating us and participating in her own professional learning and both undertakes and encourages audit.

I have used the experience of Skene Medical Group to demonstrate the enormous changes which we have seen in the development of the role of the practice manager. Perhaps an even more striking example lies in the textbook edited by R.V. Jones and published in 1985 entitled *Running a Practice* in which the four GP authors make no mention of the role of the practice manager at all.

## The future

I would now like to move on to look to the future. I confess to having had some help with my crystal ball exercise, having spent six days last year in the company of some like-minded colleagues and some outstanding speakers when we attended an RCGP course led by Marshall Marinker, surprisingly entitled 'The End of General Practice'. None of the challenges addressed will be met without professional management, both clinical and non-clinical. In my view the practice manager will be pivotal to our success in the future and during the lecture I hope managers in the audience will consider the changes in their roles which may be necessitated by the challenges I highlight. So what challenges will we face into the next millennium?

### Challenge 1 – to manage a primary care led NHS within the context of no clear government policy

I have been aware from my earliest years in general practice of the difficulties of working within an organisation which sits prominently within the political stratosphere. I believed, however, that government and those aspiring to government must have a clear 'game plan for the NHS' until I actually heard a senior civil servant from within the Department of Health state that the current government and the Labour Party had no medium or long-term policy regarding the direction and development of the NHS.

Many may see this as a threat. However, in my view it offers the professionals within the Health Service an enormous opportunity to influence change. This is particularly true of those working within primary care, where we have a significant opportunity to capitalise on the current dogma of the primary care led NHS. This opportunity may not arise again within our lifetimes, and we should pursue our beliefs and work hard to redress the imbalances which have existed between secondary and primary care since the inception of the Health Service.

### Challenge 2 – to ensure an appropriate shift of resource with the shift of activity from secondary to primary care

Inevitably, the movement of activity from secondary to primary care requires a matching movement of resource. This has been assumed to be part of the rhetoric of the primary care led NHS, but so far we have seen little or no evidence of this shift. Table 8.3.1 summarises the shift of resource within the Scottish Health Service, and clearly demonstrates that savings made as a result of the closure of long stays units have moved not to the Community but to the Acute sector. In Birmingham, £500m has been allocated for hospital development compared to £5m distributed to FHSAs for Primary Care Development.

**Table 8.3.1**  *Trends in HCHS expenditure by care programmes 1991/2–1994/5*

| | |
|---|---|
| Acute care and geriatric assessment | + £206m |
| Long stay hospitals | – £82m |
| Community | + £11m |
| New spend | + £135m |

Secondary care undoubtedly has its own problems. Several factors have been cited to explain the increasing costs within this sector, including increased demand, increased emergency admissions, increased workload in non-clinical activity, including audit and management, changes in postgraduate training leading to less 'service' time available, reduced junior doctor hours and new costly clinical procedures. I am not convinced that the majority of these arguments do not pertain equally to the primary care sector.

### Challenge 3 – to manage resources within the Health Service more effectively

One thing is clear: resources are finite and all of us working within the Health Service must look more critically at the way money is used to ensure that it is used most effectively. In this respect we are fortunate in the political profile of both health and the Health Service. The purely

237

academic view relating to improvement in the health of the nation would not support additional money being directed to the Health Service at all but rather to improving housing, providing greater employment, establishing a safer environment, and promotion of life style change, including diet.

The enormity of this challenge is crystallised by Seedhouse who states that 'a policy of purchasing services from a limited budget is simply not compatible with a policy of meeting needs regardless of ability to pay'.

### Challenge 4 – to be more open about rationing of services and setting priorities within the NHS

The current trend of empowering the general practitioner to purchase the services he/she feels appropriate to meet patients needs' is set to continue irrespective of the colour of the next government. I do not intend to explore the nuances of purchasing and commissioning within this lecture, but I have no doubt that the introduction of fundholding has brought us the ability to effect change, which in my opinion, would not have come about if the internal market had not been introduced. We should be under no illusion of the enormity of this role. It includes taking responsibility for rationing and priority setting for our patients. Rationing in many respects already happens. It is inevitable in the future, as medical advances produce an increasing capacity to provide while the capacity to pay becomes increasingly limited. I feel the time is right for the public and the professions to discuss this issue openly and to accept that the National Health Service has limitations, just as any other insurance scheme has limitations. Interestingly, open debate on this issue may be more easily held under a Labour government, who are in general more trusted with the NHS by the populace.

### Challenge 5 – to develop effective needs assessment with due attention paid to the personal and public health perspectives

Some decisions have to be taken on a wider population level, but many decisions on service development cannot be taken at a macro level and are therefore most appropriately taken at a practice or locality level, close to the patient. The argument for this can be most strikingly demonstrated by the demographic differences in SE London practices where the elderly patient population varies between 1 and 33 per cent. To be effective in needs assessment, primary care requires to develop a new set of tools, skills and knowledge and must by necessity acquire a more public health perspective of its population. Needs assessment is currently reactive by nature and little attention is paid to the non-consulting population. Andrew Harris cites the example, 'Is it ethical that mothers with no risk factors receive frequent antenatal checks (of doubtful effectiveness) whilst the majority of the elderly population suffer disability from hearing loss without adequate hearing assessment or provision of aids or education?'

### Challenge 6 – to develop cost-effective primary care services to meet the needs of the population

Within primary care itself, the nationally negotiated GP contract has, in my view, been a barrier to development within the primary care sector. It has stifled innovation and restricted a practice's ability to develop services tailored and delivered specifically for the local population. However, legislation north and south of the border will become locally based, making contracting for general practice a reality in the very near future. This will further promote the development of practice-based primary care, with more flexible and effective working between members of an expanding primary healthcare team. It will bring more freedom to shape our own services sensitive to local demand and need. Practices, regardless of size, will contract with a health board or authority to provide a specified range of services for a defined population, at an agreed cost. There will be increased specialisation by GPs within practices and procedures previously only undertaken in secondary care will be delivered closer to the patient in primary care. There is still a large number of practices who have not yet woken up to the revolution, who are still providing care in a 1970, 1960 or even 1950 setting, and it is they who may be the casualties of increased competition.

### Challenge 7 – to maintain independent contractor status and patient lists

Within this developing service I would fight strongly to retain two key elements of our current system, namely the list of patients registered with a general practitioner and independent contractor status. The GP list is the cornerstone of British general practice and distinguishes it from other primary care health systems. It focuses the responsibility of the GP, the primary healthcare team and the patient and without it I believe the ethos of current general practice would largely disappear.

Partnership is currently the organisational bedrock of general practice. Shared responsibility, effective decision-making, reduced bureaucracy, autonomy and heightened motivation are important advantages of independent contractor status. This was recently reinforced by an exercise undertaken in Aberdeen where chief executives from NHS trusts job shadowed GPs for a day. Many enlightening observations were made by these senior managers, including 'I found the level of trust shown by the patients in their GP quite staggering', and 'I attended a partnership meeting where two major decisions were made and implemented. It would have taken over a year in my trust to gain any consensus'.

Following her years at the College, Sally Irvine has together with Hilary Haman undertaken management consultancies for over 50 practices. This has built on some innovative work Sally undertook with the College. Many of the practices visited are characterised by partnership problems. The issue is not usually one of clinical diversity but where doctors operate as individuals within the organisation and where their behaviour has an immeasurably negative effect on the functioning of the partnership and indeed the whole team. With the growth of practices in both size and complexity, the whole nature of partnership will be vulnerable to external scrutiny. There needs to be a greater commitment to defining partnership and to addressing the issues of accountability as individuals within the partnership.

Peer appraisal is one tool which may be used. I am able here to speak from a personal and positive experience as I have been appraised on my management performance in the practice and my performance as an individual within the partnership. I was appraised by the practice manager who had invited, on my behalf, comments from my partners and the senior staff within the practice. It was one of the most rewarding and worthwhile two hours I have spent since becoming a principal in general practice.

### Challenge 8 – to actively promote quality in primary care and influence the setting of quality measures and standards

Local contracting of primary care services will undoubtedly bring increased accountability led by consumerism and cost containment. Accountability will be part of the contracting process where the commissioners of care, in this case the health boards or health authorities, set out their requirements which will include indicators of quality and quality standards.

Sally and Donald Irvine in their book *The Practice of Quality* highlight the differing views of patients, professionals and purchasers on what they consider as important in quality of care. They quote the evidence summarised by the US Joint Commission on the Accreditation of Healthcare Organisations which concluded that in general terms:

- quality for patients means predominantly responsiveness, politeness and relief from symptoms or improvement in function;

- quality for practitioners means primarily technical skill, freedom in care provision and desired outcome;
- quality for purchasers of care means first and foremost efficiency and savings.

We have already witnessed increasing demand made on secondary care by government and health commissioners with emphasis on targets. How long will it be until we see league tables for general practice?

There is currently considerable debate regarding the measurement of quality within healthcare. There is a trend to focus on outcome measures and indicators as the single most important method of measuring quality. Considerable research time is being devoted to the development of outcome indicators for general practice, and while agreeing that this is important, we must also recognise the quality issues which are important to the consumer and include them within our quality standards. Quality, the setting of standards and measurement, is a day's lecture in itself but I wish to emphasise its importance here, as I am sure this will be one of the major challenges for the next ten years, and one in which the manager will play a key role.

## Challenge 9 – to reduce unacceptable variations in clinical practice

I cannot leave accountability and quality without highlighting the unacceptable variations in clinical care which currently exist between practices and between individual practitioners. These variations can be demonstrated in many areas, for example, clinical management, referral, prescribing, use of laboratory services, etc. For many years the medical profession has defended the right to clinical freedom, but this position is less tenable with the increased availability of evidence-based medicine. Guidelines, audit and recertification are all relevant in this context and are being pursued actively by the Royal College. I believe that the manager has a legitimate right, as has the public, to question significant variations within clinical practice.

June Huntington summarises the issue concisely: 'Demographics and economics of healthcare make it inevitable that clinical freedom with publicly funded healthcare systems will be constrained, and re-granted only in return for greater and more specific accountability.'

## Challenge 10 – to mature into learning and caring organisations

One important vehicle to improving quality must be in education. Many practices are already involved in undergraduate and post-graduate education of doctors and nurses. With the drive to increased care in the community, more teaching of health professionals will inevitably be undertaken in the primary care setting. My crystal ball does not yet see the majority of teaching being based in the community, but certainly a much more significant proportion will be.

Those of you who have read June Huntington's book will have read her views on learning and caring organisations. Our role as educators of and within the primary healthcare team must increase over the next few years as we develop into true learning organisations.

June also highlights the differences between the human service organisation and a business in the public sector and defines the importance of developing caring organisations, not simply the caring doctor:

> While many organisations now realise that in the competitive world out there keeping customers is as important as getting them in the first place, they do not always go on to recognise the increasing complexity of the front line relationship, in which staff will not make customers feel cared for if they themselves do not feel cared for.

### Challenge 11 – research activity must increase in primary care and be linked closely to the development of primary care services

In addition to the continuing need for good education within primary care it is imperative that we continue to develop a sound research base. In comparison to secondary care the level of research activity in primary care has been pitifully low. The emergence of the primary care led NHS provides us with a catalyst to encourage research in practice. There is, I believe, a commitment by funding bodies, including government, to make more resources available to primary care, but it will take some time to develop an infrastructure and increase the critical mass of professionals with appropriate skills to attract and make good use of these resources.

Research activity must be closely linked to the development and delivery of primary care health services. Here there can be a new role for the practice manager who, while helping to promote and shape innovative development, can help ensure a rigorous evaluation of its impact and effectiveness. The current artificial divide between development and research must be closed, including in Scotland the amalgamation of the two major funding sources.

### Challenge 12 – to disseminate research evidence and worthwhile innovation more effectively

Dissemination of research evidence and innovation is currently extremely poor and we must find more effective methods of distributing the information widely and effectively to whom it is most relevant.

## Challenge 13 – to harness the advantages of IT without loss of human contact

One of the most significant changes in the last ten years, and one which is likely to be equally significant in the next ten years, has been the IT revolution. Some of us gaze in amazement at the museum piece hardware now eight years old and redundant in the store cupboard. IT has undoubtedly made an enormous impact on primary care and will further change significantly how we work and interact with our patients. Paper may become a thing of the past (this would certainly have one major plus for my staff who spend countless hours in search of patient records only to find them in some GP's car or even more surprisingly just turning up).

All records will be held on computer, links with all providers and others within the service being electronic. Patients may carry their own records on a credit card. Current best practice and management protocols will be available at the press of a button and patients will have access to more medical information through the Internet. In fact, it is not inconceivable that a patient could make it all the way to their doctor without an ounce of human contact – by dialling into the practice and making an appointment by e-mail and logging in as they arrive by swiping their card. Do they need to see the doctor at all or should they simply consult with the healthcare computer – even from their home? This is not as far-fetched as it may seem. Consider how often you require face-to-face contact with staff within your bank today compared to five years ago.

This is the point at which I begin to find the future and IT a little frightening. I believe the challenge for us, and really for the whole of society, is to use IT to facilitate what we do and to allow us to do it better, without dehumanising the system.

I don't expect any of you to know this attractive girl. This photograph was taken in 1987 shortly before Susan joined my list as a patient. She was, as you can see, just back from holiday in Cyprus, aware that something wasn't quite right but unaware that she was shortly to be diagnosed as having a rare inoperable cancer in her pelvis. For a girl who was only days older than myself this diagnosis was naturally devastating. Over the ensuing months she and I developed a close relationship, a relationship of trust and mutual understanding. She had similarly strong bonds with the district nursing staff. All the staff who worked in the practice were acutely aware of Susan's situation. This allowed, for example, the reception staff to respond in a supportive way when Susan's Dad would telephone in search of me. Towards the end of her illness I particularly remember requiring a particular drug and one of the receptionists at the end of her shift making a trip to the local hospice to fetch it for me. We were all involved in her care and in caring.

Susan was understandably frightened, but due to her trust in all round about her, I believe we were able to support her through her final days.

I am not convinced that this level of human caring and compassion is enhanced by IT. Society as we know it will fold when we spend the majority of our time gazing into the electronic screen, tapping on the keyboard or, as will be the case with the introduction of voice activation, speaking to our computer rather than interacting as fellow human beings.

## Challenge 14 – to retain current values of general practice

Information technology is not the only threat to society and to general practice as we know it. The advancement in medical technology in recent years has been almost exponential. It is predicted that by the year 2000 the human genome will have been completely exposed. We will be able to have a predictory test by donating a salivary sample or a scraping from the inside of our mouth which will document our genetic prediction for all known disease. The tools of the trade might look considerably different. A GP may use a hand-held scanner which interprets the results and which in some cases can rectify the problem, for example, unblocking an artery. There is a danger here of losing the facets of general practice which differentiate it from the other branches of medicine, namely our ability to look at the patient as a whole, as a complex human being, and to build on our previous interactions to encourage a deepening and more satisfactory relationship.

## Challenge 15 – to retain the current values of practice management

What is the future of the practice manager in this changing world? Currently the practice manager in most instances occupies a boundary role between the partners and staff. She is general manager to a board of directors formed by the partnership. She allows GPs to relinquish routine management without relinquishing their roles as directors to make strategic decisions.

At the end of the general practice course, Hamish Wilson, Director of Contracts at Grampian Health Board, attempted to define the difference between the values of general practitioners and health service managers. This is summarised in Box 1.

---

**BOX 1    DIFFERENCES BETWEEN VALUES OF HEALTH SERVICE MANAGERS AND GPs**

| **Managers** | **General practitioners** |
|---|---|
| Non-/Anti-professional | Highly professional |
| Non-/Anti-ethical | Ethical code |
| Untouched by patients | Near patients |
| Protective jargon | Language biological medicine |

---

I believe that practice managers currently occupy the middle ground between these two extremes. This is one of the major strengths of current practice management and must be maintained for the future. It facilitates the manager's ability to work with the partners while being more objective and less touched by sentiment, yet still remaining close to the patients and to the staff within the practice. She has not only a knowledge of but a 'feel' for the system and those who work within it and are served by it. Would the manager being a partner change this – I don't know.

One of the advantages of giving a lecture such as this is that it allows one to climb onto one or several of one's soap boxes. This evening is no exception and I have three soap boxes on which I will stand.

## Challenge 16 – to look more critically at our own personal development and educational needs

First, the need for us as individuals to look more critically at ourselves, our potential, and our educational and developmental needs. A great deal of literature is currently available relating to education needs assessment for general practitioners, but the need for this must equally apply to other professionals working within the Health Service including practice managers. Our education is often led by wants or availability rather than needs. How often have we looked at an advertisement for a course and thought that looks interesting and how often have we looked at our own development needs and the needs of the practice and actively sought an educational medium to meet these needs? As managers gain experience in general practice it seems increasingly difficult for them to identify both needs and appropriate stimulating education.

One possible solution may lie in peer mentoring where managers take time with a colleague at regular intervals to consider their personal development. Another solution may already lie within practice plans where practice learning plans can be identified in parallel with business plans and give a lead to managers and other staff.

### Challenge 17 – to make membership organisations relevant to the ordinary member

The second soap box relates to the difficulty professional membership organisations have in marrying the needs of the individual at the grassroots level with the national responsibilities. The RCGP developed a faculty structure soon after its inception in 1953. There is still an unacceptably low level of service to members at local level in most areas of the country and our individual members frequently complain that they do not get value for money from their subscription. The College itself has not really addressed the balance between the national and local function which is still, in the view of most ordinary Scottish members, too heavily weighted towards national. Sally Irvine in her latter years as Administrator began to improve the infrastructure to allow development of the faculties – but we are still a long way from getting it right. It is a crucial issue relating to the attraction and retention of members and requires, in my view, to be frequently reassessed. One of the major challenges within this is the geographical and intellectual disparity of the membership.

### Challenge 18 – to improve representation of primary care and the influence of AMGP

Finally, I turn to influence and representation. Box 2 summarises the constitution of the new NHS Policy Board in Scotland. Note that there is only one representative from primary care and management representation is from an NHS trust. Box 3 summarises the membership of the Joint Working Group in primary care in Scotland. This group is the prime working group at the Scottish Office concerned with the development of primary care. There is no practice manager representation.

Inequality between primary care and secondary care has existed since 1948 and continues to exist. Merit awards for hospital consultants are awarded on the 'old boys' network and can double a consultant's salary. No such system exists in primary care – nor would I want it to in such a corrupt format, but additional awards for outstanding achievement may well prove a good motivator in the future. Manager salaries in primary care compared with hospital, and the exclusion of practice staff from the NHS superannuation scheme, are examples closer to your hearts.

---

**BOX 2    MEMBERSHIP NHS POLICY BOARD IN SCOTLAND**

Secretary and Minister of State
4 Civil Servant Managers
Chief Medical Officer
Chief Nursing Officer
1 General practitioner
1 Hospital consultant
1 Hospital nurse
1 Trust chief executive
1 Patient representative
1 Scientist

---

**BOX 3    MEMBERSHIP JOINT WORKING GROUP IN PRIMARY CARE**

1 Director primary care
2 General practitioners
4 Health board managers
1 Trust chief executive
1 Dentist
3 Nurses
1 Pharmacist

---

Committee structure within the NHS has always been dominated by secondary care. The situation cannot be allowed to continue in the environment of a primary care led Health Service and both your organisation and mine require to lobby to increase the influence of those working in primary care on the development of the NHS over the next ten years.

Chairman, the years ahead will undoubtedly offer challenge – change is an integral part of the society in which we live and the environment and sector in which we work. I hope that general practitioners and practice managers continue to see the prospect of change as both challenging and exciting and that they continue to work closely together to the advantage of our healthcare system. Knowing both groups of professionals fairly well, I have little doubt that our primary health care led NHS will continue to flourish and most importantly continue to provide a caring and compassionate service for our patients.

# 8.4

# The Debate

---

**The Motion before the house:**

'People with self-inflicted illness should receive different priority for treatment'

## INTRODUCTION TO DEBATE: Dr Colin Hunter

In a cash-limited National Health Service can we afford to treat all patients – or should there be some rationalisation of who and what we treat and how we prioritise cases?

Perhaps one of the most difficult issues within the motion is to define self-infliction. Will this include individuals, for example, who sustain sports injuries as a result of trying to improve their health? We will no doubt hear from both sides what they consider to be self-infliction.

Should we be selecting the candidates who are most likely to get the greatest health gain against those who are less likely to get such gain? There has been some well-publicised evidence related to cardiac surgery and the different outcomes of surgery for smokers and non-smokers. We live in a society where the principles of the NHS so far have said that everything is available for everybody. You have undergone the Oregon exercise as part of your annual course and actually found at first hand, I guess, how difficult it is to prioritise and agree what criteria we should use. You will recall that I demonstrated in the Sally Irvine lecture yesterday how criteria for quality varied from the patient's perspective, the purchaser's perspective and the professional's. I suspect that priority setting would have a similar set of principles, which are likely to vary dependent on your personal beliefs and perspective.

I am going to introduce all the speakers now and that should allow us to roll out the debate quite quickly. Proposing the motion, Rosemary Day; Rosemary graduated in English from London University. She is an Associate of the Institute of Taxation which sounds incredibly exciting. She is a Fellow of the Royal Society of Arts, Companion of the Institute of Management. She worked with the Greater London Council for 18 years, working her way to the position of Assistant Director General. She was an Executive Director of London Transport and an Operations Director for Allied Dunbar. She is now Director and Board member for many organisations but, particularly relevant to today's debate, she is Chairman of the London Ambulance Service. She is, like me, a singer.

Rosemary's second is Tony Kennerley. Tony has just finished a ten-year stint as Chairman of the West Surrey Health Commission. His current posts include Chairman of Council of Professions Supplementary to Medicine and he is a member of the Monopolies and Mergers Commission. He has links with Glasgow. He is a former Director of Strathclyde University Business School. He has had extensive education, business and industry experience in the UK and the USA, so we are very keen to hear what Tony has to say.

Opposing the motion, Harry Burns. Harry is a home-grown chap from Glasgow who graduated in medicine in 1974 at Glasgow University. He followed a career in surgery and rose to the exalted rank of Consultant Surgeon at Glasgow Royal Infirmary. Then he became poacher turned gamekeeper when he moved to health service management, was made Medical Director of Glasgow Royal Infirmary and then became Director of Public Health at Greater Glasgow Health Board. The Director of Public Health is, in my view, one of the most challenging jobs in the Health Service, particularly in Glasgow.

Harry's second is Colin Waine. Colin has a background in general practice. He was a principal in Bishop Auckland for 22 years. He has been a member of the Regional Health Authority, the Health Education Authority. I know him well. He has chaired lots of groups in the Royal College of General Practitioners, including being Chairman of Council. His current post is Director of Health Programmes and Primary Care Development for Sunderland Health Authority. He has published extensively in disease management and has an interest in nutrition.

## SUPPORTING THE MOTION: Rosemary Day

*Rosemary Day believes it is important that the issues around the proposal are aired but that before any moves to implement such changes could be taken there would need to be much more research and extensive debate. While the main burden of discrimination would fall on GPs there would also need to be national decisions to formally change; the guidance to services such as the ambulance services, who currently may not discriminate between callers. Much remains to be reviewed and many practical aspects clarified before further steps could safely be taken even if it were desirable to take them.*

I'd like first to spend a few minutes looking at why this proposal has come up for debate today. After all, history is full of people who have been the cause of their own illness and death, to quote a few:

King John – died from over-eating – said to be a surfeit of lampreys.
Anne Boleyn – an extreme case, who through bad behaviour managed to get herself executed.
Samuel Pepys – who through an excess of Madeira suffered from gout.
The poet Samuel Taylor Coleridge – who died early from over-indulgence in the drug opium.

In the 20th century we can continue the tale with alcoholism, drug addition and add anorexia, paralysis resulting from sporting accidents, tobacco-related illnesses, obesity connected to heart diseases and unhealthy life styles resulting in a range of diseases and premature death.

So why has this question become prominent today. I believe that there may be two main reasons. First, with ever-increasing pressure on health service finance, some way needs to be found for reducing costs. The proposal is another approach to the rationing of free treatment. However, rationing by targeting those who have caused their own problem feels, on the face of it, a sensible approach: surely more sensible and equitable than rationing by ability to pay or age.

Second, to improve the health of the nation. This would be laudable but is debatable. In today's world, individual choice is emphasised and encouraged in health as in many other fields. It could be argued that forcing people into particular ways of life is unacceptable. It must be argued that it is unlikely to be achievable.

I will therefore, base my approach on the belief that adopting different priorities for self-inflicted injuries is about rationing: a more equitable distribution of healthcare focusing on those who are judged to be more deserving because their condition is not self-inflicted.

Turning to the proposition, two phrases need some exploration: *different priority* and *self-inflicted*.

## Different priority

The implication is that 'different' means worse treatment if it is to be NHS funded. In practice then:

- If the patient needs hospital treatment, the GP may decide that he or she will have to wait longer or maybe not get it at all.
- If the treatment is with costly drugs the GP will be able to refuse to prescribe these or prescribe less effective treatment if the cost is likely to prejudice treatment for other patients.
- If the patient's condition is such that without treatment or drugs he will die, then the patient may be allowed to die.

The result of this 'different priority' could therefore be that a patient who has a self-inflicted injury will become incapacitated, his or her quality of life will be seriously impaired and the patient will die probably sooner and almost certainly more painfully than if he or she had not self-inflicted the illness.

So by different priority we mean that a health professional, usually a GP, will have the right to choose whether or not to treat the patient free on the NHS, knowing what the likely consequences will be. In these circumstances, the definition of self-inflicted will be critical.

## Self-inflicted

Self-inflicted must, I suggest, be defined as 'the individual has chosen to do something which has resulted in the condition or injury which is being presented for treatment'. Logically, this could cover a huge range from pregnancy (after all we do not have to indulge in that particular activity) to over-eating and from travel to DIY. You choose to ride a bicycle and get knocked off, you choose to saw your finger off doing DIY and you choose to eat bread and butter rather than carrots.

However, pure logic gives a position that is not practicable. For the purposes of this debate, I suggest that 'self-inflicted' injury should be taken as:

- where there is an irrefutable connection between the illness and choice of behaviour;
- where there is a significant body of medical opinion linking the 'choice' to a range of illnesses;
- where the activity is not basic to 'ordinary' living.

Using these principles, I believe there are five possible categories of 'self-inflicted' injuries:

- sports;
- alcohol;

- drugs;
- obesity;
- tobacco.

There will, of course, be others that some would add. Definition of these areas will be critical to the 'equitability' of the proposal but I hope that as 'reasonable' people we could all agree that these five are definitely to be classed as leading to self-inflicted illness or injury.

I am therefore proposing that it is equitable than an individual who chooses to indulge in any in one of these five areas may from the NHS receive slower, less effective treatment or indeed no treatment at all in order to give greater priority to individuals who through no apparent fault of their own need treatment for their illness or injuries.

However, there is always a however, I would contend that this approach could only be reasonable and equitable if four conditions are accepted:

1. The approach should not be applied retrospectively. It must come into force at a point in time when individuals can be fully aware of the consequences of their choice before they make it and must be applied equally in all parts of the country.
2. The consequences of individual choices are understood by everyone who is making them. While ignorance is no defence in criminal law, ignorance of or lack of understanding about the con-sequences of such choices, given the potential impact on the indi-vidual, must be crystal clear if the equitability of the approach is to be maintained.
3. Upholding the principle of choice, an individual contracting illness or suffering injury which is 'self-inflicted', and not then eligible for free treatment, should also be able to opt for euthanasia rather than suffer significant pain and distress and/or severe reduction in the quality of life through non-treatment.
4. It can be proved that the 'choice' was the cause of the illness or injury.

I am sure there will be a few challenges to these conditions. However, I believe that when we are considering people's health and lives, choice has to be applied throughout, not just in some areas. I also maintain that given the serious nature of the consequences, it will be important to ensure that everyone accepts and understands the link between activity and illness.

## Private treatment/purchase of NHS treatment

So far, I have been looking at consequences within the National Health Service for delivery of free treatment. Before exploring the position in more depth I want to briefly look at the private health market. Will adopting this approach discriminate those who cannot afford private medicine? In short, yes.

Given the principle of choice, if somebody who chooses to over-eat, to smoke, to drink to excess, has the means and chooses to afford private health insurance, then they will be able to get treatment for their condition. Those who rely on National Health Service will not be able to. If the treatment is very expensive, this makes it even more inequitable, because a greater number of people will not be able to afford the treatment.

This is hardly a new situation. Already, and for the whole of the existence of the NHS, private healthcare has meant not necessarily better but often faster, more convenient and sometimes more individual treatment – that is what people pay for.

I contend that we cannot restrain choice by 'forbidding' private treatment and concede that there will be an inherent inequitability in the application of different priorities for people with self-inflicted injury. I also contend that if the NHS will have more money to spend on those who have not 'chosen' their illness, then the principle of the 'greatest good for the greatest number' should apply. In the end the individual has to choose, knowing the possible consequences, whether to indulge in a particular activity and pay for treatment or to avoid it and be treated free by the NHS. Provided they are aware of the consequences, there can surely be no argument on this point.

## Precedents

Just as ability to pay has always allowed some people to have a more individual service, there has always been 'rationing' or 'prioritisation' in the NHS, as your conference has been discussing. Recent examples include:

- non-removal of tattoos;
- most beauty treatment;
- in some areas, fertility treatments.

These are excluded on the basis that they are 'voluntary', i.e. not essential for health and 'ordinary' living – just as I defined earlier when looking at what should be classified as 'self-inflicted'. Non-treatment or lower priority treatment free under the NHS of life-threatening conditions – lung cancer from smoking; heart failure or stroke from obesity; cirrhosis of the liver from alcohol; ligament or muscle strain from sport – is only extending the precedents already operating.

So what does adopting the motion really mean: for the individual; for the NHS; for health?

## For the individual

If any individual chooses, knowing the consequences, to do something which will result in an injury or illness requiring medical care, then he or she will have to pay for treatment. If this is not possible, a more painful slower recovery will be the result, possibly much reduced quality of life and probably earlier death.

## For the National Health Service

More money available to treat the majority of people whose illness or injury is not self-inflicted.

## For health

The prospect of a high cost or an early death may just deter some people from indulging in activities which are known to be harmful. It may not be many, but the removal of the NHS safety net could help to prevent some avoidable illnesses if it is carefully communicated with 'gory detail' and examples from real life.

On this basis, I propose the motion – and seek the support of all reasonable people to recognise the proposal as an extension of current approaches to rationing free health services.

## SECONDING THE MOTION: Professor Tony Kennerley

Good morning, everybody. How are you feeling? No aches and pains to speak of? Untroubled and feeling relaxed and happy? Then I am pleased to tell you that you are all healthy. In fact I can tell you that you are healthy by definition. You see, WHO, the World Health Organisation has laboured long and hard to establish what health is. And now they have found it. We are healthy only when we have complete physical, emotional and social wellbeing.

There are two reasons why I want to establish that this audience is healthy. First, because at the end of this debate you will be asked to make a choice and I want that choice to be made by healthy happy people. You see, I know that healthy happy people will make rational, reasoned choice and that, of course, means supporting the motion.

Second, I want us to enjoy this debate, this conference and all the atmosphere because that is the right time to examine how we become healthy and to assess the risks to remaining healthy. Then we can exercise our prerogative of choice, an educated choice, an informed choice. Choice – the right of a free people.

Now, modern medical treatment can greatly facilitate our physical and psychological wellbeing but the social aspect is different – so let us examine how we achieve this. Partly through self-confidence they tell us – particularly in company. And what support do we require to boost our self-confidence in company? I'll tell you. A quick puff on the old cigarette at coffee time – maybe a second cream cake. Or perhaps a little drinky poos over lunch.

Need I go on? It's all a matter of choice – isn't it? Now, be honest. After all life is a social occasion – and a little bit of what you fancy does you good.

But these choices have risks and the real challenge of the motion is merely to ensure that our choice is an educated one – so that we can take an informed risk.

If I go mountaineering my life insurance premium goes up. If I smoke, the same thing is true. All that support for the motion implies is an increase in health insurance instead of life insurance – at least if we want to have the appropriate treatment when our risky behaviour catches us out and we succumb to our informed and calculated risk. But note, while our vices constitute risk, it is these very indulgences which contribute to our emotional and social wellbeing. Yes, it is necessary to indulge our peccadilloes to be completely healthy.

Consider for a moment the exact opposite. The presently prescribed 'healthy' way of life. Little meat, less bacon and eggs, no alcohol, no cigarettes and definitely no indulgence in dangerous activities such as mountaineering, horse riding – or sex. By any light this must cut across the psychological and social elements of the WHO definition of health.

Now, which of us can put their hand on their heart and claim that they live this unblemished prescribed life style. Well, you don't have to – not if you are to achieve wellbeingness. This is the great conundrum of healthy living.

Rosemary Day has given a quite splendid set of reasons why we should support the motion 'People with self-inflicted injury should receive different priority for treatment'. Her approach quite properly has been to consider the subject from the point of view of rationing. I should like to extend this to embrace the concept of choice. Choice – the very essence of individual freedom.

The life choices we face should now be extended to encompass the theme of this debate or indeed the theme of this conference with its courageous consideration of the Oregon experiment.

Perhaps we need to exchange the random rationing of the hospital waiting list for a personal list – a list of our vices if you like – particularly those vices which induce our personal sense of wellbeing. Then we can be judged for our worthiness not to be treated differently as the motion requires. There could be a scale of 'payments for peccadilloes' in order to finance their treatment. This would only be fair to offset the cost of our self-inflicted illness. But of course this process would need to be administered so that you were not overcharged on the peccadillo scale and to prevent cheating.

Imagine a new health department might be created entitled 'The Industry Promoting Perfect Life styles by Education' – TIPPLE for short. Everyone would be marked on the TIPPLE scale. (I fear some of us are already clearly marked by the scale of TIPPLE as it is.)

There would also need to be inspectors to ensure that we did not exceed our indulgence allowance. They could also encourage us to embrace the perfect life style regardless of our need for emotional and social wellbeing. These inspectors could measure us on alcohol, smoking, eating and dangerous activity scales. The points would be added up and compared with the most healthy to allow the calculated of the appropriate levy for our expected 'peccadillo treatments'. These gruesome inspectors would be known as 'social norm operatives' – abbreviated to 'snoopers'.

But to be serious, these matters were well understood in ancient times. To quote Horace:

Video melior proboque deteriora sequor.
[I see the better path but follow the worse one]

Rosemary has argued that different treatment implies rationing. This would, of course, be the case if we accept the proposition in its narrow form. However, we have seen that to be definitively healthy we are induced to indulge – engage in what may be described as unhealthy practices.

The only way to resolve this cruel dilemma is to grant the opportunity to all of us to ensure that our resultant care is not rationed. If we choose to exercise our right to indulge in risky practices we should surely be permitted to provide for parity of treatment.

There is a social precedent but quite wrongly not linked to any fairness in relation to self-inflicted damage. In fact, the reverse is the case. The people to which I refer are penalised for not indulging but for being good citizens and saving. I refer, of course, to the means testing of those in residential and nursing homes whereby you pay for your care in a very expensive way if you own assets of more than £16,000, and you continue to pay until you have spent this money. Worse is the case of those who are not sufficiently aware to be able to assign their property to be sold and whose relatives are forced to borrow to pay for care based on a notional value of the declining asset until all the value is spent. So much for incentives to save and the notion of passing on one's life savings to one's children.

Payment for peccadilloes is much kinder. It is in advance of the condition and based upon rates of presentation of disease and their cost of treatment. Let us look at some outcomes.

Alcoholism, obesity and smoking are clearly self-inflicted conditions and should have a lower priority. I have suggested that a lower priority would give equal opportunity for treatment only if the person or their insurance could pay.

Perhaps the clearest and most illuminating example relates to HIV and AIDS. Here again, we have a clearly self-inflicted condition and one that can easily be avoided if a safe sex practice is followed. The great tragedy here is that the condition is usually fatal and that even palliative treatment is hideously expensive. Following AZT we now have the protease inhibitors, but these currently cost about £10,000 per patient per year. With an excess of 27,000 AIDS patients in the UK it would cost upwards of £300m per annum merely to relieve the symptoms of AIDS sufferers.

Clearly no nation can contemplate an open-ended commitment to all who can be helped in the face of relentlessly more expensive technical advances. Currently, the resulting cruel dilemmas are left to the vagaries of the waiting list or more likely to clinical selection on criteria which involve need, age and increasingly – life style. Do we have the right to impose on already burdened clinicians and managers the added moral pressures of such decisions unaided? Our answer has to be no.

We must support and assist our decision-makers by openly accepting that there has to be a different priority for self-inflicted illness. Whether that difference means delayed treatment in a National Health Service or a health insurance scheme as I have suggested are mere details.

We have heard the arguments of the opposition. I am not sure that they can be classed as arguments for they have no substance. They are based on pious hopes and wishful thinking about a plentitude of resources. Feel sorry for them, for they are simply trapped hostages to emotion.

This conference can send a message to the world outside – a message that says, 'We know the problems, we understand the issues, we are aware that rationing decisions are being taken daily – by clinicians, by managers – decisions which leave them exposed and accountable.

Let us therefore state openly that there should be different treatment for self-inflicted illness. Let us accept this motion as the means to precipitate the true debate in a national forum.

Now, let me ask you all to have the courage to vote for reason, to vote for truth, to vote for the motion. Thank you.

## OPPOSING THE MOTION: Dr Harry Burns

I oppose the motion.

Let me start off by congratulating the proposers of this motion on the very eloquent way that they have put the case. They have presented very cogent argument, well argued. I think our position is that when we come to consider this question of different priorities of treatment judged by how we have to behave, we would want to argue two things. First of all, you can't do it. You cannot do what Rosemary has suggested and show that someone's illness is caused by his behaviour and second, even if you could, you shouldn't. The arguments we have heard are, on the face of it, full of sense. It is being suggested that if you choose to indulge in activity that has very serious consequences, you should accept those consequences. That is a very pragmatic argument. The notion of pragmatism, owes its philosophical origins to the work of an American philosopher called John Dewey. Bertrand Russell's *History of Western Philosophy* suggests that there is something of the philosophy of Hegel in Dewey's arguments: 'There is a persuasive Hegelian tendency no greater than the way in which he interacted with society'. Now of course Hegel and Nietzsche were founding fathers of national socialism and Hegel's arguments were the arguments that Hitler used to gas the mentally ill, and the mentally defective, Jews, gypsies and anyone else who disagreed with him.

When I read Russell's comments on pragmatism I thought 'Well, that's a bit steep, a bit tough for a Sunday morning!' I thought, well I had better go and find out what another philosopher is saying about pragmatism. So I went to a different book called *Christian Philosophy* written by the Professor of Philosophy at Madrid University. The philosophy of Dewey is described as 'What is good? What makes man happy? What is evil? What makes a man unhappy? The latter is pain, the former pleasure. What is true is whatever works. Whatever procures the happiness of an individual in this life, this is pragmatism, the typical American philosophy of the cult of immediacy and efficiency'.

'The varieties of materialism could be called vitalism because life, brute life by itself, becomes the basic reality. Between this vitalist materialism and this Marxist materialism there are many points of contact. You can detect pragmatism in Marxism'.

I have to say I think the proposers are very brave, because they are arguing a philosophical case, that philosophers would suggest lies somewhere between Nazism and Marxism – the two major political catastrophes of this century. We have heard a lot about smoking. The correlation between the amount you smoke and the risk of getting lung cancer is very high, and on the face of it it seems certain that if you smoke enough you get lung cancer. Should we penalise smokers? Yet some people get lung cancer who have never smoked. Well, that is fine, they get treatment. But if you think it through that means there is a population of people who get lung cancer for reasons other than smoking. How do you tell if the smoker's lung cancer is due to smoking, or due to one of these other conditions such as genetic pre-disposition? Are we going to penalise someone because they have a gene that makes them more likely to have breast cancer?

If you look across the river from this hotel you see a ship yard. From this part of Glasgow down to Clydebank, there is the highest incidence of asbestos-induced lung cancer in the world. Fifteen per cent of those lung cancers are histologically indistinguishable from the lung cancer caused by smoking. So if a patient comes to me who smokes but who also worked in the ship yards, does he get his treatment or does he not? Because it is being argued that we should penalise him for choosing to smoke, but on the other hand we shouldn't penalise him for working in an environment that increases the risk of getting lung cancer.

Supposing you can determine causality, the next question is can you determine responsibility? There is a wonderful story in the health promotion literature about maternal mothers smoking in a London tower block. The local health authority decided it wanted to get the maternal smoking rates down. For six months they tried to tell these mothers they were really going to kill themselves with their smoking. But then the interviewers noticed something interesting. They couldn't get the interviews conducted effectively because the flats were full of screaming children. The reason they were running round the house screaming all the time was because it was a tower block, and there was nowhere for the kids to play. And the answer to the smoking cessation problem was to produce an enclosed play area at the bottom of the tower block where the mothers could look out the window and see the kids were safe. The smoking rate tumbled.

Sometimes our ability to make these healthy choices is not the ability that you and I have as comfortable, well-off, middle-class people largely in control of our lives. Last winter I stopped at traffic lights in a deprived area of Glasgow. Just by these lights, in the entrance to a building, was an individual who was wearing a thin denim jacket despite the fact that it was snowing at the time. He was swaying about and his eyes were rolling in his head. You could tell from the crisp packets lying at his feet that he had been sniffing glue. He looked frozen, he looked undernourished, and he was about nine years old. Now I have a nine-year-old at home who has a different future ahead of her. She plays sport, she dances, she plays a number of musical instruments. Supposing she gets knocked down and is taken into casualty along with the glue sniffer? Are we seriously asking ourselves to agree that my child, because she doesn't have any of these risk-taking behaviours has a greater priority to healthcare than the child who staggers in front of a car because he has been put in this environment that causes him to sniff glue. Undoubtedly he has a choice. He probably knows what the consequences are. But his ability to make the correct decision is compromised by the society that we put him in. We have heard a lot about rationing and it is a load of humbug. I was staggered to see that coronary artery bypass grafts were high on the list of things to be rationed. In a study carried out two years ago in an English region it was found that 20 per cent of coronary artery bypass grafts were thought to be unnecessary. Across the UK that translates into about £10 million of unnecessary surgery. Thirty per cent of patients admitted to hospital with chest pain do not need to be admitted to hospital if we apply simple working techniques that we know are robust. That is £120 million of unnecessary expenditure. I could suggest grommets, D and Cs. I could run through a whole range of things. Back of the envelope calculations suggest we could easily find £5 to 10 billion worth of money in the NHS that is spent inappropriately. This is not a rationing decision for society. Better management of our resources is the issue.

There is of course the question of reasonable risks. Have any of you used a sun bed? How many of you have been jogging this morning? There is a risk associated with that. How many of you have had a cooked breakfast this morning with loads of cholesterol? You know that you are making choices, but society tells us that the common good is something that we organise ourselves together in a society to support and the common good is something which we as individuals agree to help each other achieve. Have you seen the advert for Nescafé? I mean the one where the guy goes over the edge of the cliff, abseils down with gripped fingers, and waves crashing at the bottom of the cliff. He is doing it to save a dog that has fallen over and broken its leg. He is risking his life to help a dog. That is something our own human nature requires us to do. Will we do less for a human being?

Jacques Maritaine pointed to the fact that if we deny that bit of our own human nature that requires us to help others, then we start at the top of slippery slope. For example, if we found ourselves walking along a river bank and saw someone floating past, obviously drowning, our natural instinct would be to jump in and save him, or at the very least find help. Maritaine argued that a society which looked on such incidents only from the point of view of self-interest would soon find itself in trouble. For example, examine this response to seeing the drowning man:

'What is your name?'
'John Smith'

'And where do you work John Smith?'
'In the factory along the road.'

The self-interested man would run to the foreman of the factory and say 'Do you know your employee John Smith? Well I wonder if I could have his job because he won't be needing it any more?'

Maritaine suggested that if society became like that it would not be long before the foreman was responding 'No you can't have his job because the guy who pushed him into the river got here five minutes before you.' A society which does not care for the weak and disadvantaged soon becomes a society in which the strong justify the imposition of their will on the weak. It becomes a dictatorship with all the horrors that totalitarianism can bring.

I began by suggesting that the philosophical principles underlying the proposition were pragmatic and that pragmatism as a way of running society has been the basis of most of the twentieth-century's social disasters. Not only is this proposition philosophically objectionable, it is, I have argued, scientifically unenforceable. I urge you to reject it.


## SECONDING THE OPPOSITION TO THE MOTION: Dr Colin Waine

Do not be fooled by the seeming reasonableness of the proposer's and seconder's approach, because it conceals an underlying sinister intent. Basically they are proposing that certain groups of people will be denied the potential benefits of our Health Service. They then cop out of decision-making, leaving it to the family doctor. Let me remind you here of the words of the late Sir James Spence:

> The essential unit in medicine is when, in the privacy of the consulting room or sick room, a person who is ill, or believes himself to be ill, seeks the help of someone he trusts.

I emphasise the 'someone he trusts'. How can anyone trust a general practitioner who has to decide whether he or she is denied treatment.

I did not become a doctor to play God and decide who should be able to benefit from advances in medicine and who should not.

Obviously, in terms of self-inflicted illness, the example of smoking comes immediately to mind — smoking is, of course, the single most preventable cause of death in the Western world. But isn't there something of a double standard operating when successive governments have lacked the courage, the moral fibre, to ban tobacco advertising? When winning motor racing grand prix is impossible without having cars carrying the logos of the tobacco barons, logos which hit the young and impressionable.

I put it to you that if we go down the path advocated by the proposer and seconder of the motion, we are certainly starting down a very slippery slope. The proposers start with five categories, make no mistake these will grow relentlessly. Those anxious to cut public spending – to whom the concept of a welfare state is anathema – will be positively jumping with glee.

The National Health Service Acts of 1946 and 1947, which led to the emergence of the NHS in 1948, represented one of the most radical, if not the most radical, pieces of social legislation of the century. They weren't built on exclusions.

Let's say we start with smoking, a major risk factor for the development of lung cancer and coronary heart disease; but that won't be the end of it. Having a raised blood cholesterol, a major factor for the development of heart disease, can be influenced by diet and by genetic factors. Adopting a healthy diet can both lower cholesterol and the risk of heart disease. So are those who have not altered their diet and have a coronary to be abandoned? Are people with genetically determined high cholesterol not to be allowed to reproduce? That's a nice slice of the NHS expenditure some £600 + million suitably sidelined and channelled into those tax cuts which some see as essential in an election manifesto.

We know that taking folic acid prior to conception and in the early months of pregnancy can protect against having a baby with a neural tube defect such as spina bifida. If a mother doesn't take it and has a baby born with spina bifida, is that baby to be denied help?

Overweight is certainly a risk factor for the development of diabetes which consumes about 5 per cent of NHS spending. You can see the scenario: 'Sorry, Mr Bloggs, we only treat people with diabetes who have a normal weight – on your bike.'

The origin of many diseases certainly lies with life style factors. The prevalence of major killing diseases like coronary heart disease and cancer is certainly influenced by people's life styles – whether they smoke, whether they eat a healthy diet, whether they take exercise.

But let me remind you of another fact – the social class gradient in health is widening. Coronary heart disease and cancer are, of course, much less prevalent in the affluent. Why? Because they have something to live for.

Adopting healthy life styles has a meaning because being alive in 20 or 30 years time has a meaning. Contrast this to a young couple, unemployed, with hungry mouths to feed. It is the concrete immediacy of the present which concerns them, not the apparent benefits of some future which they cannot even begin to contemplate. Hungry children demand that their stomachs be filled. To assuage the pangs of hunger chips are a highly effective solution, even if their consumption can bring long-term harm.

A diet high in polyunsaturated fats has little meaning for a family fallen victim to social deprivation. For a mother worried about how to pay the rent, buy food, cope with a demoralised and unemployed husband, dragging on a fag might be the only way by which she can avoid lashing out physically at one of her children who steps out of line.

I hope that by now you will be realising my repugnance at the proposition and I hope that it has not escaped your attention that such proposals usually come from the well heeled.

The proposition is contrite, smacks of nasty Nazi undertones, totally ignores the fact that the social class gap in health status is widening and does nothing to repair this wound, which a caring society should address as a number one priority.

However, in its favour I have to admit that it would probably appeal to that nasty little man with a penchant for violence and racism, who sought the supremacy of an Aryan race and who left in his wake a dreadful carnage of oppression and of man's inhumanity to man. He also had some sort of neurological abnormality which kept him raising his right arm repeatedly and uttering the words 'Sieg Heil'. In his early days he began with just burning books.

Finally, I must attack the proposition because it is so facile, so trite, and so very much the easy way out. It's like attacking crime with increasingly punitive sentences while ignoring its social origins. The real solution is to work at a system of social justice in which for everyone it's worth stopping smoking, because for everyone there is a future.

I do not deny the fact that resources are finite and that a degree of rationing is inevitable. But when we do so down this route let us start from a position that if each life counts for one, then the life of each has the same value as that of any. This is why accepting the value of life generates the principle of equality. If there is a need for decision-making dictated by scarce resources, then the decision is not medical, nor economic, nor even political, but moral. And though a democratic society has the power, through its elected representatives, to do what it chooses, it ought not to choose to do what is morally wrong.

I believe that each person is entitled to be treated with equal concern and respect, both in the way health resources are distributed and in the way they are treated by healthcare professionals, however much their personal circumstances may differ from those of others. If we choose not to provide someone with the care or treatment that he or she needs in order to say alive, then if he or she dies, we are responsible for that persons's death.

When talking about scarce resources there is a fundamental mistake of talking about the healthcare budget as opposed to the national budget. And for a country with levels of prosperity that we have, we spend remarkably little – 5 per cent of the gross national product – on health issues.

Many years ago Martin Fisher wrote:

Medicine is the one place where all the show is stripped of the human drama. You as doctors will be in a position to see the human race start naked, not only physically but mentally and morally as well.

A few years later Lord Brain wrote in defence of the medical profession:

Medicine alone takes as its province the whole man. It is not just concerned with his needs for nursing or with enquiries into the home circumstances, or with his difficulties in getting a job when he is disabled, or with this or that form of therapy. Medicine is concerned with all these but with how much more? With man in all the complexity of his body and mind from his conception to his last breath and the concern extends increasingly beyond his sickness to the conditions which enable him to lead a happy and healthy life.

Both were taking a view which was based on compassionate caring, not on judgemental exclusion.

Medicine has survived as a respected profession because of these concerns. Compassion is not a sloppy sentimental feeling for people who are underprivileged or sick. It is an absolutely practicable belief that a person, regardless of his or her ability to pay, should be provided with the best that society can offer within what society can afford.

Ladies and gentlemen I put it to you that we are all our brothers' keepers.

## CONCLUSION

There then followed one hour of lively debate with many questions and comments coming from the audience, with responses by the debaters and the chairman.

**The debate motion 'People with self-inflicted illness should receive different priority for treatment' was overwhelmingly opposed by the audience**.

AMGP hope that you will take these issues and debate them within your primary healthcare team. This is not easy, but it is essential for managers to facilitate the team in their endeavours in the prioritisation and rationing debate.

PART NINE

# APPENDICES

# Appendix I

# Health Service Guidelines

---

HSG(94)1    General ophthalmic services: Increases in NHS domiciliary sight test fees and domiciliary visiting fees

HSG(94)2    Decision of the NHS Tribunal

HSG(94)3    Health Service use of ionising radiation

HSG(94)4    Developing NHS purchasing and GP fundholding

HSG(94)5    Abortion Act 1967 – Guidance on the provision of treatment for termination of pregnancy

HSG(94)6    People with a mental illness: Local authority specific grant for 1995–6

HSG(94)7    The pay and conditions of service for general and senior managers

HSG(94)8    NHS responsibilities for meeting continuing healthcare needs

HSG(94)9    People with a mental illness supplementary credit approval for capital funding in 1994–5

HSG(94)10    Hospital infection control

HSG(94)11    Professional involvement in HA work

HSG(94)12    Decisions of the Professional Conduct Committee of the General Medical Council

HSG(94)13    Revised and expanded Patient's Charter: Implementation

HSG(94)14    General ophthalmic services: Increases in spectacle voucher values

HSG(94)15    Private finance and capital investment projects

HSG(94)16    Confidential enquiry into stillbirths and deaths in infancy

HSG(94)17    Increased NHS prescription charges: Revised prescription forms

HSG(94)18    Conditions of service for general and senior managers

HSG(94)19    Information to support the Health of the Nation

HSG(94)20    Taxation of staff benefits and allowances – Crown cars and mileage allowances

HSG(94)21    Clinical audit of suicides and other unexplained deaths

HSG(94)22    The new regional health authorities/regional offices

HSG(94)23    Charges for drugs and appliances

HSG(94)24    The education of sick children

HSG(94)25   GP fundholding: List of goods and services

HSG(94)26   GP fundholding: The National Health Service (Fundholding Practices) Amendment Regulations 1994

HSG(94)27   Guidance on the discharge of mentally disordered people and their continuing care in the community

HSG(94)28   Priority treatment for war pensioners

HSG(94)29   General medical services GP practice vacancies: Revised selection procedures

HSG(94)30   Decisions of the General Medical Council's Professional Conduct Committee

HSG(94)31   Capital investment in the NHS: The Capital Investment Manual

HSG(94)32   Decisions of the Professional Conduct Committee of the General Medical Council

HSG(94)33   Dental advice to family health services authorities

HSG(94)34   Changes to the welfare foods scheme

HSG(94)35   Secretary of State's list for dental prescribing

HSG(94)36   Distinction awards: Nominal roll of consultants

HSG(94)37   Mutual recognition of qualifications for the provision of hearing aids in the private and public sectors

HSG(94)38   Dental advice for RHAs, DHAs and FHSAs

HSG(94)39   Appointment of doctors to hospital posts: Termination of pregnancy

HSG(94)40   General ophthalmic services: Increase to the NHS sight test fees for optometrists

HSG(94)41   Interventional ventilation and organ transplant

HSG(94)42   Decision of the NHS Tribunal

HSG(94)43   Protection of children: Disclosure to NHS employers of criminal background of those with access to children

HSG(94)44   Decisions of the Professional Conduct Committee of the GMC

HSG(94)45   Abortion notification envelopes – HSA4 ENV

HSG(94)46   Removal and associated expenses – payments to staff for loss of equity and additional housing costs

HSG(94)47   Framework for local community care charters in England

HSG(94)48   NHS low income scheme. NHS optical voucher scheme. Extension of automatic entitlement to help with health costs to recipients of DWA whose capital is £8000 or less

HSG(94)49   Disciplinary procedures for hospital and community medical and hospital dental staff

HSG(94)50   Clinical waste management

HSG(94)51   Occupational Health Service for NHS Staff

HSG(94)52   Emergency planning in the NHS: Health Services arrangements for dealing with major incidents – protective clothing

HSG(94)53   Regional health authorities/regional offices: Further guidance for RHA/RO staff on the division of functions

HSG(94)54   NHS trading agencies: Future arrangements

HSG(94)55   The operation of the NHS internal market

HSG(94)56   GP fundholding management allowance

HSG(95)1   General ophthalmic services: Increases in NHS domiciliary sight fees and domiciliary visiting fees

HSG(95)2    Decision of the NHS Tribunal
HSG(95)3    Health service use of ionising radiations
HSG(95)4    Developing NHS purchasing and GP fundholding
HSG(95)5    Abortion Act 1967 – Guidance on the provision of treatment for termination of pregnancy
HSG(95)6    People with a mental illness: Local authority specific grant for 1995–6
HSG(95)7    The pay and conditions of service for general and senior managers
HSG(95)8    NHS responsibilities for meeting continuing healthcare needs
HSG(95)9    People with a mental illness: Supplementary credit approval for Capital Funding in 1994–5
HSG(95)10    Hospital infection control
HSG(95)11    Ensuring the effective involvement of professionals in health authority work
HSG(95)12    Decisions of the Professional Conduct Committee of the General Medical Council
HSG(95)13    Revised and expanded Patient's Charter: implementation
HSG(95)14    General ophthalmic services: Increases in spectacle voucher values
HSG(95)15    Private finance and capital investment project
HSG(95)16    Confidential enquiry into stillbirth and death in infancy
HSG(95)17    Increased NHS prescription charges: Revised prescription forms
HSG(95)18    Hospital laundry arrangements for used and infected linen
HSG(95)19    GP fundholding: List of goods and services
HSG(95)20    Guidance on the revised operation of notification arrangements for tertiary extra contractual referrals
HSG(95)21    Professions supplementary to medicine: issue of directions in relation to the staff of NHS contractors
HSG(95)22    Decisions of the Professional Conduct Committee of the General Medical Council
HSG(95)23    Hepatitis and blood transfusion look back
HSG(95)24    Road Traffic Act charges
HSG(95)25    NHS early retirement arrangements
HSG(95)26    Health authority drug misuse services 1995–6
HSG(95)27    Change to the Welfare Food Scheme
HSG(95)28    Key messages for community fundholders
HSG(95)29    The National Health Service (Fundholding Practices) Amendment regulations 1995
HSG(95)30    Doctors acting as observers in hospitals
HSG(95)31    Welfare Food Scheme – updated guidance
HSG(95)32    Outsourcing, Facilities Management and Managed Service for Information System and Service in the NHS
HSG(95)33    Patient referrals outside the UK and European Economic Area (EEA)
HSG(95)35    Decisions of the Professional Conduct Committee of the General Medical Council
HSG(95)36    PCR model licence for the NHS
HSG(95)37    Guidance on fundholder purchase of terminations of pregnancy

HSG(95)38 European Union Directives on public sector purchasing

HSG(95)39 Discharge from NHS inpatient care of people with continuing health or social care needs: arrangements for reviewing decisions on eligibility for NHS continuing care

HSG(95)40 National Health Service Low Income Scheme: Changes to claim forms AG1 and AG5

HSG(95)41 Regulation of nursing homes and independent hospitals

HSG(95)42 Procedures for suspensions and for early retirement in the community dental service

HSG(95)44 Provision of the National Freephone Information Service

HSG(95)45 Arrangements between Health Authorities and NHS Trusts and private and voluntary sector organisations for the provision of Community Care Services

HSG(95)46 GP Fundholding: Use of Savings

HSG(95)47 Contracting for Orthotic Services

HSG(95)48 Private Finance & Information Management & Technology (IM&T) Procurement

HSG(95)49 Decisions of the Professional Conduct Committee of the General Medical Council

HSG(95)51 The Welfare Food Scheme

HSG(95)52 Changes to Prescription Exemption Announcements

HSG(95)53 Dental Advice to FHSAs

HSG(95)54 Variations in Health

HSG(95)55 Decisions of the Professional Conduct Committee of the General Medical Council

HSG(95)56 Building Bridges: Arrangements for inter-agency working for the care and protection of severely mentally ill people

HSG(95)57 Health Authority Subscriptions

HSG(95)58 Decisions of the Professional Conduct Committee of the General Medical Council

HSG(95)59 Service Increment for Teaching: Operational Guidance

HSG(95)60 Guidance to NHS Trusts on Costing for Sift Contracts

HSG(95)61 Revised Arrangements for the Management of the Employment Contracts for Doctors in Training

HSG(95)62 The NHS Tribunal Commencement of NHS (Amendment) Act 1995

HSG(95)64 GP Fundholding: Inclusion of Community Specialist Nursing and other services in Standard and Community Fundholding from 1 April 1996

HSG(95)65 GP Fundholding: Revised lists of Goods and Services

HSG(95)67 Decisions of the Professional Conduct Committee of the General Medical Council

HSG(96)1 The pay and conditions of service for general and senior managers

HSG(96)3 Approval of doctors under Section 12 of the Mental Health Act

HSG(96)4 The NHS (Fund-holding Practices) (Functions of FHSAs) Regulations 1995

HSG(96)5 The spectrum of care – a summary of comprehensive local services for people with mental health problems

24 hour nursed beds for people with severe and enduring mental illness

An Audit pack for the Care Programme Approach

HSG(96)6 Supplementary Credit Approval to Local Authorities in 1996–7 for the development of social care services for people with a mental illness

HSG(96)7 Specific Grant to Local Authorities in 1996–7 for the development of social care services for people with a mental illness

HSG(96)8 Carers (Recognition and Services) Act 1995

HSG(96)9 Local Representative Committees

HSG(96)10 Expenditure on Staff Benefits

HSG(96)11 Guidance on supervised discharge (after-care under supervision) and related provisions

HSG(96)13 Decisions of the Professional Conduct Committee of the General Medical Council

HSG(96)14 GP Fundholding: Management and Computer Allowance

HSG(96)15 NHS Information Management and Technology Security Manual

HSG(96)16 1. Charges for Drugs, Appliances, Wigs and Supports
2. Prescription Prepayment Certificates
3. Revised Forms
4. Collection of Charges
5. Statistical Returns

HSG(96)17 New Posters and Leaflets: NHS charges, optical and travel costs

HSG(96)18 The Protection and use of Patient Information

HSG(96)21 Fourth Report of the Steering Group on Undergraduate Medical and Dental Education and Research

HSG(96)22 NHS (Fund Holding Practices) Regulation 1996

HSG(96)24 The National Health Service (Appointment of Consultants) Regulations 1996

HSG(96)25 Revised arrangements for the Management of Employment Contracts for Senior Registrars and Registrars in Public Health Medicine

HSG(96)26 Guidance on the microbiological safety of human tissues and organs used in transplantation

HSG(96)27 General Ophthalmic Services – Increases in spectacle voucher values

HSG(96)28 The Use of 'Trial Leave' under Section 17 of the Mental Health Act 1983 to transfer patients between Hospitals

HSG(96)29 Homeless Mentally Ill Initiative

HSG(96)30 Decisions of the Professional Conduct Committee of the General Medical Council

HSG(96)31 A National framework for the provision of secondary care within General Practice

HSG(96)32 Contract Energy Management

HSG(96)33 Review of Central Requirements for Information; Uses made of Information collected from the NHS

HSG(96)34 Powered indoor/outdoor wheelchairs for severely disabled people

HSG(96)35  Prescription Fraud
           Fraud Investigation Unit at the Prescription Pricing Authority
           Improving the security of prescription forms
HSG(96)38  Decisions of the NHS Tribunal
HSG(96)39  Decisions of the Professional Conduct Committee of the GMC
HSG(96)40  Mental Illness target fund to local Authorities
HSG(96)42  Travelling and other allowances for membership of NHS Boards
HSG(96)43  Electorial Registration of Patients detained under the Mental
           Health Act 1983
HSG(96)44  The Welfare Food Scheme
HSG(96)45  Dental Advice for HAs
HSG(96)46  GP Fundholding: Revised Lists of goods and services
HSG(96)49  The NHS Income Scheme and Optical Arrangements
           Changes in entitlement to help with NHS charges, optical and
           hospital travel costs
           Forms and Leaflets

# Appendix II

# Executive Letters

---

| | |
|---|---|
| EL(95)27 | Education and training in the new NHS |
| EL(95)29 | Market testing in the NHS: Update and future plans |
| EL(95)30 | Applying NHS standards when procuring computer standards |
| EL(95)31 | Future regional public health role |
| EL(95)32 | Special constabulary: Medical and nursing staff |
| EL(95)33 | Interim NHS support for MRC-funded clinical research |
| EL(95)34 | Local pay: Guidance for purchasers |
| EL(95)35 | Management of construction projects: Revised monitoring arrangements |
| EL(95)36 | Nurses, midwives and health visitors: standards for education and practice |
| EL(95)37 | Government response to the review of NHS complaints procedures |
| EL(95)38 | Family Health Services Appeal Authority |
| EL(95)39 | Community care monitoring: Report of 1994 national exercises |
| EL(95)40 | Clinical negligence scheme for Trusts |
| EL(95)41 | Community health councils |
| EL(95)43 | Health and well-being: A guide for older people |
| EL(95)44 | Review of ambulance training |
| EL(95)45 | The Human Fertilisation and Embryology Act 1990: Storage of sperm (or eggs) for cancer patients |
| EL(95)46 | Supporting R&D in the NHS: Implementation plan |
| EL(95)47 | Review of primary care projects for homeless people |
| EL(95)48 | Funding of hospital and dental training grade posts |
| EL(95)50 | Hospital doctors: Training for the future − proposals for implementing legislation: The specialist medical order |
| EL(95)51 | A policy framework for commissioning cancer services |
| EL(95)52 | Review of central requirements for information: Uses made of information collected from the NHS |
| EL(95)53 | Local elections |
| EL(95)54 | An accountability framework for GP fundholding |
| EL(95)55 | Assessing the options: cervical cytology |
| EL(95)56 | Tackling drugs together |
| EL(95)57 | The transfer of patients to shorter waiting lists |
| EL(95)58 | Making it happen: Report of the Standing Nurse and Midwifery Advisory Committee |
| EL(95)59 | NHS Performance Tables 1994−5<br>'Charter Week' |
| EL(95)60 | Code of practice on openness in the NHS: Guidance on implementation |
| EL(95)61 | New NHS number |
| EL(95)62 | Hospital doctors: Training for the future − supplementary reports on general practice, overseas doctors and academic and research medicine |
| EL(95)63 | Undergraduate medical and dental education |
| EL(95)64 | Outturn 1994−5 (non-financial information) |
| EL(95)66 | Managing in the NHS: A study of senior executives |
| EL(95)67 | Contract energy management |
| EL(95)68 | Priorities and planning guidance for the NHS: 1996−7 |

| | |
|---|---|
| EL(95)69 | Overseas work experience and professional development of NHS staff |
| EL(95)71 | Second Report of the Medical Workforce Standing Committee (MWSAC) |
| EL(95)72 | Implementing the New Deal on junior doctors' hours |
| EL(95)73 | Employee assistance for health authority staff affected by organisational change |
| EL(95)74 | The Quality Register |
| EL(95)75 | Handling confidential patient information on contract minimum data sets: Guidance for purchasers undertaking a review of compliance with data protection principles |
| EL(95)76 | Code of conduct for community health council members |
| EL(95)77 | Changing patterns of maternity care: Implications for pay and grading for midwives and midwifery senior management |
| EL(95)78 | Accountability framework for GP fundholding |
| EL(95)79 | The use of costed HRGs in the 1996–7 contracting cycle |
| EL(95)80 | Student bursaries |
| EL(95)81 | Reports of the Health Service Commissioner |
| EL(95)82 | Monitoring local pay |
| EL(95)83 | 'Maintaining medical excellence' – the review of guidance on doctor's performance |
| EL(95)84 | Building on the benefits of occupational standards and National Vocational Qualifications in the NHS |
| EL(95)85 | Publication of health authority costs |
| EL(95)86 | Nursing, midwifery and professions allied to medicine – contracts for education and training with institutions of higher education – a joint declaration of principles |
| EL(95)87 | Costing for contracting themes and issues in the community, mental health and learning disability services |
| EL(95)88 | NHS responsibilities for meeting continuing health care needs – NHS Executive/SSI Monitoring |
| EL(95)89 | Health at work in the NHS |
| EL(95)90 | Consultation document: Patient's Charter and services for children and young people |
| EL(95)91 | Costed HRG 1995–6 evaluation summary report |
| EL(95)92 | Joint medical capital projects: Guide to university/NHS capital planning interactions |
| EL(95)93 | Revised arrangements for B, A and A+ distinction awards |
| EL(95)94 | Supra-regional services: Applications for designation |
| EL(95)95 | Supra-regional services: Dedesignation of the fulminant hepatic failure |
| EL(95)96 | Non-medical education and training – planning guidance for 1996–7 education commissioning |
| EL(95)97 | New drugs for multiple sclerosis – issue delayed |
| EL(95)98 | The SCHARR report: Catching the tide: New voyages in nursing |
| EL(95)99 | Strategic review of pathology services |
| EL(95)100 | Declaration of NHS Audit & costs associated with Research and Development: Initial Guidance |
| EL(95)101 | Anonymised HIV Surveys: Revised Publicity Material |

EL(95)102   Capital Investment/Post Product Evaluation
EL(95)103   The New Health Authorities and the Clinical Audit Initiative: Outline of Planned Monitoring Arrangements
EL(95)104   'Patients Not Paper' – Implementation
EL(95)105   Improving the effectiveness of Clinical Services
EL(95)106   Legal Advice to NHS Bodies
EL(95)107   Implementation of Revised Organisation Codes and Supporting Services
EL(95)108   NHS-wide Electronic Networking Systems and Patient Confidentiality
EL(95)109   Revised arrangements for B, A, and A+ Distinction Awards: Guide to the NHS Consultant's Distinction Awards Scheme
EL(95)110   Project Contracts and Common Information
EL(95)111   NHS Trusts and Health Authorities: Employers Liability for Civil Actions by Employees
EL(95)112   Cochlear Implants
EL(95)113   Ending of the Schoolgirl Rubella Immunisation Programme
EL(95)114   Reviewing Shared Care Arrangements for Drug Misusers
EL(95)115   Decisions of the Registered Homes Tribunals 231–240
EL(95)116   Decisions of the Registered Homes Tribunals 241–250
EL(95)117   Decisions of the Registered Homes Tribunals 251–260
EL(95)118   Community Health Councils: Membership Issues
EL(95)119   Implementing the Reforms of Specialist Medical Training: Commissioning the Specialist Registrar Grade
EL(95)120   A Positive Approach to Epilepsy
EL(95)121   Implementation of New Complaints Procedure: Interim Guidance
EL(95)123   Corporate Governance in the NHS-Internal Audit
EL(95)125   Implementing the Reforms to Specialist Medical Training–the new Registrar Grade
EL(95)126   Opportunity 2000: Women in the NHS
EL(95)127   Supporting R&D in the NHS: A Declaration of NHS activities and costs associated with R&D; Guidance on Costing and making the Declaration
EL(95)128   Prescribing Expenditure: Guidance on Allocations and Budget Setting for 1996–7
EL(95)129   Policy Appraisal & Health Guide
EL(95)130   Public Expenditure on Health
EL(95)131   Management Efficiency Publications
EL(95)133   Revised Arrangements for the Management of the Employment Contracts for Doctors in Training
EL(95)134   Monitoring Local Pay
EL(95)136   Six-Monthly Report of Health Service Commissioner
EL(95)137   HIV and AIDS Health Promotion: An Evolving Strategy
EL(95)138   Implementing the Reforms to Specialist Medical Training – the new Specialist Registrar Grade
EL(95)139   NHS-wide Clearing Service
EL(95)140   NHS Performance Tables 1995–6
EL(95)141   NHS Waiting Times: Good Practice Guide

EL(95)142   Community Health Councils: Guidance on the changes in establishing arrangements

EL(95)143   Employing Disabled People in the NHS: A Guide to Good Practice

EL(95)144   Service Support for research in non-SIFTR Hospitals for 1996–7

EL(96)1   Issue Delayed

EL(96)2   Consultation Document: Patient's Charter & Mental Health Services

EL(96)3   Emergency Care Services

EL(96)4   Ethnic Minority Staff in the NHS – A Programme of Action

EL(96)5   'Acting on Complaints': Training for Local Resolution

EL(96)6   Annual Report of the Advisory Committee on Distinction Awards

EL(96)7   Core Contract for Purchasing Cancer Registration

EL(96)8   NHS Responsibilities for meeting continuing Health Care needs – Current progress and future priorities

EL(96)9   Local Pay 1996–97: Guidance for Purchasers

EL(96)10   Junior Doctors' Hours: Pay for intensive on-call rotas

EL(96)12   (1) Standards of Business Conduct: Declaration of Interests
(2) Lease Cars ('Crown Cars')

EL(96)13   Security in the NHS

EL(96)14   Implementing the Reforms of Specialist Medical Training
(1) Commissioning the Specialist Registrar Grade
(2) A guide to Specialist Registrar Training

EL(96)15   A Policy Framework for commissioning Cancer Services

EL(96)17   The Operation of Community Health Councils from April 1996

EL(96)18   Specialist Workforce Advisory Group Recommendations: higher specialist training numbers 1996–97

EL(96)19   Implementation of new Complaints Procedure: Final Guidance

EL(96)20   Guidelines on admission to and discharge from intensive care and high dependency units

EL(96)22   Paediatric Intensive Care

EL(96)23   Emergency Care Services

EL(96)24   Changing Statutory Functions of Health Authorities

EL(96)25   Joint NHS/University Capital Projects – a guide to the treatment of Embedded Accommodation in Joint Projects

EL(96)26   1996 Departmental Report for the Department of Health

EL(96)27   Patient's Charter and Services for children and young people: Implementation

EL(96)28   Children's Services

EL(96)29   Creative Career Paths in the NHS – Report No. 5: Summary of findings and agenda for action

EL(96)30   HIV/AIDS Funding

EL(96)31   Revised arrangements for the management of Employment Contracts for Doctors in Public Health Medicine

EL(96)32   NHS Top Manager Programme

EL(96)33   Occupational Exposure Standards for Anaesthetic Agents

EL(96)34   Oversight of Provision of External Quality Assessment Schemes for Pathology Laboratories

EL(96)35   Purchasing Renal Services
EL(96)36   Transfer of Health Authority Winding Up Functions
EL(96)37   Issue Delayed
EL(96)38   Continuity of Service for NHS Staff
EL(96)39   Local Elections
EL(96)41   Changes to Central Returns on Waiting Times
EL(96)42   Changes to Central Returns on the Patient's Charter
EL(96)43   Select Committee on the Parliamentary Commissioner for Administration: Report of the Health Service Ombudsman for 1994–5
EL(96)44   Health and Safety Management in the NHS
EL(96)45   NHS Priorities and Planning Guidance 1997–8
EL(96)46   Education and Training Planning Guidance
EL(96)47   R&D in the NHS – Implementing the Culyer Report
EL(96)48   Implementing the reforms of Specialist Medical Training
EL(96)50   Submission of returns on In-Patient Waiting Lists
EL(96)52   Health Service Commissioner: Annual report 1995–6 and six-monthly report for October 1995 to March 1996
EL(96)53   Paediatric Intensive Care: The Way Forward
EL(96)54   Regional Drug Misuse Databases: Core Contract Specifications
EL(96)55   GP Fundholder Budget Setting: The National Framework
EL(96)56   Extra Contractual Referrals: Changes in notification requirements and steps to reduce volume
EL(96)57   London Implementation Group (LIG), National DHA/FHSA and FMR Clearing House Scheme
EL(96)58   New NHS Complaints Procedure: Independent Review
EL(96)59   Accountable Officers
EL(96)60   Accountable Officers
EL(96)61   Introduction of a Second Dose of Measles, Mumps and Rubella Vaccine into the Pre-School Booster Immunisation Programme
EL(96)63   Monitoring Local Pay
EL(96)64   The use of Costed HRGs in the 1997–8 Contracting Cycle
EL(96)66   Improving Outcomes in Breast Cancer: Guidance for Purchasers
EL(96)68   Local Medical Workforce Advisory Groups
EL(96)69   Workforce Planning for General Medical Services
EL(96)70   Disability Discrimination Act: Implications for NHS Trusts and Health Authorities
EL(96)71   Chronic Disease Management Registers
EL(96)72   Review of Arrangements for Funding Postgraduate Medical Eduction
EL(96)73   Emergency Services
EL(96)74   Purchasing Effective Treatment and care for Drug Misusers
EL(96)76   Intensive Care Bed–State Register

# Appendix III

# NHS Trusts

---

## England

### Northern and Yorkshire

Airedale NHS Trust
Airedale General Hospital
Skipton Road
Steeton
Keighley
BD20 6TD
TEL: 01535 652511
FAX: 01535 655129

Bishop Auckland Hospitals NHS Trust
Bishop Auckland General Hospital
   Unit
Bishop Auckland
DL14 6AD
TEL: 01388 604040

Bradford Community Health NHS
   Trust
Leeds Road Hospital
Maudsley Street
Bradford
BD3 9LH
TEL: 01274 729661
FAX: 01274 725652

Bradford Hospitals NHS Trust
Trust Headquarters
Corridor III
Bradford Royal Infirmary

Duckworth Lane
Bradford
BD9 6RJ
TEL: 01274 364788
FAX: 01274 364786

Calderdale Healthcare NHS Trust
Calderdale Health Authority
Royal Halifax Infirmary
Free School Lane
Halifax
HX1 2YP
TEL: 01422 358411
FAX: 01422 342581

Carlisle Hospitals NHS Trust
Cumberland Infirmary
Newtown Road
Carlisle
CA2 7HY
TEL: 01228 23444
FAX: 01228 591889

Cheviot & Wansbeck NHS Trust
Ashington Hospital
West View
Ashington
NE63 0SA
TEL: 01670 812541

City Hospitals Sunderland NHS
   Trust
Sunderland District General Hospital
Kayll Road
Sunderland
SR4 7TP
TEL: 0191 565 6256
FAX: 0191 565 2893

Cleveland Ambulance NHS Trust
Cleveland Ambulance Headquarters
Venture House
Marton Road
Middlesbrough
TS4 3TL
TEL: 01642 850888
FAX: 01642 824905

Community Health Care, North
   Durham NHS Trust
Earls House Hospital
Lanchester Road
Durham
DH1 5RE
TEL: 0191 386 4911

Cumbria Ambulance Service NHS
   Trust
Ambulance Headquarters
Salkeld Hall
Infirmary Street
Carlisle,
Cumbria
CA2 7AN
TEL: 01228 596909
FAX: 01228 514350

Darlington Memorial Hospital NHS
   Trust
Hollyhurst Road
Darlington
Co Durham
DL3 6HX
TEL: 01325 380100
FAX: 01325 743622

Dewsbury Health Care NHS Trust
Dewsbury Health Care
Woodkirk House

Dewsbury District Hospital
Healds Road
WF13 4HS
TEL: 01924 465105
FAX: 01924 458867

Durham County Ambulance Service
   NHS Trust
Ambulance Headquarters
Finchale Road
Framwellgate Moor
Durham
DH1 5JS
TEL: 0191 386 4488

East Yorkshire Community
   Healthcare NHS Trust
Westwood Hospital
Beverley
HU17 8BU
TEL: 01482 875875
FAX: 01482 860762

East Yorkshire Hospitals NHS Trust
Castle Hill Hospital
Castle Road
Cottingham
North Humberside
HU16 5JQ
TEL: 01482 875875

Freeman Group of Hospitals NHS
   Trust
Freeman Road
High Heaton
Newcastle Upon Tyne
NE7 7DN
TEL: 0191 284 3111
FAX: 0191 213 1968

Gateshead Healthcare NHS Trust
3rd Floor
Adian House
Tynegate Precinct
Sunderland Road
Gateshead
NE8 3EP
TEL: 0191 478 3811

Gateshead Hospitals (Queen
Elizabeth & Bensham Hospitals)
NHS Trust
Queen Elizabeth Hospital
Sheriff Hill
Gateshead
Tyne & Wear
NE9 6SX
TEL: 0191 487 8989

Grimsby Health NHS Trust
Eastholme
District General Hospital
Scartho Road
Grimsby
DN33 2BA
TEL: 01472 74111

Harrogate Health Care NHS Trust
Harrogate District Hospital
Lancaster Park Road
Harrogate
HG2 7SX
TEL: 01423 506141
FAX: 01423 501391

Hartlepool and Peterlee Hospitals
NHS Trust
General Hospital
Holdforth Road
Hartlepool
TS24 9AH
TEL: 01429 266654

Hartlepool Community Care NHS
Trust
General Hospital
The Health Centre
Caroline Street
Hartlepool
Cleveland
TS26 9LE
TEL: 01429 266654

Huddersfield Health Care Services
NHS Trust
Huddersfield Royal Infirmary
Lindley

Huddersfield
DH3 3EA
TEL: 01484 654777

Hull & Holderness Community
Health NHS Trust
Project Manager
Victoria House
Park Street
Hull
HU2 8TD
TEL: 01482 675941

Humberside Ambulance Service NHS
Trust
Humberside Ambulance Service
Headquarters
Springfield House
Springfield Way
Anlaby
HU10 6RZ
TEL: 01482 54277
FAX: 01482 52069

Leeds Community & Mental Health
Services Teaching NHS Trust
Park House
Meanwood Park Hospital
Tongue Lane
Leeds
LS6 4QB
TEL: 01532 758721
FAX: 01532 745172

Newcastle City Health NHS Trust
Newcastle Mental Health
St Nicholas Hospital
Jubilee Road
Gosforth
Newcastle upon Tyne
NE3 3XT

North Durham Acute Hospitals NHS
Trust
Dryburn Hospital
Durham
DH1 5TW
TEL: 0191 386 4911

North Lakeland Healthcare NHS
Trust
The Coppice
Garlands Hospital
Carlisle
CA1 3SX
TEL: 01228 36451
FAX: 01228 515610

North Tees Health NHS Trust
North Tees General Hospital
Hardwick
Stockton on Tees
Cleveland
TS19 8PE
TEL: 01642 617 617
FAX: 01642 624 089

North Tyneside Health Care NHS
Trust
North Tyneside Health Care
Preston Hospital
North Shields
NE29 0LR
TEL: 0191 259 6660

North Yorkshire Ambulance Service
NHS Trust
Ambulance Headquarters
Fairfields
Shipton Road
York
YO3 6XW
TEL: 01904 628085
FAX: 01904 627049

Northallerton Health Services NHS
Trust
Friarage Hospital
Northallerton
North Yorkshire
DL6 1JG
TEL: 01609 779911
FAX: 01609 775749

Northgate and Prudhoe NHS Trust
Northgate Hospital
Morpeth NE61 3BP
TEL: 01670 512281

Northumberland Community Health
NHS Trust
East Cottingwood
Morpeth
Northumberland
NE61 2PD
TEL: 01670 514331

Northumberland Mental Health NHS
Trust
St Georges Hospital
East Cottingwood
Morpeth
Northumberland
NE61 2NU
TEL: 01670 512121

Northumbria Ambulance Service
NHS Trust
Ambulance Headquarters
Interlink House
Scotswood Road
Newcastle Upon Tyne
NE4 7BJ
TEL: 0191 273 1212
FAX: 0191 273 7070

Pinderfields Hospitals NHS Trust
Trust Headquarters
Rowan House
Pinderfields General Hospital
Aberford Road
Wakefield
WF1 4EE
TEL: 01924 201688
FAX: 01924 814929

Pontefract Hospitals NHS Trust
Pontefract Hospitals
Friarwood Lane
Pontefract
WF8 1PL
TEL: 01977 600600

Priority Healthcare Wearside NHS
Trust
Cherry Knowle Hospital
Ryhope
Sunderland

SR2 0NB
TEL: 0191 565 6256
FAX: 0191 523 7683

Royal Hull Hospitals NHS Trust
Hull Royal Infirmary
Anlaby Road
Hull
HU3 2KZ
TEL: 01482 28541

Royal Victoria Infirmary and
    Associated Hospitals NHS Trust
Royal Victoria and Associated
    Hospitals
Queen Victoria Road
Newcastle upon Tyne
NE1 4LP

St James's and Seacroft University
    Hospitals NHS Trust
St James's University Hospital
Beckett Street
Leeds
LS9 7TF
TEL: 01532 433144
FAX: 01532 426496

Scarborough and North East
    Yorkshire Healthcare NHS Trust
Scarborough Hospital
Scalby Road
Scarborough
North Yorkshire
YO12 6QL
TEL: 01723 368111
FAX: 01723 377223

Scunthorpe and Goole Hospitals
    NHS Trust
Scunthorpe & Goole Hospitals
Cliff Gardens
Scunthorpe
DN15 7BH
TEL: 01724 282282

Scunthorpe Community Health NHS
    Trust
Brumby Hospital

East Common Lane
Scunthorpe
South Humberside
DN16 1QQ
TEL: 01724 282282

South Durham Health Care NHS
    Trust
Claremont
Princes Street
Bishop Auckland
DL14 7BB
TEL: 01388 605811
FAX: 01388 602548

South Tees Acute Hospitals NHS
    Trust
Middlesbrough General Hospital
Ayresome Green Lane
Middlesbrough
Cleveland
TS7 0NJ
TEL: 01642 320000
FAX: 01642 324176

South Tees Community and Mental
    Health NHS Trust
Community Unit
West Lane Hospital
Acklam Road
Middlesbrough
Cleveland
TS5 4EE
TEL: 01642 813144

South Tyneside Health Care NHS
    Trust
Harton Wing
South Tyneside District Health Unit
South Shields
Tyne and Wear
NE34 0PL
TEL: 0191 454 8888
FAX: 0191 427 9908

South West Durham Mental Health
    NHS Trust (Winterton)
Winterton Hospital
Sedgefield

Cleveland
TS21 3EJ
TEL: 01740 20521
FAX: 01740 22646

The United Leeds Teaching
   Hospitals NHS Trust
Leeds General Infirmary
Great George Street
Leeds
LS1 3EX
TEL: 01532 316624
FAX: 01532 316282

Wakefield & Pontefract Health NHS
   Trust
Wakefield & Pontefract Community
   Health
Fernbank
3–5 St John's North
Wakefield
WF1 3QD
TEL: 01924 814814
FAX: 01924 814987

West Cumbria Health Care NHS
   Trust
West Cumberland Hospital
Hensingham
Whitehavan
Cumbria
CA28 8JG
TEL: 01946 693181

West Yorkshire Metropolitan
   Ambulance Service NHS Trust
West Yorkshire Metropolitan
   Ambulance Service
'Threelands'
Bradford Road
Birkenshaw
Bradford
BD11 2AH
TEL: 01274 651410
FAX: 01274 688727

York Health Services NHS Trust
Headquarters
Bootham Park

York
YO3 7BY
TEL: 01904 610700

### Trent

Barnsley Community & Priority
   Services NHS Trust
Unit II Headquarters
Kendray Hospital
Doncaster Road
Barnsley
S70 3RD
TEL: 01226 730000
FAX: 01226 296782

Barnsley District General Hospital
   NHS Trust
Barnsley District General Hospital
Gawber Road
Barnsley
S75 2EP
TEL: 01226 730000
FAX: 01226 202859

Bassetlaw Hospital and Community
   Health Services NHS Trust
Bassetlaw Hospital
Barrowby House
9 Highland Grove
Worksop
Notts
S81 0JN
TEL: 01909 500990
FAX: 01909 480879

Central Nottinghamshire Healthcare
   NHS Trust
Trust Headquarters
Southwell Road West
Mansfield
Notts
NG18 4HH
TEL: 01623 22515
FAX: 01623 634126

Central Sheffield University
   Hospitals NHS Trust
Royal Hallamshire Hospital

Glossop Road
Sheffield
S10 2JF
TEL: 01742 766222
FAX: 01742 725962

Chesterfield and North Derbyshire
Royal Hospital NHS Trust
Chesterfield & North
Derbyshire Royal Hospital
Calow
Chesterfield
Derbyshire
S44 5BL
TEL: 01246 277271

Community Health Care Service
(North Derbyshire) NHS Trust
The Shrubberies
46 Newbold Road
Chesterfield
Derbyshire
S41 7PL
TEL: 01246 200131

Community Health Services,
Southern Derbyshire NHS Trust
South Derbyshire Community Unit
'Wilderslowe'
121 Osmaston Road
Derby
DE1 2GA
TEL: 01332 363371
FAX: 01332 382131

Community Health Sheffield
Brunswick House
299 Glossop Road
Sheffield
S10 2HL
TEL: 01742 766222

Derby City General Hospital NHS
Trust
Derby City Hospital
Uttoxeter Road
Derby
DE3 3NE

TEL: 01332 40131
FAX: 01332 290559

Derbyshire Ambulance Service NHS
Trust
Ambulance Headquarters
Kingsway
Derby
DE22 3XB
TEL: 01332 372441
FAX: 01332 46824

Derbyshire Royal Infirmary
London Road
Derby
DE1 2QY
TEL: 01332 47141
FAX: 01332 295652

Doncaster Healthcare NHS Trust
St Catherines Hospital
Tickhill Road
Doncaster
DN4 8QN
TEL: 01302 853241

Doncaster Royal Infirmary & The
Montagu Hospital NHS Trust
Armthorpe Road
Doncaster
DN2 5LT
TEL: 01302 366666
FAX: 01302 730078

Fosse Health Leicestershire
Community NHS Trust
Community Unit 1 Headquarters
Leicestershire Health Authority
Gipsy Lane
Humberstone
Leicester
LE5 0TD
TEL: 01533 460100
FAX: 01533 461222

Glenfield Hospital NHS Trust
General Manager's Office
Glenfield General Hospital
Groby Road

Leicester
LE3 9QP
TEL: 01533 871471

Grantham and District Hospital NHS
  Trust
Grantham and Kesteven General
  Hospital
101 Manthorpe Road
Grantham
Lincolnshire
NG31 8DG
TEL: 01476 65232

The King's Mill Centre for Health
  Care Services
Mansfield Road
Sutton in Ashfield
NG17 4JL
TEL: 01623 22515
FAX: 01623 21770

Leicester General Hospital NHS Trust
Leicester General Hospital
Gwendolen Road
Leicester
LE5 4PW
TEL: 01533 490490

Leicester Royal Infirmary NHS Trust
Leicester Royal Infirmary
Infirmary Square
Leicester
LE1 5WW
TEL: 01533 541414
FAX: 01533 585631

Leicestershire Ambulance and
  Paramedic Service NHS Trust
The Rosings
Forest Road
Narborough
Leicestershire
LE9 5EQ
TEL: 01533 750700
FAX: 01533 751311

Leicestershire Mental Health Service
674 Melton Road

Thurmaston
Leicester
LE4 8BA
TEL: 01533 693666
FAX: 01533 693953

Lincoln District Healthcare
Gervas House
Long Leys Road
Lincoln
LN1 1EF
TEL: 01522 546546
FAX: 01522 567297

Lincoln Hospitals NHS Trust
County Hospital
Greetwell Road
Lincoln
LN2 5QY
TEL: 01522 512512

Lincolnshire Ambulance & Health
  Transport Service NHS Trust
Cross O'Cliff Court
Bracebridge Heath
Lincoln
LN4 2HL
TEL: 01522 545171
FAX: 01522 534611

Louth & District Healthcare
County Hospital
Louth
LN11 0EU
TEL: 01507 600100
FAX: 01507 609290

Mulberry NHS Trust
Holland Road
Spalding
Lincs
PE11 1UH
TEL: 01775 711551
FAX: 01775 711317

Northern General Hospital NHS
  Trust
Herries Road
Sheffield

S5 7AU
TEL: 01742 434343
FAX: 01742 560472

Nottingham City Hospital NHS Trust
Nottingham City Hospital
Hucknall Road
Nottingham
NG5 1PB
TEL: 01602 691169
FAX: 01602 627788

Nottingham Community Health
   NHS Trust
Linden House
261 Beechdale Road
Aspley
Nottingham
NG8 3EY
TEL: 01602 426000
FAX: 01602 428606

Nottingham Healthcare
Mapperley Hospital
Porchester Road
Nottingham
NG3 6AA
TEL: 01602 691300

Nottinghamshire Ambulance Service
   NHS Trust
Nottinghamshire Ambulance Service
Beechdale Road
Nottingham
NG8 3LL
TEL: 01602 296151
FAX: 01602 299415

Pilgrim Health NHS Trust
Pilgrim Hospital
Sibsey Road
Boston
PE21 9QS
TEL: 01205 364801
FAX: 01205 354395

Queens Medical Centre Nottingham
   University Hospital NHS Trust
University Hospital

Queens Medical Centre
Derby Road
Nottingham
NG7 2UH
TEL: 01602 421421
FAX: 01602 709196

Rotherham General Hospitals NHS
   Trust
Rotherham District General Hospital
Moorgate Road
Rotherham
S60 2UD
TEL: 01709 820000

Rotherham Priority Health Services
   NHS Trust
Rotherham Priority Health Services
Rivelin House
Oakwood Hall Drive
Moorgate Road
Rotherham
S60 3AJ
TEL: 01709 820000

Sheffield Childrens Hospital NHS
   Trust
Sheffield Childrens Hospital
Western Bank
Sheffield
S10 2TH
TEL: 01742 761111
FAX: 01742 721870

Southern Derbyshire Mental Health
   NHS Trust
Southern Derbyshire Mental Health
   Unit
'Thorndale'
Kingsway Hospital
Derby
DE3 3LZ
TEL: 01332 362221
FAX: 01332 31254

South Lincolnshire Community and
   Mental Health Services NHS Trust
Rauceby Hospital

Sleaford
Lincolnshire
NG34 8PP
TEL: 01529 488241

South Yorkshire Metropolitan
   Ambulance and Paramedic Service
   NHS Trust
Ambulance Service Headquarters
Fairfield
Moorgate Road
Rotherham
S60 2BX
TEL: 01709 828820
FAX: 01709 829842

The West Lindsey NHS Trust
John Coupland Hospital
Ropery Road
Gainsborough
DN21 2TJ
TEL: 01427 614751

Weston Park Hospital NHS Trust
Weston Park Hospital
Whitham Road
Sheffield
S10 2SJ
TEL: 01742 670222
FAX: 01742 684193

## Anglia and Oxford

Addenbrooke's
Addenbrooke's Hospital
Hills Road
Cambridge
CB2 2QQ
TEL: 01223 245151

Allington NHS Trust
Allington House
427 Woodbridge Road
Ipswich
Suffolk
IP4 4ER
TEL: 01473 720931
FAX: 01473 719160

Anglian Harbours NHS Trust
Northgate Hospital
Northgate Street
Great Yarmouth
Norfolk
NR30 1BU
TEL: 01493 856222
FAX: 01493 331237

Aylesbury Vale Community
   Healthcare NHS Trust
Manor House
Bierton Road
Aylesbury
Bucks
HP20 1EG
TEL: 01296 393363
FAX: 01296 392606

The Bedford and Shires Health and
   Care NHS Trust
Unit Headquarters
40 Kimbolton Road
Bedford
MK40 2NR
TEL: 01234 355122
FAX: 01234 342463

Bedford Hospitals NHS Trust
Bedford Hospital
Kempston Road
Bedford
MK42 9DJ
TEL: 01234 355122
FAX: 01234 218106

East Anglian Ambulance NHS Trust
Ambulance Headquarters
Hospital Lane
Hellesdon
Norwich
NR6 5NA
TEL: 01603 424255
FAX: 01603 485343

East Berkshire Community Health
   NHS Trust
East Berkshire Community Health
   Unit

Upton Hospital
Albert Street
Slough SL1 2BJ
TEL: 01753 821441
FAX: 01753 517163

East Berkshire NHS Trust for People
   With Learning Disabilities
Church Hill House
Crowthorne Road
Bracknell
Berkshire
RG12 7EP
TEL: 01344 422722
FAX: 01344 867990

East Suffolk Local Health Services
   NHS Trust
Anglesea Heights
1 Ivry Street
Ipswich
Suffolk
IP1 3QW
TEL: 01473 286892

Heatherwood and Wexham Park
   Hospitals NHS Trust
Wexham Park Hospital
Slough
Berkshire
SL2 4HL
TEL: 01753 534567
FAX: 01753 691343

Hinchingbrooke Health Care NHS
   Trust
Hinchingbrooke Hospital
Hinchingbrooke Park
Huntingdon
PE18 8NT
TEL: 01480 416416
FAX: 01480 416434

The Horton General Hospital NHS
   Trust
Horton General Hospital
Oxford Road
Banbury
Oxfordshire

OX16 9AL
TEL: 01295 229060
FAX: 01295 258251

Ipswich Hospital NHS Trust
Ipswich Hospital
Heath Road Wing
Ipswich
IP4 5PD
TEL: 01473 702087
FAX: 01473 703400

James Paget Hospital NHS Trust
   (Great Yarmouth)
James Paget Hospital
Lowestoft Road
Gorleston
Great Yarmouth
Norfolk
NR31 6LA
TEL: 01493 600611

Kettering General Hospital NHS Trust
Kettering General Hospital
Rothwell Road
Kettering
Northants
NN16 8UZ
TEL: 01536 410666

King's Lynn and Wisbech Hospitals
   NHS Trust
Queen Elizabeth Hospital
Gayton Road
Kings Lynn
Norfolk
PE30 4ET
TEL: 01553 766266
FAX: 01553 770154

Lifespan Health Care Cambridge
   NHS Trust
Ida Darwin
Fulbourn
Cambridge
CB4 1PT
TEL: 01223 884043
FAX: 01223 884038

Luton and Dunstable Hospital NHS
  Trust
Luton and Dunstable Hospital
Lewsey Road
Luton
Bedfordshire
LU4 0DZ
TEL: 01582 491122
FAX: 01582 598990

Mid Anglia Community Health NHS
  Trust
Community Health Unit
Hospital Road
Bury St Edmunds
Suffolk
IP33 3NR
TEL: 01284 763131

Milton Keynes Community Health
  NHS Trust
Community Health Services
District Headquarters
Standing Way
Eaglestone
Milton Keynes
MK6 5LD
TEL: 01908 660033
FAX: 01908 660539

Milton Keynes General Hospital
  NHS Trust
Milton Keynes General Hospital
Standing Way
Eaglestone
Milton Keynes
MK6 5LD
TEL: 01908 660033
FAX: 01908 669348

Norfolk and Norwich Health Care
  NHS Trust
Norfolk & Norwich Hospital
Brunswick Road
Norwich
NR1 3SR
TEL: 01603 286286

Norfolk Mental Health Care NHS
  Trust
St Andrew's Hospital (Southside)
Yarmouth Road
Norwich
NR7 0SS
TEL: 01603 31122
FAX: 01603 701768

North West Anglia Healthcare NHS
  Trust (Peterborough Priority)
Peterborough Priority Services
Tern House
Gloucester Centre
Morpeth Close
Orton Longueville
Peterborough
PE2 0JU
TEL: 01733 232321
FAX: 01733 235882

Northampton Community
  Healthcare
Clare House
St Edmund's Hospital
Wellingborough Road
Northampton
NN4 4DS
TEL: 01604 37221

Northampton General Hospital NHS
  Trust
Cliftonville
Northampton
NN1 5BD
TEL: 01604 34700

Norwich Community Health
  Partnership NHS Trust
The Old Hall
Little Plumstead
Hospital Road
Norwich
NR13 5EW
TEL: 01603 711227

Nuffield Orthopaedic NHS Trust
Windmill Road
Headington

Oxford OX3 7LJ
TEL: 01865 741155
FAX: 01865 742348

Oxford Radcliffe Hospital NHS
  Trust
John Radcliffe Site
Headley Way
Headington
Oxford
OX3 9DU
TEL: 01865 221610
FAX: 01865 741408

Oxfordshire Ambulance
Churchill Drive
Old Road
Headington
Oxford
OX3 7LH
TEL: 01865 225577

Oxfordshire Community Health
Radcliffe Infirmary
Woodstock Road
Oxford
OX2 6HE
TEL: 01865 224639

Oxfordshire Learning Disabilities
  NHS Trust
Slade Hospital Resource Centre
Horspath Driftway
Headington
Oxford
OX3 7JH
TEL: 01865 747455
FAX: 01865 228182

Oxfordshire Mental Healthcare
Littlemore Hospital
Littlemore
Oxford
OX4 4XN
TEL: 01865 223001
FAX: 01865 223061

Papworth Hospital NHS Trust
Papworth Hospital

Papworth Everard
Cambridge
CB3 8RE
TEL: 01480 830541
FAX: 01480 831147

Peterborough Hospitals NHS Trust
Peterborough District Hospital
Thorpe Road
Peterborough
PE3 6DA
TEL: 01733 67451
FAX: 01733 891082

The Radcliffe Infirmary NHS Trust
Radcliffe Infirmary
Woodstock Road
Oxford
OX2 6HE
TEL: 01865 311188
FAX: 01865 224566

Rockingham Forest NHS Trust
St Mary's Hospital
London Road
Kettering
Northants
NN15 7PW
TEL: 01536 410141

Royal Berkshire Ambulance Service
  NHS Trust
Royal Berkshire Ambulance Service
41 Barkham Road
Wokingham
Berkshire
RG11 2RE
TEL: 01734 771200
FAX: 01734 773923

Royal Berkshire & Battle Hospitals
  NHS Trust
Royal Berkshire Hospital
London Road
Reading
Berkshire
RG1 5AN
TEL: 01734 875111
FAX: 01734 878041

South Bedfordshire Community
Healthcare NHS Trust
Fairfield Hospital
Stotfold
Nr Hitchin
Hertfordshire
SG5 4AA
TEL: 01462 730123
FAX: 01462 733449

South Buckinghamshire NHS Trust
(Wycombe)
Wycombe Health Authority
Oakengrove
Shrubbery Road
High Wycombe
Buckinghamshire
HP13 6PS
TEL: 01494 526161
FAX: 01494 426114

Stoke Mandeville Hospital NHS Trust
Stoke Mandeville Hospital
Mandeville Road
Aylesbury
Buckinghamshire
HP21 8AL
TEL: 01296 315000
FAX: 01296 316208

The Two Shires Ambulance NHS
Trust
Ambulance Service Headquarters
39 Billing Road
Northampton
NN1 5BB
TEL: 01604 230555
FAX: 01604 233999

West Berkshire Priority Care
Services NHS Trust
Fair Mile Hospital
Wallingford
Oxford
OX10 9HH

West Suffolk Hospitals NHS Trust
Hardwick Lane

Bury St Edmunds
Suffolk
IP33 2QZ
TEL: 01284 763131
FAX: 01284 701993

## North Thames

Barnet Community Healthcare NHS
Trust
Trust Headquarters
Colindale Hospital
Colindale Avenue
London
NW9 5HG
TEL: 0181 200 1555
FAX: 0181 200 9499

Basildon and Thurrock General
Hospitals NHS Trust
Basildon Hospital
Nethermayne
Basildon
Essex
SS16 5NL
TEL: 01268 533911
FAX: 01268 280548

Bedfordshire and Hertfordshire
Ambulance Service NHS Trust
Bedfordshire Ambulance Service
Ambulance Headquarters
Hammond Road
Bedford
MK41 0RG
TEL: 01234 270099
FAX: 01234 215399

BHB Community Health Care NHS
Trust
Barking, Havering and Brentwood
Community Services
The Willows
117 Suttons Lane
Hornchurch
Essex
RM12 6RS
TEL: 014024 52577
FAX: 014024 41049

Camden & Islington Community
  Health Services NHS Trust
National Temperance Hospital
Vesey Strong Wing
Hampstead Road
London
NW1 2LT
TEL: 0171 380 0717

Central Middlesex Hospital NHS
  Trust
Acton Lane
London
NW10 7NS
TEL: 0181 965 5733
FAX: 0181 961 0012

Chase Farm Hospitals NHS Trust
  (Enfield Acute)
Chase Hospital
The Ridgeway
Enfield
Middlesex
EN2 8JL
TEL: 0181 366 6600
FAX: 0181 366 1361

Chelsea and Westminster Healthcare
  NHS Trust
Chelsea and Westminster Hospital
369 Fulham Road
London
SW10 9NH

The City and Hackney Community
  Services
East London and City Health
  Authority
Tredegar House
97–99 Bow Road
London E3 2AN
TEL: 0171 739 8484

Ealing Hospital NHS Trust
Ealing Hospital
Uxbridge Road
Southall
Middlesex
UB1 3HW

TEL: 0181 574 2444
FAX: 0181 574 3619

East Hertfordshire NHS Trust
Queen Elizabeth II Hospital
Howlands
Welwyn Garden City
Hertfordshire
AL7 4HQ
TEL: 01707 328111
FAX: 01707 373359

Enfield Community Care NHS
  Trust
Community Premises
Chase Farm Hospital
The Ridgeway
Enfield
Middlesex
EN2 8JL
TEL: 0181 366 6600

Essex Ambulance Service NHS Trust
Ambulance Headquarters
Court Road
Broomfield
Chelmsford
Essex
CM1 5EP
TEL: 01245 443344
FAX: 01245 441854

Essex and Herts Community NHS
  Trust
Rutherford House
Haymeads Lane
Bishop's Stortford
CM23 5JH
TEL: 01279 444455
FAX: 01279 465873

Essex Rivers Healthcare NHS Trust
Colchester General Hospital
Turner Road
Colchester
Essex
CO4 5JL
TEL: 01206 853535
FAX: 01206 852332

Forest Healthcare NHS Trust
PO Box 13
Claybury Hall
Woodford Green
Essex
IG8 8DB
TEL: 0181 505 6241
FAX: 0181 505 6756

The Hammersmith Hospitals NHS
  Trust
Hammersmith Hospital
Du Cane Road
London
W12 0HS
TEL: 0181 743 2030
FAX: 0181 742 9098

Harefield Hospital NHS Trust
Harefield Hospital
Harefield
Middlesex
UB9 6JH
TEL: 01895 278631
FAX: 01895 822870

Haringey Health Care NHS Trust
St Anns Hospital
St Anns Road
London
N15 3TH
TEL: 0181 442 6000
FAX: 0181 442 6567

Harrow and Hillingdon Healthcare
  NHS Trust
Harrow Community Health Services
Siddons House
Roxeth Hill
Harrow
Middlesex
HA2 0JX

Havering Hospitals NHS Trust (BHB
  Acute Services)
Harold Wood Hospital
Gubbins Lane
Romford
Essex
RM3 0BE

TEL: 01708 345533
FAX: 01708 384730

Hillingdon Hospital NHS Trust
Pield Field Heath Road
Hillingdon
Middlesex
UB8 3NN
TEL: 01895 238282
FAX: 01895 811687

The Homerton Hospital NHS Trust
Management Offices
Homerton Row
Homerton
London
E9 6SR
TEL: 0171 985 5555
FAX: 0171 985 6376

Horizon NHS Trust
Harperbury Hospital
Harper Lane
Shenley
Radlett
Hertfordshire
WD7 9HQ
TEL: 01923 855912
FAX: 01923 855909

Hounslow and Spelthorne
  Community & Mental Health
  NHS Trust
Phoenix Court
531 Staines Road
Hounslow
Middlesex
TW4 5DP
TEL: 0181 565 2345
FAX: 0181 565 2249

Mid Essex Community and Mental
  Health NHS Trust
Collingwood Road
Witham
Essex
CM8 2TT
TEL: 01376 501888
FAX: 01376 510843

Mid Essex Hospital Services NHS
   Trust
Mid Essex Hospital Services
Broomfield Court
Pudding Wood Lane
Broomfield
Chelmsford
Essex
CM1 5WE
TEL: 01245 440761
FAX: 01245 443528

Mount Vernon and Watford
   Hospitals NHS Trust
Mount Vernon Hospital
Rickmansworth Road
Northwood
Middlesex
HA6 2RN
TEL: 01923 844132
FAX: 01923 844460

New Possibilities NHS Trust
Turner House
Turner Village
Turner Road
Colchester
Essex
CO4 5JP
TEL: 01206 844840
FAX: 01206 842301

Newham Community Health Services
Community House
430 Barking Road
London
E13 8HJ
TEL: 0171 511 5665

Newham Healthcare NHS Trust
Newham Health Care
1 Helena Road
Plaistow
London
E13 0DZ
TEL: 0181 472 1444
FAX: 0181 552 0848

North East Essex Mental Health
   NHS Trust
Mental Health Services
Severalls Hospital
Boxted Road
Colchester
Essex
CO4 5HG
TEL: 01206 852271
FAX: 01206 844435

North Hertfordshire NHS Trust
Lister Hospital
Coreys Mill Lane
Stevenage
Herts
SG1 4AB
TEL: 01438 314333
FAX: 01438 781033

North Middlesex Hospital NHS
   Trust
Sterling Way
Edmonton
London
N18 1QX
TEL: 0181 887 2000
FAX: 0181 887 4219

North West London Mental Health
   NHS Trust
IKEA Tower
255 North Circular Road
Brent Park
London
NW10 0JQ
TEL: 0181 830 0033

Northwick Park & St Mark's NHS
   Trust
Northwick Park Hospital
Watford Road
Harrow
Middlesex
HA1 3UJ
TEL: 0181 869 2001
FAX: 0181 869 2009

Parkside NHS Trust
Paddington Community Hospital
Woodfield Road
London
W9 2BB
TEL: 0171 286 6669
FAX: 0171 286 9479

The Princess Alexandra Hospital
  NHS Trust
(West Essex Acute)
Princess Alexandra Hospital
Hamstel Road
Harlow
Essex
CM20 1QX
TEL: 01279 444455
FAX: 01279 429371

Redbridge Health Care NHS Trust
Barley Lane
Goodmayes
Ilford
Essex
IG3 8XJ
TEL: 0181 554 8811

Riverside Community Health Care
  NHS Trust
5–7 Parsons Green
London
SW6 4UL
TEL: 0181 846 6711
FAX: 0181 846 6749

Riverside Mental Health NHS Trust
Commonwealth House
2–4 Chalkhill Road
London
W6 8DW
TEL: 0181 746 8954
FAX: 0181 746 8978

Royal Free Hampstead NHS Trust
Royal Free Hospital
Pond Street
Hampstead
London
NW3 2QG

TEL: 0171 794 0500
FAX: 0171 435 5342

Royal Hospital of St Bartholomew,
  the Royal London Hospital and
  London Chest Hospital
The Royal London Hospital
53 Philpot Street
Whitechapel
London
E1 1BB
TEL: 0171 377 7000
FAX: 0171 377 7361

Royal London Homoeopathic
  Hospital NHS Trust
The Royal London Homoeopathic
  Hospital
Great Ormond Street
London
WC1N 3NR
TEL: 0171 837 8833

Royal National Orthopaedic
  Hospital NHS Trust
Brockley Hill
Stanmore
Middlesex
HA7 4LP
TEL: 0181 954 2300
FAX: 0181 954 7249

Royal National Throat, Nose & Ear
  Hospital NHS Trust
Gray's Inn Road
London
WC1X 8DA
TEL: 0171 837 8855
FAX: 0171 833 5518

St Albans and Hemel Hempstead
  NHS Trust
St Albans City Hospitals
Normandy Road
St Albans
Hertfordshire
AL3 5PN
TEL: 01727 866122

St Mary's NHS Trust
St Mary's Hospital
Praed Street
London
W2 1NY
TEL: 0171 725 6666
FAX: 0171 725 1017

Southend Community Care NHS
   Trust
Community House
Union Lane
Rochford
Essex
SS4 1RB
TEL: 01702 546354
FAX: 01702 546383

Southend Health Care NHS Trust
Southend Hospital
Prittlewell Chase
Westcliff On Sea
Essex
SS0 0RY
TEL: 01702 435853
FAX: 01702 435926

Tavistock and Portman NHS Trust
Tavistock and Portman Clinics
Tavistock Centre
120 Belsize Park
London
NW3 5BA
TEL: 0171 435 7111

Thameside Community Healthcare
   NHS Trust
Community Headquarters
South Ockendon Hospital
South Road
South Ockendon
Essex
RM15 6SB
TEL: 01708 851901
FAX: 01708 851463

Tower Hamlets Healthcare
Elizabeth Fry House
Mile End Hospital

Bancroft Road
London
E1 4DG
TEL: 0171 377 7920/21
FAX: 0171 377 7931

University College London
   Hospitals NHS Trust
25 Grafton Way
London
WC1E 6DB

Wellhouse NHS Trust
Edgware General Hospital
Burnt Oak Broadway
Edgware
Middlesex
HA8 0AD
TEL: 0181 952 2381
FAX: 0181 951 3078

West Hertfordshire Community
   Health NHS Trust
Head Office
99 Waverley Road
St Albans
Hertfordshire
AL3 5TL

The West London Healthcare NHS
   Trust
Ealing Hospital
Uxbridge Road
Southall
Middlesex
UB1 3EU
TEL: 0181 574 2444
FAX: 0181 574 3619

West Middlesex University
   Hospitals NHS Trust
Twickenham Road
Isleworth
Middlesex
TW7 6AF
TEL: 0181 565 2121

The Whittington Hospital NHS Trust
The Whittington Hospital

Highgate Hill
London
N19 5NF
TEL: 0171 272 3070
FAX: 0171 288 5550

## Special health authorities

The Great Ormond Street Hospital
   for Children
Great Ormond Street
London
WC1N 3JH
TEL: 0171 405 9200

Moorfields Eye Hospital
162 City Road
London
EC1V 2PD
TEL: 0171 253 3411

Royal Brompton Hospital NHS Trust
Sydney Street
London
SW3 6NP
TEL: 0171 352 8121
FAX: 0171 351 8290

The Royal Marsden NHS Trust
Fulham Road
London
SW3 6JJ
TEL: 0171 352 8171

## South Thames

Ashford Hospital NHS Trust
Ashford Hospital
London Road
Middlesex
TW15 3AA
TEL: 01784 264200
FAX: 01784 255696

Bournewood Community and
   Mental Health NHS Trust
Botley Park & St Peter's Hospital

Guildford Road
Chertsey
Surrey
KT16 0QA
TEL: 01483 728201

Brighton Healthcare NHS Trust
Royal Sussex County Hospital
Eastern Road
Brighton
BN2 5BE
TEL: 01273 696011

Bromley Hospitals NHS Trust
   (Bromley Acute)
Bromley Health Authority
Farnborough Hospital
Farnborough Common
Orpington
Kent
BR6 8ND
TEL: 01689 862422
FAX: 01689 862423

The Canterbury & Thanet
   Community Healthcare NHS
   Trust
St Martin's Hospital
Littlebourne Road
Canterbury
Kent CT1 1TD
TEL: 01227 459371
FAX: 01227 455509

Chichester Priority Care Services
   NHS Trust
9 College Lane
Chichester
West Sussex
PO19 4FX
TEL: 01243 787970

Crawley and Horsham NHS Trust
Crawley Hospital
West Green Drive
Crawley
West Sussex
RH11 7DH
TEL: 01293 527866

Croydon Community NHS Trust
12–18 Lennard Road
Croydon
CR9 2RS
TEL: 0181 680 2008
FAX: 0181 666 0495

Dartford & Gravesham NHS Trust
Joyce Green Hospital
Joyce Green Lane
Dartford
Kent
DA1 5PL
TEL: 01322 227242
FAX: 01322 283496

East Surrey Hospital and Com-
    munity Healthcare NHS Trust
East Surrey Hospital
Three Arch Road
Redhill
Surrey
RH1 5RH
TEL: 01737 768511

East Surrey Priority Care NHS Trust
Royal Earlswood
Brighton Road
Redhill
Surrey
RH1 6JL
TEL: 01737 556700
FAX: 01737 556701

Eastbourne & County Healthcare
    NHS Trust
Woodhill
The Drive
Hellingly
Hailsham
East Sussex
BN27 4EP
TEL: 01323 441000
FAX: 01323 842868

Eastbourne Hospitals NHS Trust
Eastbourne Hospitals
c/o District General Hospital

Kings Drive
Eastbourne
East Sussex
BN21 2UD
TEL: 01323 417400
FAX: 01323 36705

Epsom Health Care NHS Trust
Epsom General Hospital
Dorking Road
Epsom
Surrey
KT18 7EG
TEL: 01372 726100
FAX: 01372 745527

Frimley Park Hospital NHS Trust
Frimley Park Hospital
Portsmouth Road
Frimley
Surrey
GU16 5UJ
TEL: 01276 692777
FAX: 01276 691663

Greenwich Healthcare NHS Trust
Greenwich Health Authority
Memorial Hospital
Shooters Hill Road
London
SE18 3RZ
TEL: 0181 856 5511
FAX: 0181 856 8712

Guy's and St Thomas' NHS Trust
Guy's Hospital
St Thomas Street
London
SE1 9RT
TEL: 0171 955 5000

Hastings and Rother NHS Trust
St Annes House
729 The Ridge
St Leonards On Sea
East Sussex
TN37 7PT
TEL: 01424 754488
FAX: 01424 754263

Heathlands Mental Health NHS
    Trust
Heathlands House
The Ridgewood Centre
Old Bisley Road
Frimley
Camberley
Surrey
GU16 5QE
TEL: 01276 692919

Kent Ambulance NHS Trust
Heath Road
Coxheath
Maidstone
Kent
ME17 4BG
TEL: 01622 747010
FAX: 01622 743565

Kent and Canterbury Hospitals NHS
    Trust
Kent & Canterbury Hospital
Canterbury
CT1 3NG
TEL: 01227 766877

Kent & Sussex Weald NHS Trust
Pembury Hospital
Pembury
Tunbridge Wells
Kent
TN2 4OJ
TEL: 01892 511577

Kingston & District Community
    NHS Trust
Claremont
60 St James Road
Surbiton
Surrey
KT6 4QL
TEL: 0181 390 4511
FAX: 0181 390 5049

Kingston Hospital NHS Trust
Kingston Hospital
Glasworthy Road
Kingston Upon Thames

Surrey
KT2 7QB
TEL: 0181 546 7711
FAX: 0181 547 3345

King's Healthcare NHS Trust
King's College Hospital
Denmark Hill
London
SE5 9RS
TEL: 0171 274 6222

Lewisham and Guy's Mental Health
    NHS Trust
Trust Headquarters
Leegate House
Burnt Ash Road
Lee Green
London
SE12 8RG
TEL: 0181 297 0707
FAX: 0181 297 0377

Lewisham Hospital NHS Trust
Lewisham Hospital
Lewisham High Street
Lewisham
London
SE13 6LH
TEL: 0181 690 4311

Lifecare NHS Trust
St Lawrence's Hospital
Coulsdon Road
Caterham
Surrey
CR3 5YA
TEL: 01883 346411
FAX: 01883 347822

Maidstone Priority Care NHS Trust
The Pagoda
Hermitage Lane
Maidstone
Kent
ME16 9PD
TEL: 01622 721818
FAX: 01622 751919

Mayday Health Care NHS Trust
(Croydon)
Mayday Hospital
Mayday Road
Thornton Heath
Surrey
CR4 7YE
TEL: 0181 684 6999

The Medway NHS Trust
Medway Hospital
Windmill Lane
Gillingham
Kent
ME7 5NY
TEL: 01634 830000

Merton and Sutton Community NHS
Trust
Merton & Sutton Community Health
Care Services
Orchard Hill
Queen Mary's Avenue
Carshalton
Surrey
SM5 4NR
TEL: 0181 770 8375
FAX: 0181 643 5807

Mid-Kent Healthcare NHS Trust
The Maidstone Hospital
Hermitage Lane
Barming
Maidstone
Kent
ME16 9QQ
TEL: 01622 729000
FAX: 01622 720807

Mid-Sussex NHS Trust
The Princess Royal Hospital
Lewes Road
Haywards Heath
West Sussex
RH16 4EX
TEL: 01444 441881

North Downs Community Health
NHS Trust

Farnham Hospital
Hale Road
Farnham
Surrey
GU9 9QL
TEL: 01252 726666

North Kent Healthcare NHS Trust
Keycol Hospital
Newington
Nr Sittingbourne
Kent
ME9 8NG
TEL: 01634 407311

Optimum Health Services NHS Trust
Elizabeth Blackwell House
Wardells Grove
Avonley Road
London
SE14 5ER
TEL: 0171 639 2050
FAX: 0171 252 8026

Oxleas NHS Trust
Bexley Hospital
Old Bexley Lane
Bexley
Kent
DA5 2BW
TEL: 01322 526282

Pathfinder NHS Trust
(Wandsworth Mental Health)
Springfield Hospital
61 Glenburnie Road
London
SW17 7DJ
TEL: 0181 672 9911
FAX: 0181 767 7608

Queen Mary's, Sidcup, NHS Trust
Queen Mary's Hospital
Sidcup
Kent
DA14 6LT
TEL: 0181 302 2678

Queen Victoria Hospital NHS Trust
The Queen Victoria Hospital
Holtye Road
East Grinstead
West Sussex
RH19 3DZ
TEL: 01342 410210

Ravensbourne Priority Health NHS
   Trust
Bassetts House
Broadwater Gardens
Farnborough
Orpington
Kent
BR6 7UA
TEL: 01689 853339
FAX: 01689 855662

Richmond, Twickenham and Roe-
   hampton Healthcare NHS Trust
Roehampton House
Roehampton Lane
London
SW15 5PN
TEL: 0181 789 6611
FAX: 0181 780 1089

The Royal Surrey County & St
   Luke's Hospital NHS Trust
Royal Surrey County Hospital
Egerton Road
Guildford
Surrey
GU2 5XX
TEL: 01483 571122
FAX: 01483 37747

The Royal West Sussex NHS Trust
St Richard's Hospital
Chichester
West Sussex
PO19 4SE
TEL: 01243 788122

St George's Healthcare NHS Trust
St George's Health Care Group
St George's Hospital
Blackshaw Road

London
SW17 0QT
TEL: 0181 672 1255

The St Helier's NHS Trust
St Helier's Hospital
Wrythe Lane
Carshalton
Surrey
SM5 1AA
TEL: 0181 644 4343
FAX: 0181 641 4546

St Peters Hospital NHS Trust
St Peters Hospital
Guildford Road
Chertsey
Surrey
KT16 0PZ
TEL: 01932 872000
FAX: 01932 874757

South Downs Health NHS Trust
Brighton General Hospital
Elm Grove
Brighton
East Sussex
BN2 3EW
TEL: 01273 696011
FAX: 01273 697671

South Kent Community Healthcare
   NHS Trust
Radnor Park West
Folkstone
Kent
CT19 5HL
TEL: 01303 850202

South Kent Hospitals NHS Trust
William Harvey Hospital
Broomfield
Kennington Road
Willesborough
Ashford
Kent
TN24 0LZ
TEL: 01233 633331
FAX: 01233 612771

Surrey Ambulance Service NHS Trust
The Horseshoe
Bolters Lane
Banstead
Surrey
SM7 2AS
TEL: 01737 353333
FAX: 01737 370868

Surrey Heartlands
St Ebba's
Hook Road
Epsom
Surrey
KT19 8QJ
TEL: 01372 722212
FAX: 01372 725068

Sussex Ambulance Service NHS Trust
Ambulance Headquarters
Southfields Road
Eastbourne
BN21 1BZ

Teddington Memorial Hospital NHS
  Trust
Hampton Road
Teddington
Middlesex
TW11 0JL
TEL: 0181 977 2212
FAX: 0181 977 1914

Thameslink Healthcare Services NHS
  Trust
Archery House
Bow Arrow Lane
Dartford
Kent
DA2 6PB
TEL: 01322 227211
FAX: 01322 223492

Thanet Health Care NHS Trust
Thanet District General Hospital
St Peter's Road
Margate,
Kent
CT9 4AN

TEL: 01843 225544

Wandsworth Community Health
  NHS Trust
Clare House
St George's Hospital
Blackshaw Road
London
SW17 0QT
TEL: 0181 672 1255

Weald of Kent Community NHS
  Trust
Blackhurst
Halls Hole Road
Tunbridge Wells
Kent
TN2 4RG
TEL: 01892 539144
FAX: 01892 535522

West Lambeth Community Care
  NHS Trust
Tooting Beck Hospital
Church Lane
Tooting
London
SW17 8BL
TEL: 0171 326 5400
FAX: 0171 326 5574

Worthing Priority Care Services
  NHS Trust
Priority Care Services Unit HQ
Swandean Hospital
Arundel Road
Worthing
West Sussex
BN13 3EP
TEL: 01903 264121
FAX: 01903 691179

Worthing & Southlands Hospital
  NHS Trust
Park Avenue
Worthing
West Sussex
BN11 2OH
TEL: 01903 205111

**Special Health Authority**

The Bethlem and Maudsley NHS
    Trust
The Bethlem Royal Hospital
Monks Orchard Road
Beckenham
Kent
BR3 3BX
TEL: 0171 703 6333

## South West

Andover District Community NHS
    Trust
War Memorial Community Hospital
Andover
SP10 3LB
TEL: 01264 358811

Avalon, Somerset, NHS Trust
Tone Vale Hospital
Norton Fitzwarren
Taunton
Somerset
TA4 1DB
TEL: 01823 432375

Avon Ambulance Service NHS Trust
Ambulance Service Headquarters
Central Ambulance Station
Tower Hill
Bristol
BS2 0JA
TEL: 0117 9277046
FAX: 0117 9251419

The Bath and West Community NHS
    Trust
Avon & Somerset House
St Martins Hospital
Midford Road
Bath
BA2 5RP
TEL: 01225 832383
FAX: 01225 840407

Bath Mental Health Care NHS Trust
St Martins Hospital
Midford Road
Bath
BA2 5RP
TEL: 01225 832255
FAX: 01225 835940

Cornwall & Isles of Scilly Learning
    Disabilities NHS Trust
4 St Clement Vean
Tregolls
Truro
Cornwall
TR1 1NR
TEL: 01872 74242
FAX: 01872 40046

Cornwall Healthcare NHS Trust
Penrice Hospital
Porthpean Road
St Austell
Cornwall
PL26 6AD
TEL: 01726 68232

Dorset Ambulance Service NHS Trust
Headquarters
Ringwood Road
St Leonards
Ringwood
BH24 2SP
TEL: 01202 896111
FAX: 01202 891978

Dorset Community NHS Trust
Grove House
Millers Close
Dorchester
Dorset
DT1 1SS
TEL: 01305 264479
FAX: 01305 264474

Dorset Healthcare NHS Trust
Unit Headquarters
Shelley Road
Bournemouth
BH1 4JQ
TEL: 01202 303400
FAX: 01202 391565

East Gloucestershire NHS Trust
Burlington House
Lypiatt Road
Cheltenham
Gloucestershire
GL50 2QN
TEL: 01242 221188
FAX: 01242 221214

East Somerset Hospital NHS Trust
Yeovil District Hospital
Higher Kingston
Yeovil
Somerset
BA21 4AT
TEL: 01935 75122
FAX: 01935 26850

East Wiltshire Health Care NHS
  Trust
Community Care Unit
Victoria Hospital
Okus Road
Swindon
Wiltshire
SN1 4HZ
TEL: 01793 488991
FAX: 01793 432369

Exeter Community Services NHS
  Trust
Dean Clarke House
Southernhay East
Exeter
EX1 1PQ
TEL: 01392 411222
FAX: 01392 406157

Frenchay Healthcare NHS Trust
Frenchay
Bristol
BS16 1LE
TEL: 0117 970 1070
FAX: 0117 970 1070

Gloucestershire Ambulance Service
  NHS Trust
Ambulance Headquarters
Horton Road

Gloucester
GL1 3PX
TEL: 01452 395055
FAX: 01452 302184

Gloucestershire Royal NHS Trust
Gloucestershire Royal Hospital
Great Western Road
Gloucester
GL1 3NN
TEL: 01452 328555

Hampshire Ambulance Service NHS
  Trust
10 City Road
Winchester
Hants
SO23 8SD
TEL: 01962 860421
FAX: 01962 842156

Isle of Wight Community Healthcare
  NHS Trust
Whitecroft
Sandy Lane
Newport
Isle of Wight
PO30 3EB
TEL: 01983 526011
FAX: 01983 822142

North Hampshire Hospitals NHS
  Trust
Basingstoke District Hospital
Aldermaston Road
Basingstoke
Hampshire
RG24 9NA
TEL: 01256 473202

The North Hampshire, Loddon
  Community NHS Trust
Clock Tower House
Park Prewett
Aldermaston Road
Basingstoke
Hants
RG24 9LZ

TEL: 01256 473202
FAX: 01256 56275

Northern Devon Healthcare NHS
    Trust
Trust Headquarters
Riversvale
Litchdon Street
Barnstaple
North Devon
EX32 8ND
TEL: 01271 22577
FAX: 01271 75008

Phoenix NHS Trust
Stoke Park Hospital
Stapleton
Bristol
BS16 1QU
TEL: 01272 585000
FAX: 01272 592308

Plymouth Community Services NHS
    Trust
Mount Gould Hospital
Mount Gould Road
Plymouth
PL4 7QD
TEL: 01752 268011
FAX: 01752 272371

Plymouth Hospitals NHS Trust
Derriford Hospital
Derriford Road
Plymouth
PL6 8DH
TEL: 01752 777111

The Poole Hospital NHS Trust
Poole General Hospital
Longfleet Road
Poole
Dorset
BH13 2JB
TEL: 01202 675100
FAX: 01202 669277

Portsmouth Health Care NHS Trust
St James Hospital

Locksway Road
Portsmouth
Hants
PO4 8LD
TEL: 01705 822331

Portsmouth Hospitals NHS Trust
District Offices
St Mary's Hospital
Portsmouth
PO3 6AD
TEL: 01705 822331

Royal Bournemouth and
    Christchurch Hospitals NHS Trust
The Royal Bournemouth Hospital
Castle Lane East
Bournemouth
Dorset
BH7 7DW
TEL: 01202 303626
FAX: 01202 309538

The Royal Cornwall Hospitals NHS
    Trust
The Royal Cornwall Hospital
    (Treliske)
Truro
Cornwall
TR1 3LJ
TEL: 01872 74242
FAX: 01872 40574

The Royal Devon & Exeter NHS
    Trust
Royal Devon and Exeter Hospital
Barrack Road
Exeter
EX2 5DW
TEL: 01392 402361

Royal National Hospital for
    Rheumatic Diseases NHS Trust
Upper Borough Walls
Bath
BA1 1RL
TEL: 01225 465941
FAX: 01225 4212022

Royal United Hospital, Bath, NHS Trust
Royal United Hospital
Combe Park
Bath
BA1 3NG
TEL: 01225 823142
FAX: 01225 332886

Salisbury Health Care NHS Trust
Salisbury District Hospital
Salisbury
Wiltshire
SP2 8BJ
TEL: 01722 336262

Severn NHS Trust
Rikenal
Montpellier
Gloucester
GL1 1LY
TEL: 01452 29421

South Devon Health Care NHS Trust
Hengrave House
Torbay Hospital
Lawes Bridge
Torquay
TQ2 7AA
TEL: 01803 614567
FAX: 01803 616334

Southampton Community Health Services NHS Trust
Central Health Clinic
East Park Terrace
Southampton
SO9 4WN
TEL: 01703 634321
FAX: 01703 634375

Southampton University Hospitals NHS Trust
Southampton General Hospital
Tremona Road
Shirley
Southampton
Hants
SO9 4XY

TEL: 01703 777222

Southmead Health Services NHS Trust
Southmead Hospital
Westbury on Trym
Bristol
BS10 5NS
TEL: 0117 950 5050
FAX: 0117 950 0902

St Mary's Hospital NHS Trust (Isle of Wight Acute)
St Mary's Hospital
Parkhurst
Newport
Isle of Wight
PO30 5TG
TEL: 01983 524081
FAX: 01983 822569

Swindon & Marlborough NHS Trust
Princess Margaret Hospital
Okus Road
Swindon
Wiltshire
SN1 4JU
TEL: 01793 536231

Taunton & Somerset Hospital NHS Trust
Musgrove Park Hospital
Taunton
TA1 1DA
TEL: 01823 333444
FAX: 01823 336877

United Bristol Healthcare NHS Trust
Trust Headquarters
Marlborough Street
Bristol
BS1 3UN
TEL: 0117 928 3604
FAX: 0117 925 6588

West Country Ambulance Service NHS Trust
Heathlands Business Park (Unit 6B)
Heathlands Road

Liskeard
Cornwall
PL14 4DH
TEL: 01579 340454
FAX: 01579 340455

West Dorset General Hospitals NHS
  Trust
Dorset County Hospital
Princes Street
Dorchester
Dorset
DT1 1TS
TEL: 01305 263123
FAX: 01305 262877

Weston Area Health NHS Trust
Weston General Hospital
Grange Road
Uphill
Weston Super Mare
Avon BS23 4TQ
TEL: 01934 636363
FAX: 01934 619275

Wiltshire Ambulance Service NHS
  Trust
Ambulance Service Headquarters
Malmesbury Road
Chippenham
SN15 5LN
TEL: 01249 443939
FAX: 01249 443217

Wiltshire Healthcare NHS Trust
St Johns Hospital
Bradley Road
Trowbridge
Wiltshire
BA14 0QU
TEL: 01225 753610
FAX: 01225 777697

Winchester and Eastleigh Healthcare
  NHS Trust
Royal Hampshire County Hospital
Romsey Road
Winchester

SO22 5DG
TEL: 01962 863535

## West Midlands

Alexandra Healthcare NHS Trust
The Alexandra Hospital
Woodrow Drive
Redditch
B98 7UB
TEL: 01527 503030
FAX: 01527 517432

Birmingham Children's Hospital
  NHS Trust
The Children's Hospital
Ladywood Middleway
Ladywood
Birmingham
B16 8ET
TEL: 0121 454 4851

Birmingham Heartlands Hospital
  NHS Trust
51 Bordesley Green East
Birmingham
B9 5ST
TEL: 0121 766 6611
FAX: 0121 773 6736

Birmingham Women's Health Care
  NHS Trust
Birmingham Maternity Hospital
Queen Elizabeth Medical Centre
Edgbaston
Birmingham
B15 2TG
TEL: 0121 627 2601
FAX: 0121 627 2602

Black Country Mental Health NHS
  Trust
(Sandwell Mental Health)
48 Lodge Road
West Bromwich
West Midlands
B70 8NY
TEL: 0121 553 7676
FAX: 0121 607 3579

Burton Hospitals NHS Trust
Burton District Hospital Centre
Belvedere Road
Burton on Trent
DE13 0RB
TEL: 01283 66333

City Hospitals NHS Trust
Dudley Road
Birmingham
B18 7QH
TEL: 0121 554 3801
FAX: 0121 551 5562

Coventry Healthcare NHS Trust
Gulson Clinic
Gulson Road
Coventry
CV1 2JL
TEL: 01203 844064

Dudley Group of Hospitals NHS
   Trust
Dudley Road Hospital
Dudley Road
Birmingham
B18 7QH
TEL: 0121 554 3801
FAX: 0121 551 5562

Dudley Priority Health NHS Trust
Ashwoodhay
Ridge Hill
Brierley Hill Road
Stourbridge
DY8 5ST
TEL: 01384 401401
FAX: 01384 400217

First Community Health NHS Trust
Mellor House
Corporation Street
Stafford
ST16 3SR
TEL: 01785 222888
FAX: 01785 54640

The Foundation NHS Trust
St George's Hospital

Corporation Street
Stafford
ST16 3SR
TEL: 01785 57888
FAX: 01785 54640

The George Eliot Hospital NHS Trust
George Eliot Hospital
College Street
Nuneaton
Warwickshire
CV10 7DJ
TEL: 01203 865072

Good Hope Hospital NHS Trust
Rectory Road
Sutton Coldfield
West Midlands
B75 7RR
TEL: 0121 378 2211
FAX: 0121 378 0929

Hereford and Worcester Ambulance
   Service NHS Trust
Ambulance Headquarters
Powick
Worcester
WR2 4SS
TEL: 01905 830630

Hereford Hospitals NHS Trust
County Hospital
Hereford
HR1 2ER
TEL: 01432 355444
FAX: 01432 354066

Herefordshire Community Health
   NHS Trust
St Mary's Hospital
Burghill
Hereford
HR4 7RF
TEL: 01432 760324
FAX: 01432 761174

Kidderminster Health Care NHS Trust
Kidderminster General Hospital
Bewdley Road

Kidderminster
DY11 6RJ
TEL: 01562 823424

Mid Staffordshire General Hospitals
  NHS Trust
Stafford District General Hospital
Weston Road
Stafford
ST16 3SA
TEL: 01785 57731

The North East Worcestershire
  Community Healthcare NHS
  Trust
Smallwood Health Centre
Church Green West
Redditch
B97 4DJ
TEL: 01527 60121

Northern Birmingham Community
  Health NHS Trust
Family & Preventive Services Unit
Carnegie Centre
Hunters Road
Hockley
Birmingham
B19 1DR
TEL: 0121 554 3899

Northern Birmingham Mental Health
  NHS Trust
All Saints Hospital
Lodge Road
Birmingham
B18 5SD
TEL: 0121 523 5151
FAX: 0121 515 2311

North Staffordshire Hospital NHS
  Trust
City General Hospital
Newcastle Road
Stoke on Trent
ST4 6QG
TEL: 01782 715444

North Staffordshire Combined
  Healthcare NHS Trust
Bucknall Hospital
Eaves Lane
Bucknall
Stoke on Trent
ST2 8LD
TEL: 01782 273510
FAX: 01782 213682

The North Warwickshire NHS Trust
139 Earls Road
Nuneaton
CV11 5HP
TEL: 01203 328411

Premier Health NHS Trust
Imex
Shobnall Road
Burton on Trent
Staffordshire
DE14 2AU
TEL: 01283 515616
FAX: 01283 30630

The Princess Royal Hospital NHS
  Trust
The Princess Royal Hospital
Apley Castle
Telford
Shropshire
TF6 6TF
TEL: 01952 641222

Robert Jones & Agnes Hunt
  Orthopaedic & District Hospital
  NHS Trust
Oswestry
Shropshire
SY10 7AG
TEL: 01691 655311

The Royal Orthopaedic Hospital
  NHS Trust
Woodlands
Northfields
Birmingham
B31 2AP
TEL: 0121 627 1627

Royal Shrewsbury Hospitals NHS
    Trust
Royal Shrewsbury Hospital North
Mytton Oak Road
Shrewsbury
SY3 8YF
TEL: 01743 231122
FAX: 01743 243856

The Royal Wolverhampton
    Hospitals NHS Trust
New Cross Hospital
Wednesfield Road
Wolverhampton
WV10 0QP
TEL: 01902 307721

The Rugby NHS Trust
17 Warwick Street
Rugby
CV21 3DN
TEL: 01788 572831
FAX: 01788 61561

Sandwell Healthcare NHS Trust
Sandwell District General Hospital
Lyndon
West Bromwich
B71 4HJ
TEL: 0121 553 1831

Shropshire Community Health
    Service NHS Trust
Brayford House
Cross Houses
Shrewsbury
SY5 6JN
TEL: 01743 761242
FAX: 01743 761032

Shropshire's Mental Health NHS
    Trust
The Royal Shrewsbury Hospital
Shelton
Bicton Heath
Shrewsbury
SY3 8DN
TEL: 01743 231122

Solihull Healthcare NHS Trust
Berwicks Lane
Marston Green
Birmingham
B37 7XR
TEL: 0121 779 6035
FAX: 0121 779 5926

South Birmingham Mental Health
    NHS Trust
Vincent Drive
Edgbaston
Birmingham
B15 2TZ
TEL: 0121 4722294
FAX: 0121 4711866

South Warwickshire General NHS
    Trust
South Warwickshire Hospital
Lakin Road
Warwick
CV34 5BW
TEL: 01926 493491

South Warwickshire Health Care
    NHS Trust
Community Health Offices
Alcester Road
Stratford upon Avon
CV37 6PW
TEL: 01789 269264
FAX: 01789 413608

South Warwickshire Mental Health
    Services NHS Trust
Central Hospital
Hatton
Warwick
CV35 7EE
TEL: 01926 496241
FAX: 01926 401690

South Worcestershire Community
    NHS Trust
The Community Unit
Isaac Maddox House
Shrub Hill Road
Worcester

WR4 9RW
TEL: 01905 763333
FAX: 01905 610292

Southern Birmingham Community
   Health NHS Trust
West Heath Hospital
Rednall Road
West Heath
Birmingham
B38 8HR
TEL: 0121 627 1627
FAX: 0121 627 8228

Staffordshire Ambulance Service
   NHS Trust
Ambulance Service Headquarters
70 Stone Road
Stafford
ST16 2RS
TEL: 01785 53521
FAX: 01785 46238

University Hospital Birmingham
   NHS Trust
Selly Oak Hospital
Oak Tree Lane
Birmingham
B29 6JF
TEL: 0121 627 1627
FAX: 0121 627 8641

Walsall Community Health NHS
   Trust
Community Health Services Unit
Lichfield House
27–31 Lichfield Street
Walsall
WS1 1TE
TEL: 01922 720255
FAX: 01922 656040

Walsall Hospitals NHS Trust
Manor Hospital
Moat Road
Walsall
West Midlands
WS2 9PS
TEL: 01922 721172
FAX: 01922 722951

The Walsgrave Hospitals NHS Trust
Walsgrave Hospital
Clifford Bridge Road
Walsgrave
Coventry
CV2 2DX
TEL: 01203 602020

Warwickshire Ambulance Service
   NHS Trust
Ambulance HQ
50 Holly Walk
Leamington Spa
CV32 4HY
TEL: 01926 881331

West Midlands Ambulance Service
   NHS Trust
West Midlands Metropolitan
   Ambulance Service Headquarters
4th Floor
6 The Minories
Dudley
DY2 8NP
TEL: 01384 455644

Wolverhampton Health Care NHS
   Trust
Cleveland/Leasowes
10/12 Tetterhall Road
Wolverhampton
WV1 4SA
TEL: 01902 310641
FAX: 01902 716834

Worcester Royal Infirmary NHS
   Trust
Newtown Branch
Newtown Road
Worcester
WR5 1JG
TEL: 01905 763333

## North West

Aintree Hospitals NHS Trust
Aintree House
Fazakerley Hospital
Longmoor Lane

Liverpool
L9 7AL
TEL: 0151 525 3622
FAX: 0151 525 6086

Blackburn, Hyndburn & Ribble
Valley Health Care NHS Trust
Queens Park Hospital
Haslingden Road
Blackburn
BB2 3HH
TEL: 01254 263555
FAX: 01254 293803

Blackpool Victoria Hospital NHS
Trust
Whinney Heys Road
Blackpool
FY3 8NR
TEL: 01253 300000

Blackpool, Wyre and Fylde
Community Health Services NHS
Trust
Wesham Park Hospital
Derby Road
Wesham
Preston
PR4 3AL
TEL: 01253 303256

Bolton Hospitals NHS Trust
Bolton General Hospital
Minerva Road
Farnworth
Bolton
BL4 0JR
TEL: 01204 22444
FAX: 01204 390794

Burnley Health Care NHS Trust
Burnley General Hospital
Casterton Avenue
Burnley
Lancashire
BB10 2PQ
TEL: 01282 474520
FAX: 01282 56239

Bury Health Care NHS Trust
Bury Health Authority
21 Silver Street
Bury
BL9 0EN
TEL: 0161 764 6081
FAX: 0161 705 3028

Calderstones NHS Trust
Burnley Pendle & Rossendale Health
Authority
Unit Office
Calderstones
Mitton Road
Whalley
Blackburn
BB6 9PE
TEL: 01254 822121

The Cardiothoracic Centre Liverpool
NHS Trust
Thomas Drive
Liverpool
L14 3LB
TEL: 0151 228 1616
FAX: 0151 220 8573

Central Manchester Healthcare NHS
Trust
2nd Floor Cobbett House
Manchester Royal Infirmary
Oxford Road
Manchester
M13 9WL
TEL: 0161 276 1234
FAX: 0161 273 5642

The Cheshire Community Healthcare
NHS Trust
Cheshire Community Healthcare
NHS Trust Headquarters
Barony Road
Nantwich
Cheshire
CW5 5QU
TEL: 01270 610000
FAX: 01270 627469

Chester & Halton Community NHS
   Trust
Countess of Chester Hospital
Moston Lodge
Liverpool Road
Chester
CH2 1BQ
TEL: 01244 364877
FAX: 01244 366001

Chorley and South Ribble NHS Trust
Chorley District Hospital
Preston Road
Chorley
PR7 1PP
TEL: 01257 261222
FAX: 01257 245309

Christie Hospital NHS Trust
Wilmstow Road
Withington
Manchester
M20 9BX
TEL: 0161 446 3000
FAX: 0161 446 3820

Clatterbridge Centre for Oncology
   NHS Trust
Clatterbridge Hospital
Clatterbridge Road
Bebington
L63 4JY
TEL: 0151 334 4000
FAX: 0151 334 0882

CommuniCare NHS Trust
Accrington Victoria Community
   Hospital
Heywood Road
Accrington
BB5 6AS
TEL: 01254 687160
FAX: 01254 687074

Community Healthcare Bolton NHS
   Trust
St Peter's House
Silverwell Street
Bolton
BL1 1PP

TEL: 01204 390093
FAX: 01204 390193

The Countess of Chester Hospital
   NHS Trust
Countess of Chester Hospital
Liverpool Road
Chester
CH2 1BQ
TEL: 01244 365000

East Cheshire NHS Trust
Macclesfield District General
   Hospital
Westpark Branch
Prestbury Road
Macclesfield
Cheshire
SK10 3BL
TEL: 01625 421000
FAX: 01625 661644

Furness Hospitals NHS Trust
Furness General Hospital
Dalton Lane
Barrow in Furness
Cumbria
LA14 4LF
TEL: 01229 870870

Greater Manchester Ambulance
   Service NHS Trust
Ambulance Service Headquarters
Bury Old Road
Whitefield
Manchester
M25 6AQ
TEL: 0161 231 7921
FAX: 0161 223 1351

Guild Community Healthcare NHS
   Trust
Unit Offices
Whittingham Hospital
Whittingham
Preston
PR3 2JH
TEL: 01772 865531
FAX: 01772 862293

Halton General Hospital NHS Trust
Halton General Hospital
Runcorn
Cheshire
WA7 2DA
TEL: 01928 714567


Lancashire Ambulance Service NHS
    Trust
Ambulance Service Headquarters
Broughton House
449–451 Garstang Road
Broughton
Nr Preston
PR3 5LN
TEL: 01772 711278
FAX: 01772 711692


Lancaster Acute Hospitals NHS
    Trust
Trust Headquarters
PO Box 15
Lancaster Moor Hospital
Lancaster
LA1 3SN
TEL: 01524 65241
FAX: 01524 61645


Lancaster Priority Services NHS
    Trust
Lancaster Moor Hospital
Quernmore Road
Lancaster
LA1 3JR
TEL: 01524 65241
FAX: 01524 61645


Liverpool Women's Hospital NHS
    Trust
Mill Road Maternity Hospital
Mill Road
Liverpool
L6 2AH
TEL: 0151 260 8787
FAX: 0151 263 9152


Manchester Children's Hospitals
    NHS Trust

Royal Manchester Children's
    Hospitals
Hospital Road
Pendlebury
Manchester
M27 1HA
TEL: 0161 795 7000
FAX: 0161 741 5510


Mancunian Community Health NHS
    Trust
Mancunian Trust
Mauldeth House
Mauldeth Road West
Chorlton
Manchester
M21 2RL
TEL: 0161 881 7233
FAX: 0161 881 9366


Mental Health Services of Salford
    NHS Trust
Prestwick Hospital
Bury New Road
Prestwick
Manchester
M25 7BL
TEL: 0161 773 9121
FAX: 0161 773 8186


Mersey Regional Ambulance Service
    NHS Trust
Ambulance Headquarters
Elm House
Belmont Grove
Liverpool
L6 4EG
TEL: 0151 260 5220
FAX: 0151 206 4475


Mid Cheshire Hospitals NHS Trust
Leighton Hospital
Middlewich Road
Crewe
Cheshire
CW1 4QJ
TEL: 01270 255 141
FAX: 01270 587 696

North Manchester Healthcare NHS
Trust
North Manchester General Hospital
Decaunays Road
Crumpsall
Manchester
M8 6RL
TEL: 0161 740 9781
FAX: 0161 740 4450

The North Mersey Community NHS
Trust
Rathbone Hospital
Mill Lane
Liverpool
L13 4AW
TEL: 0151 250 3000
FAX: 0151 228 0486

The Oldham NHS Trust
District Headquarters
Westhulme Avenue
Oldham
OL1 2PN
TEL: 0161 624 0420
FAX: 0161 627 3130

Preston Acute Hospitals NHS Trust
Royal Preston Hospital
Sharoe Green Lane
Fulwood
Preston
PR2 4HT
TEL: 01772 710692
FAX: 01772 711692

Rochdale Healthcare NHS Trust
Birch Hill Hospital
Rochdale
OL12 9QB
TEL: 01706 377777
FAX: 01706 755130

Royal Liverpool and Broadgreen
University Hospitals NHS Trust
Royal Liverpool University Hospital
Prescott Street
Liverpool
L7 8XP

TEL: 0151 706 2000
FAX: 0151 706 5806

The Royal Liverpool Children's
Hospital NHS Trust Alder Hey
Eaton Road
Liverpool
L12 2AP
TEL: 0151 228 4811
FAX: 0151 228 0328

Salford Community Health Care
NHS Trust
Joule House
49 The Crescent
Salford
M5 4NW
TEL: 0161 743 0477
FAX: 0161 743 0462

Salford Royal Hospitals NHS Trust
Hope Hospitals
Stott Lane
Salford
Manchester
M6 8HD
TEL: 0161 789 7373
FAX: 0161 787 4670

St Helens and Knowsley Community
Health NHS Trust
The Hollies
Cowley Hill Lane
St Helens
Merseyside
WA10 2AP
TEL: 01744 457238
FAX: 01744 453615

St Helen's & Knowsley Hospital
NHS Trust
Whiston Hospital
Prescot
Merseyside
L35 5DR
TEL: 0151 426 1600
FAX: 0151 430 8478

South Cumbria Community and
  Mental Health NHS Trust
Community Health Offices
2 Fairfield Lane
Barrow in Furness
Cumbria
LA13 9AJ
TEL: 01229 833056
FAX: 01229 823224

South Manchester University
  Hospitals NHS Trust
Trust Headquarters
Wythenshawe Hospital
Southmoor Road
Manchester
M23 9LT
TEL: 0161 998 7070
FAX: 0161 946 2037

Southport and Formby Community
  Health Services NHS Trust
Hesketh Centre
Albert Road
Southport
Merseyside
PR9 8BL
TEL: 01704 547471
FAX: 01704 211415

Southport and Formby NHS Trust
Southport and Formby District
  General Hospital
Town Lane
Kew
Southport
Merseyside
PR8 6NJ
TEL: 01704 547471
FAX: 01704 500962

Stockport Acute Services NHS Trust
Oak House
Stepping Hill Hospital
Stockport
SK2 7JG
TEL: 0161 419 5001
FAX: 0161 419 5003

Stockport Healthcare NHS Trust
Oak Hill
Stepping Hill Hospital
Poplar Grove
Stockport
SK2 7JE
TEL: 0161 419 5029
FAX: 0161 419 5003

Tameside and Glossop Acute
  Services NHS Trust
Tameside General Hospital
Fountain Street
Ashton Under Lyne
TEL: 0161 330 8373

Tameside and Glossop Community
  & Priority Services NHS Trust
Tameside General Hospital
Fountain Street
Ashton Under Lyne
TEL: 0161 330 8373

Trafford Healthcare NHS Trust
Urmston District Headquarters
Moorside Road
Urmston
Manchester
M31 3FP
TEL: 0161 456 7214

The Walton Centre for Neurology
  and Neurosurgery NHS Trust
Walton Hospital
Rice Lane
Liverpool
L9 1AE
TEL: 0151 525 3611
FAX: 0151 525 3857

Warrington Community NHS Trust
Winwick Hospital
Winwick
Warrington
WA2 8RR
TEL: 01925 55221

Warrington Hospital NHS Trust
Warrington District General Hospital

Lovely Lane
Warrington
Cheshire
WA5 1QG
TEL: 01925 35911

West Cheshire NHS Trust
Liverpool Road
Chester
CH2 1UL
TEL: 01244 364228
FAX: 01244 364227

The West Lancashire NHS Trust
Ormskirk & District General
    Hospital
Wigan Road
Ormskirk
L39 2AZ
TEL: 01695 577111

Westmoreland Hospital NHS Trust
    (Kendal Acute)
Westmoreland General Hospital
Burton Road
Kendal
Cumbria
LA9 7RG
TEL: 01539 732288
FAX: 01539 740852

Wigan & Leigh Health Services NHS
    Trust
Whelley Hospital
Bradshaw Street
Wigan
WN1 3XN
TEL: 09142 822820

Wirral Community Healthcare NHS
    Trust
Victoria Central Hospital
Mill Lane
Wallasey
L44 5UP
TEL: 0151 678 5111
FAX: 0151 639 2478

The Wirral Hospitals NHS Trust
Arrowe Park
Upton
Wirral
L49 5PE
TEL: 0151 334 4000
FAX: 0151 606 9609

Wrightington Hospital NHS Trust
Wrightington Hospital
Hall Lane
Wrightington
Wigan
Lancashire
WN6 9EP
TEL: 01257 56214
FAX: 01257 53809

## New NHS Trusts 1996

Birmingham Heartlands and Solihull
    (Teaching) NHS Trust
Birmingham Heartlands NHS Trust
    and Solihull Hospital

London Ambulance Service NHS
    Trust
Ambulance Headquarters
220 Waterloo Road
London
SE1 8SD

University College London
    Hospitals NHS Trust
9th Floor
St Martin's House
140 Tottenham Court Road
London
W1P 9LN

## Other mergers

Hartlepool & East Durham NHS
    Trust
Hartlepool General Hospital
Holdforth Road
Hartlepool
Cleveland
TS24 9AH

Lincoln and Louth NHS Trust
County Hospital
Greetwell Road
Lincoln
LN2 5QY

South Durham NHS Trust
Winterton Hospital
Sedgefield
County Durham
TS21 3EJ

Worcestershire Community
  Healthcare NHS Trust
Isaac Maddox House
Shrub Hill Road
Worcester
WR4 9RW

## Northern Ireland

Altnagelvin Hospitals HSS Trust
Altnagelvin Area Hospital
Glenshane Road
Londonderry
BT47 1SB
TEL: 01504 45171
FAX: 01504 611222

Armagh and Dungannon HSS Trust
Gosford Place
The Mall
Armagh
BT61 9AR
TEL: 01861 522262
FAX: 01861 522544

Belfast City Hospital HSS Trust
51 Lisburn Road
Belfast
BT9 7AB
TEL: 01232 329241
FAX: 01232 326614

Causeway HSS Trust
8E Coleraine Road
Ballymoney
BT53 6BP

TEL: 012656 66600
FAX: 012656 66630

Craigavon Area Hospital Group HSS
  Trust
68 Lurgan Road
Portadown
Craigavon
BT63 5QQ
TEL: 01762 334444
FAX: 01762 350068

Craigavon and Banbridge
  Community HSS Trust
Bannvale House
Moyallen Road
Gilford
BT63 5JX
TEL: 01762 831983
FAX: 01762 831993

Down Lisburn HSS Trust
Lisburn Health Centre
25 Linenhall Street
Lisburn
BT28 1BH
TEL: 01846 665181
FAX: 01846 665179

Foyle HSS Trust
Riverview House
Abercorn Road
Londonderry
BT48 6SA
TEL: 01504 266111
FAX: 01504 260806

Green Park HSS Trust
20 Stockman's Lane
Belfast
BT9 7JB
TEL: 01232 669501
FAX: 01232 382008

Homefirst Community HSS Trust
The Cottage
5 Greenmount Avenue
Ballymena
Co Antrim

BT43 6DA
TEL: 01266 633700
FAX: 01266 633733

Mater Infirmorum Hospital HSS
  Trust
45–51 Crumlin Road
Belfast
BT14 6AB
TEL: 01232 741211
FAX: 01232 741342

Newry and Mourne HSS Trust
5 Downshire Place
Newry
BT34 1DZ
TEL: 01693 60505
FAX: 01693 69064

North and West Belfast HSS
  Trust
Glendinning House
6 Murray Street
Belfast
BT1 6DP
TEL: 01232 327156
FAX: 01232 249109

North Down and Ards Community
  HSS Trust
23–25 Regent Street
Newtownards
BT23 4AD
TEL: 01247 816666
FAX: 01247 820140

Northern Ireland Ambulance Service
  HSS Trust
Ambulance Service Headquarters
12/22 Linenhall Street
Belfast BT2 8BS
TEL: 01232 246113
FAX: 01232 333090

Royal Group of Hospitals and Dental
  Hospital HSS Trust
274 Grosvenor Road
Belfast
BT12 6BP

TEL: 01232 240503
FAX: 01232 240899

South and East Belfast HSS Trust
Trust Headquarters
Knockbracken Healthcare Park
Saintfield Road
Belfast
BT8 8BH
TEL: 01232 790673
FAX: 01232 796632

Sperrin Lakeland HSS Trust
15 Elliott Place
Enniskillen
BT74 7HQ
TEL: 01365 322500
FAX: 01365 326556

Ulster, North Down and Ards
  Hospitals HSS Trust
700 Upper Newtonards Road
Dundonald
Belfast
BT16 0RH
TEL: 01232 484511
FAX: 01232 481753

United Hospitals HSS Trust
Antrim Area Hospital
45 Bush Road
Antrim
BT41 2RL
TEL: 01849 424000
FAX: 01849 424654

## Scotland

Aberdeen Royal Hospitals NHS
  Trust
Foresterhill House
Ashgrove Road West
Aberdeen
AB9 1ZB
TEL: 01224 681818
FAX: 01224 840597

Angus NHS Trust
Whitehills Hospital

Forfar
Angus
DD8 3DY
TEL: 01307 464551
FAX: 01307 465129

Argyll & Bute Unit NHS Trust
Trust Headquarters
Aros
Lochgilphead
Argyll
PA31 8LB
TEL: 01546 606600
FAX: 01546 606622

Ayrshire & Arran Community
   Healthcare NHS Trust
1a Hunters Avenue
Ayr
KA8 9DW
TEL: 01292 281821
FAX: 01292 610213

Borders Community Health Services
   NHS Trust
Headquarters
Huntlyburn House
Melrose
TD6 9BP
TEL: 01896 662300
FAX: 01896 822887

Borders General Hospital NHS
   Trust
Borders General Hospital
Near Melrose
TD6 9BS
TEL: 01896 754333
FAX: 01896 662291

Caithness & Sutherland NHS
   Trust
Caithness General Hospital
Wick
Caithness
KW1 5LA
TEL: 01955 605050
FAX: 01955 604606

Central Scotland Healthcare NHS
   Trust
Trust Headquarters
Royal Scottish National Hospital
Old Denny Road
Larbert
FK5 4SD
TEL: 01324 570700
FAX: 01324 563552

Dumfries & Galloway Acute &
   Maternity Hospitals NHS Trust
Dumfries & Galloway Royal
   Infirmary
Bankend Road
Dumfries
DG1 4AP
TEL: 01387 246246
FAX: 01387 241639

Dumfries & Galloway Community
   Health NHS Trust
Campbell House
Crichton Royal Hospital
Glencaple Road
Dumfries
DG1 4TG
TEL: 01387 255301
FAX: 01387 244101

Dundee Healthcare NHS Trust
Liff Hospital
Dundee
DD2 5NF
TEL: 01382 580441
FAX: 01382 581329

Dundee Teaching Hospitals NHS
   Trust
Ninewells Hospital
Dundee
DD1 9SY
TEL: 01382 660111
FAX: 01382 660445

East & Midlothian NHS Trust
Edenhall Hospital
Pinkie Burn

Musselburgh
EH21 7TZ
TEL: 0131 536 8000
FAX: 0131 536 8153

Edinburgh Healthcare NHS Trust
Astley Ainslie Hospital
133 Grange Loan
Edinburgh
EH9 2HL
TEL: 0131 537 9000
FAX: 0131 537 9500

Edinburgh Sick Children's NHS Trust
Royal Hospital for Sick Children
Sciennes Road
Edinburgh
EH9 1LF
TEL: 0131 536 0000
FAX: 0131 536 0001

Falkirk & District Royal Infirmary
    NHS Trust
Falkirk & District Royal Infirmary
Major's Loan
Falkirk
FK1 5QE
TEL: 01324 624000
FAX: 01324 612340

Fife Healthcare NHS Trust
Cameron House
Cameron Bridge
Leven
KY8 5RG
TEL: 01592 712812
FAX: 01592 712762

Glasgow Dental Hospital & School
    NHS Trust
378 Sauchiehall Street
Glasgow
G2 3JZ
TEL: 0141 211 9600
FAX: 0141 211 9800
FAX: 0141 311 2798 (School)

Glasgow Royal Infirmary University
    NHS Trust
Glasgow Royal Infirmary
84 Castle Street
Glasgow
G4 0SF
TEL: 0141 552 3535
FAX: 0141 304 4889

Grampian Healthcare NHS Trust
Westholme
Woodend General Hospital
Eday Road
Aberdeen
AB2 6LR
TEL: 01224 663131
FAX: 01224 840790

Greater Glasgow Community &
    Mental Health Services NHS
    Trust
Trust Headquarters
Gartnavel Royal Hospital
1055 Great Western Road
Glasgow
G12 0XH
TEL: 0141 211 3600
FAX: 0141 334 0875

Hairmyres & Stonehouse Hospitals
    NHS Trust
Hairmyres Hospital
East Kilbride
G75 8RG
TEL: 013552 20292
FAX: 013552 34064

Highland Communities NHS Trust
Royal Northern Infirmary
Ness Walk
Inverness
IV2 5SF
TEL: 01463 704000
FAX: 01463 713844

Inverclyde Royal NHS Trust
Inverclyde Royal Hospital
Larkfield Road
Greenock

PA16 0XN
TEL: 01475 633777
FAX: 01475 631700

Kirkcaldy Acute Hospitals NHS
Trust
Victoria Hospital
Hayfield Road
Kirkcaldy
KY2 5AH
TEL: 01592 643355
FAX: 01592 647041

Lanarkshire Healthcare NHS Trust
Unit Office
Strathclyde Hospital
Airbles Road
Motherwell
ML1 3B2
TEL: 01698 230500
FAX: 01698 275674

Law Hospital NHS Trust
Law Hospital
Carluke
ML8 5ER
TEL: 01698 361100
FAX: 01698 376671

Lomond Healthcare NHS Trust
Vale of Leven District General
Hospital
Alexandria
Dunbartonshire
G83 0UA
TEL: 01389 754121
FAX: 01389 755948

Monklands & Bellshill Hospital NHS
Trust
Monklands District General Hospital
Monkscourt Avenue
Airdrie
ML6 0JS
TEL: 01236 748748
FAX: 01236 760015

Moray Health Services NHS Trust
Maryhill House

317 High Street
Elgin
Moray
IV30 1AJ
TEL: 01343 543131
FAX: 01343 540834

North Ayrshire & Arran NHS Trust
Crosshouse Hospital
Kilmarnock
KA2 0BE
TEL: 01563 521133
FAX: 01563 539787

Perth & Kinross Healthcare NHS
Trust
Trust Headquarters
Taymount Terrace
Perth
PH1 1NX
TEL: 01738 623311
FAX: 01738 473278

Queen Margaret Hospital NHS Trust
Queen Margaret Hospital
Whitefield Road
Dunfermline
KY12 0SU
TEL: 01383 623623
FAX: 01383 624156

Raigmore Hospital NHS Trust
Raigmore Hospital
Old Perth Road
Inverness
IV2 3UJ
TEL: 01463 704000
FAX: 01463 711322

Renfewshire Healthcare NHS Trust
Trust Headquarters
Dykebar Hospital
Grahamston Road
Paisley
PA2 7DE
TEL: 0141 884 5122
FAX: 0141 884 5425

Royal Alexandra Hospital NHS
Trust
Royal Alexandra Hospital
Corsebar Road
Paisley
PA2 9PN
TEL: 0141 887 9111
FAX: 0141 887 6701

Royal Infirmary of Edinburgh NHS
Trust
Royal Infirmary of Edinburgh
1 Lauriston Place
Edinburgh
EH3 9YW
TEL: 0131 536 1000
FAX: 0131 536 3002

Scottish Ambulance Service NHS
Trust
National Headquarters
Tipperlinn Road
Edinburgh
EH10 5UU
TEL: 0131 447 7711
FAX: 0131 447 4789

South Ayrshire Hospitals NHS Trust
The Ayr Hospital
Daimelington Road
Ayr
KA6 6DX
TEL: 01292 610555
FAX: 01292 288952

Southern General Hospital NHS
Trust
Southern General Hospital
1345 Govan Road
Glasgow
G51 4TF
TEL: 0141 201 1200
FAX: 0141 201 2999

Stirling Royal Infirmary NHS Trust
Stirling Royal Infirmary
Livilands
Stirling
FK8 2AU

TEL: 01786 434000
FAX: 01786 450588

Stobhill NHS Trust
Stobhill General Hospital
133 Balomock Road
Glasgow
G21 3UW
TEL: 0141 201 3000
FAX: 0141 201 3887

The Victoria Infirmary NHS Trust
Queen's Park House
Langside Road
Glasgow
G42 9TT
TEL: 0141 201 6000
FAX: 0141 201 5825

West Glasgow Hospitals University
NHS Trust
Administration Building
Western Infirmary
Dumbarton Road
Glasgow
G11 6NT
TEL: 0141 211 2000
FAX: 0141 211 1920

West Lothian NHS Trust
St John's Hospital at Howden
Livingston
West Lothian
EH54 6PP
TEL: 01506 491666
FAX: 01506 416484

Western General Hospitals NHS
Trust
Western General Hospital
Crewe Road South
Edinburgh
EH4 2XU
TEL: 0131 537 1000
FAX: 0131 537 1001

The Yorkhill NHS Trust
Royal Hospital for Sick Children
Yorkhill

Glasgow
G3 8SJ
TEL: 0141 201 0000
FAX: 0141 201 0836

## Wales

Bridgend and District NHS Trust
Nurses Home Offices
Bridgend General Hospital
Quarella Road
Bridgend
Mid Glamorgan
CF31 1YE
TEL: 01656 752752
FAX: 01656 665377

Cardiff Community Healthcare NHS
    Trust
'Trenewydd'
Fairwater Road
Llandaff
Cardiff
CF5 2LD
TEL: 01222 552212
FAX: 01222 578032

Carmarthen and District NHS Trust
West Wales General Hospital
Glangwili
Carmarthen
Dyfed
SA31 2AF
TEL: 01267 235151
FAX: 01267 237662

Ceredigion and Mid Wales NHS
    Trust
Bronglais General Hospital
Caradog Road
Aberystwyth
Dyfed
SY23 1ER
TEL: 01970 623131
FAX: 01970 635922

Derwen NHS Trust
St David's Hospital
Carmarthen

Dyfed
SA31 3HB
TEL: 01267 237481
FAX: 01267 221895

East Glamorgan NHS Trust
East Glamorgan General Hospital
Church Village
Pontypridd
Mid Glamorgan
CF38 1AB
TEL: 01443 218218
FAX: 01443 217213

Glan Hafren NHS Trust
Royal Gwent Hospital
Cardiff Road
Newport
Gwent
NP9 2UB
TEL: 01633 234234
FAX: 01633 221217

Glan Clwyd District General
    Hospital NHS Trust
Ysbyty Glan Clwyd
Bodelwyddan
Rhyl
Clwyd
LL18 5UJ
TEL: 01745 583910
FAX: 01745 583143

Glan-y-Môr NHS Trust
21 Orchard Street
Swansea
SA1 5BE
TEL: 01792 651501
FAX: 01792 458730

Gofal Cymuned Clwydian
    Community Care NHS Trust
Catherine Gladstone House
Hawarden Way
Deeside
Clwyd
CH5 2EP
TEL: 01244 538883
FAX: 01244 538884

Gwent Community Health NHS
Trust
Grange House
Llanfrechfa Grange Hospital
Cwmbran
Gwent
NP44 8YN
TEL: 01633 838521
FAX: 01633 643864

Gwynedd Community Health NHS
Trust
Bryn-y-Neuadd Hospital
Llanfairfechan
Gwynedd
LL33 0HH
TEL: 01248 682682
FAX: 01248 681832

Gwynedd Hospitals NHS Trust
Ysbyty Gwynedd
Penrhos Garnedd
Bangor
Gwynedd
LL57 2PW
TEL: 01248 384384
FAX: 01248 370629

Llandough Hospital and Community
NHS Trust
Llandough Hospital
Penlan Road
Llandough
Penarth
South Glamorgan
CF64 2XX
TEL: 01222 711711
FAX: 01222 708973

Llanelli Dinefwr NHS Trust
Prince Philip General Hospital
Bryngwynmawr
Dafen
Llanelli
Dyfed
SA14 8QF
TEL: 01554 756567
FAX: 01554 772271

Mid Glamorgan Ambulance NHS
Trust
Ambulance Service Headquarters
Main Avenue
Treforest Industrial Estate
Treforest
Mid Glamorgan
CF37 9AD
TEL: 01443 841213

Morriston Hospital NHS Trust
Morriston Hospital
Morriston
Swansea
SA6 6NL
TEL: 01792 703331
FAX: 01792 799574

Nevill Hall & District NHS Trust
Nevill Hall Hospital
Abergavenny
Gwent
NP7 7EG
TEL: 01873 852091
FAX: 01873 859168

North Wales Ambulance NHS Trust
'Delfryn'
HM Stanley Hospital
St Asaph
Clwyd
LL17 0RS
TEL: 01745 585106
FAX: 01745 584101

North Glamorgan NHS Trust
Prince Charles Hospital
Merthyr Tydfil
Mid Glamorgan
CF47 9DT
TEL: 01685 721721
FAX: 01685 388001

Pembrokeshire NHS Trust
Withybush General Hospital
Fishguard Road
Haverfordwest
Dyfed

SA61 2PZ
TEL: 01437 774000
FAX: 01437 774300

Powys Health Care NHS Trust
Unit Offices
Felindre
Bronllys Hospital
Bronllys
Brecon
Powys
LD3 0LS
TEL: 01874 711661
FAX: 01874 711601

Rhondda Health Care NHS Trust
Llwynypia Hospital
Llwynypia
Rhondda
CF40 2LX
TEL: 01443 440440
FAX: 01443 431611

South and East Wales Ambulance
NHS Trust
Ambulance Headquarters
Caerleon House
Mamhilad Park Estate
Pontypool
Gwent
NP4 0XF
TEL: 01495 765400
FAX: 01495 765418

Swansea NHS Trust
Singleton Hospital
Sketty
Swansea
SA2 0FB
TEL: 01792 205666
FAX: 01792 208647

University Hospital of Wales
Healthcare NHS Trust
Heath Park
Cardiff
CF4 4XW
TEL: 01222 747747
FAX: 01222 742968

University Dental Hospital NHS
Trust
Heath Park
Cardiff
CF4 4XY
TEL: 01222 742422
FAX: 01222 743838

Velindre NHS Trust
Velindre Hospital
Velindre Road
Whitchurch
Cardiff
CF4 7XL
TEL: 01222 615888
FAX: 01222 522694

West Wales Ambulance NHS Trust
Ty Maes-y-Griffydd
Ceefn Coed Hospital
Cockett
Swansea
SA2 0GP
TEL: 01792 562900
FAX: 01792 281184

Wrexham Maelor Hospital NHS
Trust
Wrexham Maelor General Hospital
Croesnewydd Road
Wrexham
Clwyd
LL13 7TD
TEL: 01978 291100
FAX: 01978 310326

# Appendix IV

# Health Authorities

## England

### *Anglia and Oxford*

Bedfordshire Health Authority
Charter House
Alma Street
Luton
LU1 2PL
TEL: 01582 744800

Berkshire Health Authority
Pendragon House
59 Bath Road
Reading
RG3 2BA
TEL: 01734 503094

Buckinghamshire Health Authority
Merlin Centre
Gatehouse Close
Aylesbury
HP19 3DP
TEL: 01296 310000

Cambridge and Huntingdon Health
  Authority
Fulbourn
Cambridge
CB1 5EF
TEL: 01223 218829

East Norfolk Health Authority
St Andrew's Hospital
Yarmouth Road
Norwich
NR7 0SS
TEL: 01603 300600

North West Anglia Health Authority
St John's
Thorpe Road
Peterborough
PE3 6JG
TEL: 01733 882288

Northamptonshire Health Authority
Highfield
Cliftonville Road
Northampton
NN1 5DN
TEL: 01604 615000

Oxfordshire Health Authority
Old Road
Headington
Oxford
OX3 7LG
TEL: 01865 741741

Suffolk Health Authority
PO Box 55
Foxhall Road
Ipswich
IP3 8NN
TEL: 01473 712272

## North West

Bury & Rochdale Health Authority
21 Silver Street
Bury
BL9 0EN
TEL: 0161 762 3100

East Lancashire Health Authority
31/33 Kenyon Road
Lomeshaye Estate
Nelson
BB9 5SZ
TEL: 01282 619909

Liverpool Health Authority
Hamilton House
Pall Mall
Liverpool
L3 6AL
TEL: 0151 236 4747

Manchester Health Authority
Gateway House
Piccadilly South
Manchester
TEL: 0161 237 2000

Morecambe Bay Health Authority
Tenterfield
Brigsteer Road
Kendal
LA9 5EA
TEL: 01539 735565

North Cheshire Health Authority
Lister Road
Astmoor
Runcorn
WA7 1TW
TEL: 01928 593000

North West Lancashire Health
   Authority
Wesham Park Hospital
Derby Road
Wesham
Kirkham
PR4 2AL
TEL: 01253 306305

St Helens & Knowsley Health
   Authority
Cowley Hill Lane
St Helens
WA10 2AP
TEL: 01744 733722

Salford & Trafford Health Authority
Peel House
Albert Street
Eccles
M30 0NJ
TEL: 0161 789 7373

Sefton Health Authority
3rd Floor
Burlington House
Crosby Road North
Waterloo
Liverpool
L22 0QP
TEL: 0151 920 5056

South Cheshire Health Authority
1829 Building
Countess of Chester Health Park
Chester
CU2 1UL
TEL: 01244 650300

South Lancashire Health Authority
Grove House
Langton Brow
The Green
Eccleston
PR7 7PD
TEL: 01257 452222

Stockport Health Authority
Healthcare House

Bramhall Moor Lane
Hazel Grove
Stockport
SK7 5BY
TEL: 0161 419 6000

West Pennine Health Authority
Westhulme Avenue
Oldham
OL1 2PN
TEL: 0161 455 5700

Wigan & Bolton Health Authority
Bryan House
61 Standishgate
Wigan
WN1 1AH
TEL: 01204 390000

Wirral Health Authority
St Catherine's Hospital
1st Floor
Administration Block
Church Road
Tranmere
Wirral
L42 0LQ
TEL: 0151 651 0011

## West Midlands

Birmingham Health Authority
1 Vernan Road
Edgbaston
Birmingham
B16 9SA
TEL: 0121 456 5566

Coventry Health Authority
Christchurch House
Greyfriars Lane
Coventry
West Midlands
CV1 2GQ
TEL: 01203 552225

Dudley Health Authority
12 Bull Street

Dudley
West Midlands
DY1 2DD
TEL: 01384 239376

Herefordshire Health Authority
Victoria House
Eign Street
Hereford
Herefordshire
HR4 0AN
TEL: 01432 272021

North Staffordshire Health
    Authority
District Offices
PO Box 652
Princes Road
Hartshill
Stoke on Trent
Staffordshire
ST4 7QJ
TEL: 01782 715444

Sandwell Health Authority
Kingston House
438 High Street
West Bromwich
West Midlands
B70 9LD
TEL: 0121 553 1774

Shropshire Health Authority
William Farr House
Shrewsbury
Shropshire
SY3 8XL
TEL: 01743 261300

Solihull Health Authority
21 Poplar Road
Solihull
West Midlands
B91 3AD
TEL: 0121 704 5191

South Staffordshire Health Authority
Mellor House

Corporation Street
Stafford
Staffordshire
ST16 3SR
TEL: 01785 52233

Walsall Health Authority
Lichfield House
27–31 Lichfield Street
Walsall
West Midlands
WS1 1TE
TEL: 01922 720255

Warwickshire Health Authority
Westgate House
Market Street
Warwick
Warwickshire
CV34 3DH
TEL: 01926 493491

Wolverhampton Health Authority
Coniston House
Chapel Ash
Wolverhampton
West Midlands
WV3 0XE
TEL: 01902 20202

Worcestershire Health Authority
Isaac Maddox House
Shrub Hill Road
Worcester
WR4 9RW
TEL: 01905 763333

## Trent

Barnsley Health Authority
Hillder House
49/51 Gawber Road
Barnsley
S75 2PY
TEL: 01226 779922

Doncaster Health Authority
White Rose House
Ten Pound Walk

Doncaster
DN4 5DJ
TEL: 01302 320111

Leicestershire Health Authority
Gwendolen Road
Leicester
LE5 4QS
TEL: 0116 273 1173

Lincolnshire Health Authority
Cross O'Cliff Court
Bracebridge Heath
Lincoln
LN4 2HL
TEL: 01522 513355

North Derbyshire Health Authority
Scarsdale Hospital
Newbold Road
Chesterfield
S41 7PF
TEL: 01246 231255

North Nottinghamshire Health
    Authority
Ransom Hospital
Mansfield
Notts
NG21 0ER
TEL: 01623 22515

Nottingham Health Authority
1 Standard Court
Park Row
Nottingham
NG1 6GN
TEL: 0115 912 3344

Rotherham Health Authority
220 Badsley Moor Lane
Rotherham
S65 1QU
TEL: 01709 382647

Sheffield Health Authority
Fulwood House
5 Old Fulwood Road
Sheffield

S10 3TG
TEL: 0114 267 0333

South Derbyshire Health Authority
Southern Derbyshire Health
Derwent Court
1 Stuart Street
Derby
DE1 2FZ
TEL: 01332 363971

South Humber Health Authority
Health Place
Wrawby Road
Brigg
DN20 8GS
TEL: 01652 659659

## Northern and Yorkshire

Bradford Health Authority
New Mill
Victoria Road
Saltaire
Shipley
West Yorkshire
BD18 3LD
TEL: 01274 366007

County Durham Health Commission
Appleton House
Lanchester Road
Durham
Co Durham
DH1 5XZ
TEL: 0191 333 2333

East Riding Health Authority
Grange Park Lane
Willerby
Hull
North Humberside
HU10 6DT
TEL: 01482 658822

Leeds Healthcare
St Marys House
St Marys Road

Leeds
Yorkshire
LS7 3JX
TEL: 0113 278 1341

Newcastle and North Tyneside
  Health Authority
Benfield Road
Walkergate
Newcastle upon Tyne
Tyne & Wear
NE6 4PF
TEL: 0191 281 5011

North Cumbria Health Authority
Unit 2
Lakeland Business Park
Lamplugh Road
Cockermouth
Cumbria
CA13 0QT
TEL: 01900 822155

North Yorkshire Health Authority
Sovereign House
Kettlestring Lane
Clifton Moor
York
North Yorkshire
YO3 4XF
TEL: 01904 693322

Northumberland Health Authority
East Cottingwood
Morpeth
Northumberland
NE61 2PD
TEL: 01670 514331

South of Tyne Health Commission
Horsley Hill Road
South Shields
Tyne & Wear
NE33 3BN
TEL: 0191 427 5444

Sunderland Health Commission
Durham Road

Sunderland
Tyne & Wear
SR3 4AF
TEL: 0191 565 6256

Tees Health Authority
Poole Hospital
Nunthorpe
Middlesbrough
Cleveland
TS7 0NJ
TEL: 01642 320000

Wakefield Health Authority
White Rose House
West Parade
Wakefield
West Yorkshire
WF1 1LT
TEL: 01924 814400

West Yorkshire Health Authority
St Lukes House
Blackmoorfoot Road
Crosland Moor
Huddersfield
West Yorkshire
HD4 5RH
TEL: 01484 466000

## South Thames

Bexley and Greenwich Health
    Authority
221 Erith Road
Bexleyheath
Kent DA7 6HA
TEL: 0181 301 2333

Bromley Health Authority
Global House
10 Station Approach
Hayes
Bromley
Kent BR2 7EH
TEL: 0181 462 2211

East Kent Health Authority
Protea House

New Bridge
Marine Parade
Dover
CT17 9BW
TEL: 01304 227227

Croydon Health Authority
Knollys House
17 Addiscombe Road
Croydon
CR9 6HS
TEL: 0181 401 3913

East Surrey Health Authority
Health Commission Offices
West Park Road
Horton Lane
Epsom
Surrey
KT19 8PB
TEL: 01372 731111

East Sussex Health Authority
250 Willington Road
Eastbourne
East Sussex
BN20 9AL
TEL: 01323 520000

Kingston and Richmond Health
    Authority
17 Upper Brighton Road
Surbiton
Surrey
KT6 6LH
TEL: 0181 390 1111

Lambeth, Southwark and Lewisham
    Health Authority
1 Lower Marsh
London
SE1 7RJ
TEL: 0171 716 7000

Merton, Sutton and Wandsworth
    Health Authority
Wilson Hospital
Cranmer Road

Mitcham
Surrey
CR4 4TP
TEL: 0181 648 3021

West Kent Health Authority
Preston Hall
Aylesford
Kent
ME20 7NJ
TEL: 01622 710161

West Surrey Health Authority
The Ridgewood Centre
Old Bisley Road
Frimley
Camberley
Surrey
GU16 5QE
TEL: 01276 671718

West Sussex Health Authority
West Sussex District Health
   Authority
PO Box 3009
Worthing
West Sussex
BN12 6BN
TEL: 01903 245554

## North Thames

Barking and Havering Health
   Authority
The Grange
Gubbins Lane
Romford
Essex
RM3 0DD
TEL: 01708 349511

Barnet Health Authority
District Offices
Colindale Hospital
Colindale Avenue
London
N9 5HG
TEL: 0181 205 1777

Brent and Harrow Health Authority
Grace House
Harrovian Business Centre
Bessborough Road
Harrow
London
HA1 3EX
TEL: 0181 422 6644

Camden and Islington Health
   Authority
110 Hampstead Road
London
NW1 2LJ
TEL: 0171 383 4888

Ealing, Hammersmith and Hounslow
   Health Authority
1 Armstrong Way
Southall
Middlesex
UB2 4SA
TEL: 0181 893 0303

East and North Hertfordshire Health
   Authority
c/o North Thames Regional Office
40 Eastbourne Terrace
London
W2 3QR
TEL: 0171 725 5300

East London and the City Health
   Authority
Tredegar House
97–99 Bow Road
London
E3 2AN
TEL: 0181 983 2900

Enfield and Haringey Health
   Authority
Alexander Place
Lower Park Road
New Southgate
London
N11 1ST
TEL: 0181 361 7272

Hillingdon Health Authority
Kirk House
97–109 High Street
Yiewsley
West Drayton
Middlesex
UB7 7HJ
TEL: 01895 452000

Kensington & Chelsea and
    Westminster Health Authority
Kensington & Islington Health
    Authority
50 Eastbourne Terrace
London
W2 6LX
TEL: 0171 725 3333

North Essex Health Authority
Collingwood Road
Witham
Essex
CM8 2TT
TEL: 01376 516515

Redbridge and Waltham Forest
    Health Authority
West Wing
713 Eastern Avenue
Ilford
Essex
IG2 7SJ
TEL: 0181 518 2299

South Essex Health Authority
Charles House
Norsey Road
Billericay
Essex
CM11 1AG
TEL: 01277 633006

West Hertfordshire Health Authority
c/o North Thames Regional Office
40 Eastbourne Terrace
London
W2 3QR
TEL: 0171 725 5300

## South and West

Avon Health Authority
Avon Health
10 Dighton Street
Bristol
BS2 8EE
TEL: 0117 976 6600

Cornwall and Isles of Scilly Health
    Authority
John Keay House
St Austell
PL25 4DJ
TEL: 01726 77777

Dorset Health Authority
Victoria House
Princes Road
Ferndown
BH22 9JR
TEL: 01202 893000

Gloucestershire Health Authority
Victoria Warehouse
The Docks
Gloucester
G11 2EL
TEL: 01455 2300222

Isle of Wight Health Authority
Whitecroft Hospital
Sandy Lane
Newport
Isle of Wight
PO30 3ED
TEL: 01983 526011

North and East Devon Health
    Authority
Dean Clarke House
Southernhay East
Exeter
EX1 1PQ
TEL: 01392 406192

North and Mid Hampshire Health
    Authority
Harness House

Basingstoke District Hospital
Basingstoke
RG24 9NB
TEL: 01256 332288

Portsmouth and South East
  Hampshire Health Authority
Finchdean House
Milton Road
Portsmouth
PO3 6DP
TEL: 01705 838340

Somerset Health Authority
Wellsprings Road
Taunton
TA2 7PQ
TEL: 01823 333491

South and West Devon Health
  Authority
District Headquarters
Powisland Drive
Plymouth
PL6 6AB
TEL: 01752 793793

Southampton and South West
  Hampshire Health Authority
Oakley Road
Southampton
SO16 4GX
TEL: 01703 725400

Wiltshire Health Authority
Wiltshire & Bath Health Authority
Southgate House
Pans Lane
Devizes
SN10 5EQ
TEL: 01380 728899

## Northern Ireland

Eastern Health and Social Services
  Board (EHSSB)
Champion House
12–22 Linenhall Street

Belfast
BT2 8BS
TEL: 01232 321313

Northern Health and Social Services
  Board (NHSSB)
County Hall
182 Galgorm Road
Ballymena
BT42 1QB
TEL: 01266 662083

Southern Health and Social Services
  Board (SHSSB)
Tower Hill
Armagh
BT61 9DR
TEL: 01861 410041

Western Health and Social Services
  Board (WHSSB)
15 Gransha Park
Clooney Road
Londonderry
BT47 1TG
TEL: 01504 860086

## Scotland

Argyll and Clyde Health Board
Gilmour House
Paisley
PA1 1DQ
TEL: 0141 887 0131

Ayrshire and Arran Health Board
PO Box 13
Seafield House
Doonfoot Road
Ayr
KA7 4DW
TEL: 01298 611040

Borders Health Board
Huntlyburn House
Melrose
TD6 9BP
TEL: 08198 682 2662

Dumfries and Galloway Health Board
Nithbank
Dumfries
DG1 2SD
TEL: 01387 46246

Fife Health Board
Springfield House
Cupar
Fife
KY15 5UP
TEL: 01334 56200

Forth Valley Health Board
33 Spittal Street
Stirling
FK8 1DX
TEL: 01786 63031

Grampian Health Board
Summerfield House
2 Eday Road
Aberdeen
AB9 8Q

Greater Glasgow Health Board
112 Ingram Street
Glasgow
G1 1ET
TEL: 0141 552 6222

Highland Health Board
Reay House
17 Old Inverness Road
Inverness
IV2 3HG
TEL: 01463 239851

Lanarkshire Health Board
14 Beckford Street
Hamilton
ML3 0TA
TEL: 01698 281313

Lothian Health Board
148 The Pleasance
Edinburgh
EH8 9RR
TEL: 0131 229 5888

Orkney Health Board
Gordon House
New Scapa Road
Kirkwall
KW15 1BQ
TEL: 01856 2762

Shetland Health Board
Gilbert Bain Hospital
Lerwick
ZE1 0RB
TEL: 01595 5678

Tayside Health Board
PO Box 75
Vernonholme
Riverside Drive
Dundee
DD1 9N
TEL: 01382 645151

Western Isles Health Board
37 South Beach Street
Stornoway
PA87 2BN
TEL: 01851 702997

Health Education Board for Scotland
Woodburn House
Caanan Lane
Edinburgh
EH10 4SG
TEL: 0131 447 8044

Common Services Agency
Trinity Park House
South Trinity Road
Edinburgh
EH5 3SE
TEL: 0131 552 6355

## Wales

Bro Taf Health Authority
6th Floor
Churchill House
Churchill Way
Cardiff

CF1 4TW
TEL: 01222 226216

Dyfed Powys Health Authority
St David's Hospital
Carmarthen
Dyfed SA31 3HB
TEL: 01267 234501

Gwent Health Authority
Mamhilad House
Mamhilad
Pontypool
Gwent
NP4 0YP
TEL: 01495 765065

Iechyd Morgannwg Health
41 High Street
Swansea
SA1 1LT
TEL: 01792 458066

North Wales Health Authority
Preswylfa
Hendy Road
Mold
Clwyd CH7 1PZ
TEL: 01352 700227

# Appendix V

# Useful Addresses

ACAS (Advisory, Consiliation &
Arbitration Council)
Clifton House
83 Euston Road
London
NW1 2RB
TEL: 0171 396 5100
FAX: 0171 396 5159

Association of Community Health
Councils
30 Drayton Park
London
N5 1PB
TEL: 0171 609 8405
FAX: 0171 700 1152

Association of Managers in General
Practice (AMGP)
Suite 308 The Foundry
156 Blackfriars Rd
London
SE1 8EN
TEL: 0171 721 7080
FAX: 0171 721 7090

Association of Personal Injury
Lawyers
33 Pilchergate
Nottingham
NG7 7QF

TEL: 0115 958 0585
FAX: 0115 958 0885

Audit Commission
1 Vincent Square
London
SW1 2PN
TEL: 0171 828 1212
FAX: 0171 976 6187

British Medical Association
General Medical Services Committee
BMA House
Tavistock Square
London WC1H 9JP
TEL: 0171 387 4499

Carers National Association
20–25 Glasshouse Yard
London
EC1A 4JS
FAX: 0171 490 8824

Council for Professions
Supplementary to Medicine
Park House
184 Kennington Park Road
London
SE11 4BI
TEL: 0171 582 0866
FAX: 0171 820 9684

CPHVA (Community Practitioner's
and Health Visitors Association)
50 Southwark Street
London
SE1 1UN
TEL: 0171 717 4000
FAX: 0171 717 4010

Department of Health
Quarry House
Quarry Hill
Leeds
Yorkshire
LS2 7UE
TEL: 0113 254 5000
FAX: 0113 254 6346

Eastleigh GP Consortium
Eastleigh Health Centre
Newtown Road
Eastleigh
SO50 9AG
TEL: 01703 399925
FAX: 01703 399926

Feamus Kehoe
General Practice Finance Committee
Tavistock House North
Tavistock Square
London
WC1H 9JL
TEL: 0171 387 5274
FAX: 0171 388 5860

The Freemen's Common Health
Centre
Freemen's Cottages
161 Welford Road
Leicester
LE2 6BF
TEL: 0116 255 4776
FAX: 0116 254 9518

General Medical Counsil
178–203 Gt Portland Street
London
W1N 6JE
TEL: 0171 580 7642
FAX: 0171 915 3641

General Practice Finance Committee
Tavistock House North
Tavistock Square
London
WC1H 9JL
TEL: 0171 387 5274
FAX: 0171 388 5860

Greenhalgh and Company Ltd
GCL House
Gunco Lane
Macclesfield
Cheshire
SK11 7JL
TEL: 01625 612261
FAX: 01625 611219

Health and Safety Executive
Health Directorate
Magdalen House
Trinity Road
Bootle
Merseyside
L20 3QZ
TEL: 0151 951 3786
FAX: 0151 951 4703

HEA (Health Education Authority)
Hamilton House
Mabledon Place
London
WC1H 9TX
TEL: 0171 383 3833
FAX: 0171 387 0550

The Help for Health Trust
Highcroft
Romsey Road
Winchester
Hampshire
SO22 5DH
TEL: 01962 849100
FAX: 01962 840454

Hillsborough Medical Practice
The Health Centre
Ballynahinch Street
Hillsborough

County Down
BT26 6AW
Northern Ireland
TEL: 01846 682216
FAX: 01846 689721

HSE Books
PO Box 1999
Sudbury
Suffolk
CO10 6FS
TEL: 01787 881165
FAX: 01787 313995

HSE Information Centre
Broad Lane
Sheffield
S3 7HQ
TEL: 0114 2892345
FAX: 0114 2892333

The Industrial Society
Quadrant Court
49 Calthorpe Road
Edgbaston
Birmingham
B15 1TH
TEL: 0121 454 6769
FAX: 0121 456 2715

Institute of General Practice
Postgraduate Medical School
University of Exeter
Barrack Road
Exeter
EX2 5DW
TEL: 01392 403020
FAX: 01392 403223

Institute of Health and Care
  Development
(formerly the NHSTD)
St Bartholomew's Court
18 Christmas Street
Bristol
BS1 5BT
TEL: 0117 9291029
FAX: 0117 9250574

Institute of Health Policy Studies
University of Southampton
Faculty of Social Science
129 University Road
Highfield
Southampton
SO17 1BJ
TEL: 01703 593394
FAX: 01703 593177

King's Fund Organisational Audit
11–13 Cavendish Square
London
W1M 0AN
TEL: 0171 307 2526
FAX: 0171 307 2804

D G Love & Partners
Chartered Valuation Surveyors
6 Rockstone Place
Southampton SO15 2EP
TEL: 01703 223828
FAX: 01703

MDU (Medical Defence Union)
3 Devonshire Place
London
W1N 2EA
TEL: 0171 486 6181
FAX: 0171 935 5503

MDDUS (Medical & Dental Defence
  Union of Scotland)
Mackintosh House
120 Blythswood Street
Glasgow
G2 4EA
Scotland
TEL: 0141 221 5858
FAX: 0141 228 1208

MPS (Medical Protection Society)
50 Hallam Street
London
W1N 6DE
TEL: 0171 637 0541
FAX: 0171 636 0690

Medi-Commercial Ltd
Oxford House
College Street
Southampton
SO14 3EJ
TEL: 01703 333536
FAX: 01703 632186

NHS Confederation (previously
    NAHAT and NHS Trust
    Federation)
Birmingham Research Park
Vincent Drive
Birmingham
B15 2SQ
TEL: 0121 471 4444
FAX: 0121 414 1120

NHS Executive
Quarry House
Quarry Hill
Leeds
LS2 7UE
TEL: 0113 2545000

National Association of Patient
    Participation Groups
Max Reed, Affiliation Secretary
'Cograh'
Chalngate House
Iron Acton
Bristol
TEL: 01454 228893
FAX: 01454 228893

National Counselling Service for Sick
    Doctors
1 Park Square West
London
NW1 4LJ
TEL: 0171 935 5982
FAX: 0171 935 8601

New Milton Health Centre
Spencer Road
New Milton
BH25 6EN
TEL: 01425 620393
FAX: 01425 620646

The Patients Association
8 Guildford Street
London
WC1N 1DT
TEL: 0171 242 3460
FAX: 0171 242 3560

Public Concern at Work
42 Kingsway
London
WC2B 6BR
TEL: 0171 404 6609
FAX: 0171 404 6576

Royal College of General
    Practitioners
14 Princes Gate
Hyde Park
London
SW7 1PU
TEL: 0171 581 3232
FAX: 0171 225 3047

RCM (Royal College of Midwives
    Trust)
15 Manfield Street
London
W1M 0BE
TEL: 0171 872 5100
FAX: 0171 872 5101

RCN (Royal College of Nursing)
20 Cavendish Square
London
W1M 0AB
TEL: 0171 409 3333
FAX: 0171 495 6104

The Royal Institution of Chartered
    Surveyors
12 Great George Street
Parliament Square
London SW1P 3AD
TEL: 0171 222 7000
FAX: 0171 222 9430

Sedgwick Noble Lowndes
    Occupational Health
Washford House

Claybrook Drive
Redditch
Worcestershire
B98 0DU
TEL: 01527 517747
FAX: 01527 525934

Small Practices Association
19 York Street
Heywood
Lancashire
OL10 4NN
TEL: 01706 620920
FAX: 01706 620780

Southampton East Multifund (SEM)
Multifund Central Officer
St Luke's Surgery
St Luke's Close
Off Shamblehurst Lane South
Hedge End
Southampton
SO30 2US
TEL: 01489 789988
FAX: 01489 789992

The Stationery Office
(previously HMSO Publications
   Centre)
PO Box 276
London
SW8 5DT
TEL: 0171 873 0011
FAX: 0171 873 8247

David M. Towner. MSc
Victoria Cottage
3 George Mews
Winchcombe
Glos
GL54 5LJ
TEL: 01242 603970
FAX: 01242 603970

UKCC (United Kingdom Central
   Council for Nursing, Midwifery &
   Health Visiting)
23 Portland Place
London
W1N 4JT
TEL: 0171 637 7181
FAX: 0171 436 2924

Vale of Trent Faculty of the Royal
   College of General Practition
The Department of General Practice
Queens Medical Centre
Nottingham
NG7 2UH
TEL: 01159 709391
FAX: 01159 709389

The Wellness Forum
131 Great Peter Street
London SW1P 3LR.
TEL: 0345 622 633

# Index

References in italic indicate figures or tables

# Index of Advertisers